MARKOV CHAINS

North-Holland Mathematical Library

VOLUME 11

NORTH-HOLLAND PUBLISHING COMPANY – AMSTERDAM · OXFORD
AMERICAN ELSEVIER PUBLISHING COMPANY, INC. – NEW YORK

Markov Chains

D. REVUZ

Université de Paris VII
Paris, France

1975

NORTH-HOLLAND PUBLISHING COMPANY – AMSTERDAM · OXFORD
AMERICAN ELSEVIER PUBLISHING COMPANY, INC. – NEW YORK

Library of Congress Catalog Card Number: 74–80112
North-Holland ISBN for the series: 0 7204 2450 X
North-Holland ISBN for this volume: 0 7204 2460 7
American Elsevier ISBN: 0 444 10752 5

982174

Published by:
North-Holland Publishing Company – Amsterdam
North-Holland Publishing Company, Ltd. – Oxford

Sole distributors for the U.S.A. and Canada:
American Elsevier Publishing Company, Inc.
52 Vanderbilt Avenue
New York, N.Y. 10017

PREFACE

This book grew out of a lecture course given at the "3me cycle" level of the universities of Paris during recent years. The first part is thus intended for students at that level; the later chapters are designed for more advanced readers.

Our purpose is to provide an introduction to homogeneous Markov chains with general (measurable) state space, or perhaps more accurately to the study of "sub-Markovian kernels" or "transition probabilities". This contains as special cases the study of pointwise transformations and ergodic theory, potential theory, random walks on groups and homogeneous spaces, etc. It would be preposterous to attempt a comprehensive treatment of all these topics within this book, in as much as some of them are far from being complete and offer still challenging problems.

Roughly speaking, the first four chapters – at least parts of them – are foundations that must be learnt by every beginner in the field. It will be no surprise that they include a short chapter on potential theory, since its fruitful relationship with Markov phenomena has been long and widely known. They include also the basic classification of chains according to their asymptotic behaviour and the celebrated Chacon–Ornstein Theorem. After these first chapters we proceed to some portions of the theory such as renewal theory for abelian groups, an introduction to Martin Boundary Theory and the study – the most thorough in this book – of chains recurrent in the Harris sense. The last chapter deals with the construction of chains starting from a kernel satisfying some maximum principle. These topics do not depend very strictly on one another and the reader may skip some according to his own interest. An interdependence table is given below, but this is merely a guide, and some idea of all the previous results will always come in useful.

Other important subjects such as invariant measures, pointwise transformations or random walks on non-abelian groups are barely alluded to. Relevant references will be given in the "Notes and Comments" at the end of the book.

We tried to present at the end of each section a large selection of exercises. We feel that the reader will not benefit greatly from reading the book if he does not tackle a large number of them. They are in particular designed to provide examples and counter-examples; some of them are results which might have been included in the text. With a few exceptions they can be worked out with a knowledge of the previous sections and of classical calculus.

References and credits do not appear in the text but are collected under the "Notes and Comments". We have in no way tried to draw a historical picture of the field, and apologize in advance to anyone who may feel slighted. We merely indicate the papers we have actually used; as a result insufficient tribute is paid to those who have founded the theory of chains, such as A. A. Markov, N. Kolmogoroff, W. Doeblin, J. L. Doob and K. L. Chung.

The book is divided into chapters; each chapter is divided into sections and starts with a fresh section 1. In every section, items such as theorems, examples, exercises, paragraphs, remarks, are numbered. The references are given in the following way: the nth chapter is quoted as ch. n; the pth section of ch. n is quoted as ch. n, §p. Finally, the qth numbered item in ch. n, §p is quoted as ch. n, Theorem $p.q$, etc.; however, for quotations within the same chapter we shall drop "ch. n" and write simply Theorem $p.q$, etc.

It is a pleasure to acknowledge a few of my debts. Like many French probabilists, I owe everything to J. Neveu and P. A. Meyer; but for their teaching and advice I would never have been really introduced to Markov theory. I must especially thank M. Duflo, who first aroused my interest in discrete time, and A. Brunel for the work we have done together, part of which finds its way into the present book. Many students and colleagues were kind enough to comment on preliminary drafts of the first chapters, in particular M. Brancovan, P. Jaffard and P. Priouret, and I wish to thank them all. My warm thanks go to M. Sharpe, who read through the entire manuscript and removed the most important inaccuracies in the use of English language (a very difficult language indeed); he is not responsible for any awkward points remaining. We hope they will not hamper understanding and that the native speaker will make allowances for the "exotic flavour".

Finally I must thank Martine Mirey, who typed the entire manuscript, and E. Fredriksson of the staff of North-Holland Publishing company for his understanding help.

D. REVUZ

INTERDEPENDENCE GUIDE

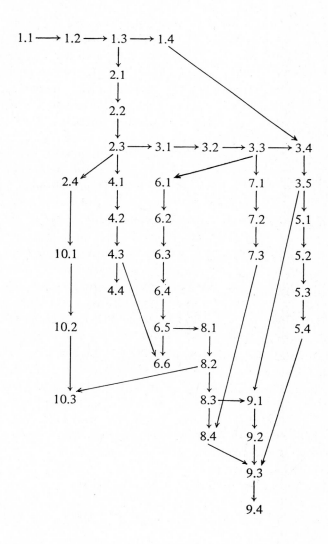

CONTENTS

CHAPTER 0

PRELIMINARIES

This chapter is devoted to a list of some basic notations and facts which will be used throughout the sequel without further explanation. We assume that the reader is familiar with measure theory and probability theory as may be found for instance in the first four chapters of the book by Neveu [2], with point set topology, and that he has some knowledge of topological groups and Fourier transforms, for which we refer to the books by Rudin [1] and by Hewitt and Ross [1].

1. Notation

1.1. Let $\mathbf{N}$ denote the set of positive integers, $\mathbf{Z}$ the set of integers and $\mathbf{R}$ the set of real numbers; $\bar{\mathbf{R}}$ will denote the extended real numbers $\{-\infty\} \cup \mathbf{R} \cup \{+\infty\}$ with the usual topology. For a and b in $\bar{\mathbf{R}}$, we write

$$a \vee b = \max(a, b), \qquad a \wedge b = \min(a, b).$$

If E is a set and f a numerical function on E, we shall write

$$\|f\| = \sup_{x \in E} |f(x)|, \qquad f^+ = f \vee 0, \qquad f^- = -(f \wedge 0).$$

1.2. If $(E, \mathscr{E})$ and $(F, \mathscr{F})$ are measurable spaces, we shall write $f \in \mathscr{E}/\mathscr{F}$ to indicate that the function $f : E \to F$ is measurable with respect to $\mathscr{E}$ and $\mathscr{F}$. In the case where F is $\mathbf{R}$ and $\mathscr{F}$ the σ-algebra of Borel subsets we write simply $f \in \mathscr{E}$. The symbol $\mathscr{E}$ thus denotes the σ-algebra as well as the set of real-valued measurable functions on E.

If A is a subset of E, we denote the indicator function of A by 1_A, so that the statements $1_A \in \mathscr{E}$ and $A \in \mathscr{E}$ have the same meaning. When $A = E$ we shall often write 1 for 1_E.

1.3. If $\mathscr{H}$ is any set of numerical functions, then $\mathscr{H}_+$ denotes the set of non-negative functions in $\mathscr{H}$ and $b\mathscr{H}$ the set of bounded functions. For instance

1

if $(E, \mathscr{E})$ is a measurable space, $b\mathscr{E}$ is the set of bounded measurable functions and $b\mathscr{E}_+$ the set of non-negative bounded measurable functions. We recall that $b\mathscr{E}$ is a Banach space for the supremum norm $\|\cdot\|$ described above. We shall denote by $\mathscr{U}$ the unit ball of $b\mathscr{E}$. The set $\mathscr{U}_+$ is thus the set of measurable numerical functions on $(E, \mathscr{E})$ such that for every $x \in E$, $0 \leqslant f(x) \leqslant 1$.

1.4. Let Ω be a set and $\{(E_i, \mathscr{E}_i)\}_{i \in I}$ a collection of measurable sets. For each $i \in I$ let f_i be a map from Ω to E_i; the σ-algebra on Ω generated by the sets $\{f_i^{-1}(A_i): A_i \in E_i\}$ is the smallest σ-algebra on Ω relative to which all the f_i are measurable, and it will be denoted by $\sigma(f_i, i \in I)$. If $\mathscr{F}$ is any collection of subsets of E, we denote by $\sigma(\mathscr{F})$ the σ-algebra generated by $\mathscr{F}$. A measurable space $(E, \mathscr{E})$ will be said to be *separable* if $\mathscr{E}$ is generated by a countable collection of sets.

1.5. We denote by $\mathscr{M}(\mathscr{E})$ the space of σ-finite measures on $(E, \mathscr{E})$ and by $b\mathscr{M}(\mathscr{E})$ the space of finite measures. We shall call μ^+ and μ^- the positive and negative parts of the measure μ and set $|\mu| = \mu^+ + \mu^-$. The space $b\mathscr{M}(\mathscr{E})$ is a Banach space when endowed with the norm $\|\mu\| = |\mu|\,(E)$.

If $f \in \mathscr{E}$ and the integral of f with respect to the positive measure μ exists, we shall write it in any of the forms

$$\int_E f \, d\mu, \qquad \mu(f), \qquad \langle \mu, f \rangle, \qquad \langle f, \mu \rangle.$$

The space of integrable functions will be denoted by $\mathscr{L}^1(\mu)$, and as usual $L^1(\mu)$ will be the Banach space of equivalence classes of integrable functions endowed with the norm $\|f\|_1 = \int_E f \, d\mu$. There is a canonical isometry of $L^1(\mu)$ into $b\mathscr{M}(\mathscr{E})$ which maps f onto the measure $\lambda: A \to \int_A f \, d\mu$; λ is absolutely continuous with respect to μ $(\lambda \ll \mu)$.

1.6. If $(\Omega, \mathscr{F}, P)$ is a probability space we shall, as is customary, use the words random variable and expectation in place of measurable function and integral, and we shall write

$$\int_\Omega X \, dP = E[X].$$

If $\mathscr{G}$ is a sub-σ-algebra of $\mathscr{E}$, we denote $E[X \mid \mathscr{G}]$ the conditional expectation of X (assumed to be quasi-integrable) given $\mathscr{G}$. When $X = 1_A$, $A \in \mathscr{E}$, we write $P(A \mid \mathscr{G})$ instead of $E[1_A \mid \mathscr{G}]$, and if $\mathscr{G}$ is the smallest σ-algebra relative to which the random variable Y is measurable, we may write $E[X \mid Y]$ and $P(A \mid Y)$. When we apply conditional expectation successively, we shall often abbreviate $E[E[X \mid \mathscr{G}_1] \mid \mathscr{G}_2]$ by $E[X \mid \mathscr{G}_1 \mid \mathscr{G}_2]$. We recall that conditional expectations are defined up to P-equivalence; in the sequel we shall often omit the qualifying phrase "almost everywhere relative to P" in the relations involving conditional expectations.

2. Martingales

Let $(\Omega, \mathscr{F}, P)$ be a probability space and $\{\mathscr{F}_n\}_{n \geqslant 0}$ an increasing sequence of sub-σ-algebras of $\mathscr{F}$. A sequence $\{X_n\}_{n \geqslant 0}$ of random variables over $(\Omega, \mathscr{F}, P)$ is said to be a *supermartingale* with respect to $\{\mathscr{F}_n\}$ if
   (i) $X_n \in \mathscr{F}_n$ for every $n \geqslant 0$,
   (ii) $E[X_n^-] < + \infty$ for every $n \geqslant 0$,
   (iii) $E[X_n \mid \mathscr{F}_m] \leqslant X_m$ whenever $m \leqslant n$.
It is a *submartingale* if $\{-X_n\}$ is a supermartingale and a *martingale* provided it is both a supermartingale and a submartingale.

The proof of the following result, which we shall use freely in the sequel, may be found in the books by Doob [2], Loeve [0], Meyer [2] or Neveu [2].

Theorem 2.1. *Let $\{X_n\}_{n \in \mathbf{N}}$ be a supermartingale such that $\sup_n E[X_n^-] < \infty$; then $\lim_n X_n$ exists almost surely.*

As a result the positive supermartingales converge almost surely. We shall also need the following.

Proposition 2.2. *Let $\mathscr{F}_n$ be an increasing sequence of sub-σ-algebras of $\mathscr{F}$ such that $\bigcup_n \mathscr{F}_n$ generates $\mathscr{F}$. Let X_n be a sequence of random variables converging almost surely to a random variable X, and Y an integrable random variable such that $|X_n| \leqslant Y$ for every n. Then the sequence $E[X_n \mid \mathscr{F}_n]$ converges almost surely to $E[X \mid \mathscr{F}]$.*

Proof. Pick $\varepsilon > 0$ and set

$$U = \inf_{n \geqslant m} X_m, \qquad V = \sup_{n \geqslant m} X_n,$$

where m is chosen such that $E[V - U] < \varepsilon$. Then for $n \geqslant m$ we have

$$E[U \mid \mathscr{F}_n] \leqslant E[X_n \mid \mathscr{F}_n] \leqslant E[V \mid \mathscr{F}_n],$$

and applying Theorem 2.1 yields

$$E[U \mid \mathcal{F}] \leqslant \varliminf_n E[X_n \mid \mathcal{F}_n] \leqslant \varlimsup_n E[X_n \mid \mathcal{F}_n] \leqslant E[V \mid \mathcal{F}]$$

as well as

$$E[U \mid \mathcal{F}] \leqslant E[X \mid \mathcal{F}] \leqslant E[V \mid \mathcal{F}].$$

It follows that

$$E[\varlimsup E[X_n \mid \mathcal{F}_n] - \varliminf E[X_n \mid \mathcal{F}_n]] \leqslant \varepsilon,$$

which implies that $E[X_n \mid \mathcal{F}_n]$ converges almost surely and that the limit equals $E[X \mid \mathcal{F}]$.

In the sequel we write P-a.s. for "almost surely relative to P" and more simply a.s. when there is no risk of mistake.

3. The monotone class theorem

Definition 3.1. Let Ω be a set; a collection $\mathcal{S}$ of subsets of Ω will be called a *monotone class* if:

    (i) $\Omega \in \mathcal{S}$;
    (ii) if $A, B \in \mathcal{S}$, $A \subseteq B$, then $B - A \in \mathcal{S}$;
    (iii) if $\{A_n\}$ is an increasing sequence of elements of $\mathcal{S}$, then $\bigcup A_n \in \mathcal{S}$.

Plainly a σ-algebra is a monotone class. It is also clear that the intersection of an arbitrary number of monotone classes is a monotone class; hence for any collection $\mathcal{F}$ of subsets of Ω there is a smallest monotone class containing $\mathcal{F}$, which we call $\mathcal{S}(\mathcal{F})$. Clearly $\mathcal{S}(\mathcal{F}) \subseteq \sigma(\mathcal{F})$.

Theorem 3.2. *If $\mathcal{F}$ is closed under finite intersections, then $\mathcal{S}(\mathcal{F}) = \sigma(\mathcal{F})$.*

Proof. Clearly, it suffices to show that $\mathcal{S}(\mathcal{F})$ is a σ-algebra, and for this it suffices to show that it is closed under finite intersections.

To this end we define

$$\mathcal{S}_1 = \{B \in \mathcal{S}(\mathcal{F}): B \cap A \in \mathcal{S}(\mathcal{F}) \quad \text{for all } A \in \mathcal{F}\}.$$

It is easily checked that $\mathcal{S}_1$ is a monotone class, and since $\mathcal{F}$ is closed under finite intersections, $\mathcal{S}_1 \supset \mathcal{F}$, and hence $\mathcal{S}_1 \supset \mathcal{S}(\mathcal{F})$. Since by definition $\mathcal{S}_1 \subseteq \mathcal{S}(\mathcal{F})$, we get $\mathcal{S}_1 = \mathcal{S}(\mathcal{F})$. Now define

$$\mathcal{S}_2 = \{B \in \mathcal{S}(\mathcal{F}): B \cap A \in \mathcal{S}(\mathcal{F}) \quad \text{for all } A \in \mathcal{S}(\mathcal{F})\}.$$

Again $\mathscr{S}_2$ is a monotone class, and by the preceding argument $\mathscr{S}_2 \supset \mathscr{F}$; hence $\mathscr{S}_2 \supset \mathscr{S}(\mathscr{F})$, and as before we get $\mathscr{S}_2 = \mathscr{S}(\mathscr{F})$. But this is precisely the statement that $\mathscr{S}(\mathscr{F})$ is closed under finite intersections. The proof is thus complete.

One generally has to deal with functions rather than sets and then may use the following version of Theorem 3.2.

Theorem 3.3. *Let $\mathscr{F}$ be a collection of subsets of Ω closed under finite intersection and $\mathscr{H}$ a vector space of real valued functions on Ω such that*
  (i) *$1_E \in \mathscr{H}$ and $1_A \in \mathscr{H}$ for all $A \in \mathscr{F}$,*
  (ii) *if h_n is an increasing sequence of elements of $\mathscr{H}_+$ such that $h = \sup h_n$ is finite (bounded), then $h \in \mathscr{H}$.*
Then $\mathscr{H}$ contains all real-valued (bounded) functions on Ω that are $\sigma(\mathscr{F})$-measurable.

Proof. Left to the reader as an exercise. [*Hint*: Set $\mathscr{D} = \{A : 1_A \in \mathscr{H}\}$ and prove that $\mathscr{D} = \mathscr{S}(\mathscr{F}) = \sigma(\mathscr{F})$.]

The above theorems will be used in the following setup: let Ω be a set and $(E_i, \mathscr{E}_i)$ a family of measurable spaces indexed by a set I. For each $i \in I$, let $\mathscr{F}_i$ be a class of subsets of E_i closed under finite intersections and such that $\mathscr{E}_i = \sigma(\mathscr{F}_i)$. Finally let f_i be a map from Ω to E_i.

Proposition 3.4. *The collection $\mathscr{F}$ of all sets of the form $\bigcap_{i \in J} f_i^{-1}(A_i)$, where $A_i \in \mathscr{F}_i$ for $i \in J$ and J ranges over all finite subsets of I, is closed under finite intersections and $\mathscr{S}(\mathscr{F}) = \sigma(f_i, i \in I)$.*

Proposition 3.5. *Let $\mathscr{H}$ be a vector space of real-valued functions on Ω such that:*
  (i) *$1 \in \mathscr{H}$;*
  (ii) *if h_n is an increasing sequence of elements of $\mathscr{H}_+$ such that $h = \sup h_n$ is finite (bounded), then $h \in \mathscr{H}$;*
  (iii) *$\mathscr{H}$ contains all products of the form $\prod_{i \in J} 1_{A_i} \circ f_i$ where J is a finite subset of I and $A_i \in \mathscr{F}_i$.*
Then $\mathscr{H}$ contains all real-valued (bounded) functions in $\sigma(f_i, i \in I)$.

We shall also use the following corollary of the monotone class theorem.

Proposition 3.6. *Let μ and ν be two finite measures on $(E, \mathscr{E})$ and let $\mathscr{F} \subset \mathscr{E}$ be closed under finite intersections. Then if μ and ν agree on $\mathscr{F}$ they agree on $\sigma(\mathscr{F})$.*

Proof. One shows that $\mathcal{D} = \{A \in \mathcal{E} : \mu(A) = \nu(A)\}$ is a monotone class.

4. Topological spaces and groups

Except for Banach spaces of functions, the topological spaces we shall have to consider will be locally compact. If E is such a space, then $C(E) \subset C_0(E) \subset C_K(E)$ denote respectively the bounded real-valued continuous functions on E, the real-valued continuous functions vanishing at infinity, and the real-valued continuous functions with compact support. The first two of these spaces are Banach spaces under the supremum norm $\|\cdot\|$. We shall also denote by $\mathcal{E}$ the σ-algebra of Borel sets of E.

Almost always, the spaces E we shall deal with have a countable basis and we shall write for short: E is an LCCB. In that case we recall that:

(i) The σ-algebra $\mathcal{E}$ of Borel sets is generated by any open countable basis for the topology (hence $(E, \mathcal{E})$ is separable) as well as by the space $C_K(E)$.

(ii) The space E is metrizable, and one can choose a metric d compatible with the topology such that (E, d) is a separable complete metric space in which every closed and d-bounded set is compact.

(iii) The space E possesses a countable dense subset.

If E is an LCCB, a positive measure μ on $(E, \mathcal{E})$ will be called a *Radon measure* if $\mu(K) < \infty$ for every compact K. In particular, a Radon measure is σ-finite. If L is a non-negative linear functional on C_K, there is a unique Radon measure on $(E, \mathcal{E})$ such that $L(f) = \mu(f)$ for all $f \in C_K$. Every Radon measure is regular, that is for $B \in \mathcal{E}$

$$\mu(B) = \sup\{\mu(K) : K \subset B, K \text{ compact}\}$$
$$= \inf\{\mu(G) : G \supset B, G \text{ open}\}.$$

The space of Radon measures on E will be endowed with the vague topology, which is the coarsest topology for which all the functions $\mu \to \mu(f)$, $f \in C_K$, are continuous. We shall need the following compactness criterion.

Proposition 4.1. *A set $\{\mu_i, i \in I\}$ of measures is vaguely relatively compact if and only if for every compact subset K of E the sets of numbers $\{\mu_i(K), i \in I\}$ is bounded.*

A locally compact metrizable group G is a group which is also an LCCB such that the transformation from $G \times G$ onto G which sends (x, y) into $x^{-1}y$ is continuous. (We denote by x^{-1} the inverse of the element x and by V^{-1} the set of inverses of elements x in V.)

One can choose a metric compatible with the topology of G and invariant by left translations (or right translations) in G. If e is the identity of G, the filter $\mathscr{V}$ of neighbourhoods of e has the following properties:

(i) For every $U \in \mathscr{V}$ there is a set $V \in \mathscr{V}$ such that $VV^{-1} \subset U$;

(ii) If $U \in \mathscr{V}$ and x is any element of G then there exists a set $V \in \mathscr{V}$ such that $x^{-1}Vx \subset U$.

By (i) the class of symmetric ($V = V^{-1}$) neighbourhoods is a base for $\mathscr{V}$. Finally the filter of neighbourhoods of $x \in G$ is equal to $x\mathscr{V}$.

On every LCCB group G there is a left (right) invariant Radon measure, unique up to a multiplicative constant, called the left (right) Haar measure of G. Let m be the left Haar measure on G; then for every integrable function f,

$$\int f(x) \, \mathrm{d}m(x) = \int f(yx) \, \mathrm{d}m(x)$$

for every y in G. The group G is *unimodular* if the left Haar measure is also a right Haar measure. Abelian and compact groups are unimodular.

Finally, the convolution $\mu * \nu$ of two measures μ and ν is defined by

$$\langle \mu * \nu, f \rangle = \int\int f(xy) \, \mu(\mathrm{d}x) \, \nu(\mathrm{d}y),$$

provided the integral on the right is meaningful for all $f \in C_K$. The convolution of two functions f and g is defined by

$$(f * g)(x) = \int f(y) \, g(y^{-1}x) \, m(\mathrm{d}y)$$

if m is a left Haar measure. We shall use the fact that the convolution of a function in $\mathscr{L}^\infty$ and a function in $\mathscr{L}^1$ is a continuous function.

CHAPTER 1

TRANSITION PROBABILITIES. MARKOV CHAINS

This chapter is of an introductory nature; in it we discuss the basic data of our study. Throughout the sequel a measurable space $(E, \mathscr{E})$ is assumed given.

1. Kernels. Transition probabilities

Definition 1.1. A *kernel* on E is a mapping N from $E \times \mathscr{E}$ into $]-\infty, +\infty]$ such that:

(i) for every x in E, the mapping $A \to N(x, A)$ is a measure on $\mathscr{E}$ which will often be denoted by $N(x, \cdot)$;

(ii) for every A in $\mathscr{E}$, the mapping $x \to N(x, A)$ is a measurable function with respect to $\mathscr{E}$ which will often be denoted by $N(\cdot, A)$.

The kernel N is said to be *positive* if its range is in $[0, +\infty]$. It is said to be *σ-finite* if all the measures $N(x, \cdot)$ are σ-finite; it is said to be *proper* if E is the union of an increasing sequence $\{E_n\}_{n \geqslant 0}$ of subsets of E such that the functions $N(\cdot, E_n)$ are bounded.

Definition 1.2. In the sequel we shall deal mainly with positive kernels. If f is in $\mathscr{E}_+$, it is then easily seen by approximating f with simple functions that one defines a function in $\mathscr{E}_+$ denoted Nf or $N(f)$ by setting

$$Nf(x) = \int_E N(x, \mathrm{d}y)\, f(y) = \langle N(x, \cdot), f \rangle.$$

By defining $Nf = Nf^+ - Nf^-$, we may extend this to every function in $\mathscr{E}$ such that Nf^+ and Nf^- are not both infinite. We sometimes write $N(x, f)$ for $Nf(x)$; in particular $N(x, A) = N1_A(x)$.

In the same way, let m be a positive measure on $\mathscr{E}$, and define for $A \in \mathscr{E}$,

$$mN(A) = \int_E m(\mathrm{d}x)\, N(x, A) = \langle m, N(\,\cdot\,, A)\rangle;$$

it is easily seen that mN is a positive measure on $\mathscr{E}$, and as above this may be extended to signed measures. The two mappings thus defined are linear and, whenever the two members are meaningful, we have

$$\langle mN, f\rangle = \langle m, Nf\rangle.$$

Notice further that if we call ε_x the Dirac measure of the point x, we have $\varepsilon_x N(\,\cdot\,) = N(x, \cdot\,)$.

The mappings of $\mathscr{E}_+$ into itself defined by positive kernels are characterized by the following property.

Proposition 1.3. *An additive and homogeneous mapping V of $\mathscr{E}_+$ into itself is associated with a positive kernel if and only if for every increasing sequence $\{f_n\}$ of functions in $\mathscr{E}_+$ one has*

$$V\left(\lim_n f_n\right) = \lim_n Vf_n.$$

Proof. Easy and left to the reader as Exercise 1.9.

We proceed to a few examples of kernels.

Examples 1.4. (i) Let λ be a positive σ-finite measure on $\mathscr{E}$ and n a real-valued function defined on $E \times E$ and measurable with respect to the product σ-algebra $\mathscr{E} \otimes \mathscr{E}$.

One may then define a kernel N on E by setting

$$N(x, A) = \int_A n(x, y)\, \lambda(\mathrm{d}y).$$

Such a kernel is called an *integral kernel* with basis λ. When $E = \mathbf{R}^d$, $d \geqslant 3$, λ is the Lebesgue measure, and $n(x, y) = |x - y|^{-d+2}$, we thus get the kernel of newtonian potential theory.

If n is a positive function, then N is a positive kernel and for $f \in \mathscr{E}_+$,

$$Nf(x) = \int_E n(x, y)\, f(y)\, \lambda(\mathrm{d}y).$$

If $n(x, y) = a(x)\, b(y)$, where a, b are two measurable functions on E, then

$$Nf(x) = a(x) \int b(y) \, f(y) \, \lambda(dy) = \langle fb, \lambda \rangle \, a(x).$$

In that case we write $N = a \otimes b\lambda$, and simply $N = a \otimes \lambda$ if $b = 1$.

A case which has been extensively studied is the case where E is countable and $\mathscr{E}$ the discrete σ-algebra on E. The measure may be taken equal to the counting measure of E $(\lambda(\{x\}) = 1$ for every x in $E)$ and the integrals then reduce to sums, that is

$$Nf(x) = \sum_{y \in E} n(x, y) \, f(y).$$

But since in that case $N(x, \{y\}) = n(x, y)$, we shall mix the two notational devices and write more simply

$$Nf(x) = \sum_{y \in E} N(x, y) \, f(y).$$

It thus suffices to give the numbers $N(x, y)$ to define on E a kernel, which may then be viewed as an infinite square matrix indexed by the elements of E. The measures (functions) will be "row" ("column") vectors and the operators of Definition 1.2 are just the usual operators on vectors defined by square matrixes.

(ii) Let G be a multiplicative locally compact semi-group and μ a positive Radon measure on the Borel sets of G; one defines a positive kernel N on G by setting

$$N(x, A) = (\mu * \varepsilon_x) \, (A),$$

where $*$ denotes the convolution in G. For a Borel function f

$$Nf(x) = \int_G f(yx) \, \mu(dy)$$

and for a positive measure m on G, $mN = \mu * m$. Such a kernel is called a *convolution kernel*. The newtonian kernel of (i) is a convolution kernel.

The case where G is a group will of course be of special interest in the sequel. We remark that it is not true that $Nf = \mu * f$ since (whenever it makes sense)

$$(\mu * f) \, (x) = \int_G f(y^{-1}x) \, \mu(dy).$$

If we call $\hat{\mu}$ the image of μ by the mapping $x \to x^{-1}$, then $Nf = \hat{\mu} * f$.

This may be put in the following more general setting. We say that G (the elements of which are henceforth written $g, g', h, \ldots$) *operates* on the topological space M, or that M is a G-*space*, if there is a continuous mapping $g \times x \to gx$ from $G \times M$ to M such that $(g_1 g_2)\, x = g_1(g_2 x)$. With a positive measure μ on G we associate a kernel N on M, by setting, for a Borel function f on M,

$$Nf(x) = \int_G f(gx)\, \mu(dg);$$

if m is a positive measure on M then $mN = \mu * m$, where the convolution $*$ is defined by the formula

$$\langle \mu * m, f \rangle = \int_{G \times M} f(gx)\, \mu(dg)\, m(dx).$$

By letting G operate to the left on itself, we see that the former example is a special case of the latter.

(iii) A measurable mapping θ of E into itself $(\theta \in \mathscr{E}/\mathscr{E})$ is called a *point transformation* of E. With such a mapping we may associate a kernel by setting

$$N(x, A) = 1_A(\theta(x)) = 1_{\theta^{-1}(A)}(x).$$

Definition 1.5. The *composition* or *product* of two positive kernels M and N is defined by

$$MN(x, A) = \int_E M(x, dy)\, N(y, A).$$

It is easily seen that MN is a kernel and we have

Proposition 1.6. *The composition of positive kernels is an associative operation.*

Proof. By approximating $f \in \mathscr{E}_+$ by simple functions, it is easily checked that

$$((LM)N)\, f = (LM)\, (\cdot\, , Nf) = L(\cdot\, , (MNf)) = (L(MN))\, f,$$

which is the desired conclusion.

From now on, unless the contrary is stated, we deal only with positive kernels. By virtue of the preceding proposition we may therefore define the powers N^n of a positive kernel N; they are the kernels defined inductively by the formula

$$N^n(x, f) = N(x, N^{n-1}f) = N^{n-1}(x, Nf).$$

For $n = 0$, we set $N^0 = I$, where $I(x, \cdot) = \varepsilon_x(\cdot)$. The convolution powers of a positive probability measure μ on a group will be denoted μ^{*n} or more simply μ^n.

Let us give yet another definition that we shall need in the sequel.

Definition 1.7. Let M and N be two kernels; we say that M is *smaller than* N and write $M \leqslant N$ if for every $f \in \mathscr{E}_+$ we have $Mf \leqslant Nf$. We write $M < N$ if in addition there exists an $f \in \mathscr{E}_+$ such that $Mf < Nf$.

The following definitions are basic.

Definition 1.8. A kernel N such that $N(x, E) \leqslant 1$ for all x in E is called a *transition probability* or a *submarkovian* kernel. It is said to be *markovian* if $N(x, E) = 1$ for all x in E. In the sequel we shall often write T.P. instead of writing in full the words "transition probability."

Throughout almost all the sequel our basic datum will be a transition probability, denoted by the letter P, the properties of which we shall study from the probabilistic point of view as well as from the potential or ergodic theoretical points of view. The powers of P will be denoted P_n rather than P^n; this integer n will appear as a "time" in the sequel.

We close this section with a few useful remarks. If P is a T.P., the operators associated with P according to Definition 1.2 will also be denoted by P. They are *positive operators*, that is, they map positive functions (measures) into positive functions (measures). Moreover, they are linear and continuous operators on the Banach spaces $b\mathscr{E}$ and $b\mathscr{M}(\mathscr{E})$, and their norm is less than or equal to 1. This may be stated: P is a *positive contraction* of these Banach spaces. Finally notice that the product of two T.P.'s is itself a T.P.

Exercise 1.9. Prove Proposition 1.3.

[*Hint*. Define the kernel N by setting $N(x, A) = V1_A(x)$.]

Exercise 1.10. By using the convolution kernels associated with the three following measures on $\mathbf{R}$, prove that Proposition 1.6 may fail to be true if the kernels are not positive: (i) the Lebesgue measure, (ii) $\varepsilon_1 - \varepsilon_0$, (iii) the restriction of the Lebesgue measure to $\mathbf{R}_+$.

Exercise 1.11. Compute the powers of the kernels defined in Example 1.4 (ii).

Exercise 1.12. If $N = a \otimes \lambda$ compute MN and NM for an arbitrary positive kernel M.

Exercise 1.13. Let N and A be two positive kernels on $(E, \mathscr{E})$. Prove that the kernel $S = \sum_{n \geqslant 0} (NA)^n N$ satisfies the relation

$$S = N + NAS = N + SAN.$$

If B is another positive kernel, then

$$\sum_{n \geqslant 0} (SB)^n S = \sum_{n \geqslant 0} (N(A + B))^n N.$$

2. Homogeneous Markov chains

Let $(\Omega, \mathscr{F}, P_0)$ be a probability space and $X = \{X_n\}_{n \geqslant 0}$ a sequence of random variables defined on Ω with their range in E. Let $\mathscr{F}_n = \sigma(X_m, m \leqslant n)$ and $\mathscr{G}_n$ be an increasing sequence of σ-algebras such that $\mathscr{G}_n \supset \mathscr{F}_n$ for every n.

Definition 2.1. *The sequence* $X = \{X_n\}_{n \geqslant 0}$ *is said to be a Markov chain with respect to the σ-algebras* $\mathscr{G}_n$ *if, for every* n, *the σ-algebras* $\mathscr{G}_n$ *and* $\sigma(X_m, m \geqslant n)$ *are conditionally independent with respect to* X_n; *in other words, if for every* $A \in \mathscr{G}_n$ *and* $B \in \sigma(X_m, m \geqslant n)$

$$P_0[A \cap B \mid X_n] = P_0[A \mid X_n] \, P_0[B \mid X_n] \quad \text{a.s.}$$

If $\mathscr{G}_n = \mathscr{F}_n$, we say simply that X_n is a Markov chain; the "past" $\sigma(X_m, m \leqslant n)$ and the "future" $\sigma(X_m, m \geqslant n)$ then play totally symmetric roles in this definition, the intuitive meaning of which is clear: given the present X_n, the past and the future are independent.

Notice that if the above property is true with the σ-algebras $\mathscr{G}_n$, it is a fortiori true with the σ-algebras $\mathscr{F}_n$. Finally we emphasize the importance of P_0 in this definition.

Proposition 2.2. *The sequence* X *is a Markov chain if and only if for every random variable* $Y \in b\sigma(X_m, m \geqslant n)$,

$$E_0[Y \mid \mathscr{G}_n] = E_0[Y \mid X_n]. \tag{2.1}$$

Proof. Pick A in $\mathscr{G}_n$ and B in $\sigma(X_m, m \geqslant n)$; then, since $\mathscr{G}_n \supset \sigma(X_n)$

$$E_0[1_A 1_B \mid X_n] = E_0[1_A 1_B \mid \mathscr{G}_n \mid X_n] = E_0[1_A E[1_B \mid \mathscr{G}_n] \mid X_n],$$

and if the property in the statement is true, this is equal to

$$E_0[1_A E_0[1_B \mid X_n] \mid X_n] = E_0[1_A \mid X_n] E_0[1_B \mid X_n],$$

which proves that $\{X_n\}_{n \geqslant 0}$ is a Markov chain.

Conversely it suffices to show the above property when $Y = 1_B$ with B in $\sigma(X_m, m \geqslant n)$, and this amounts to showing that for every A in $\mathscr{G}_n$,

$$E_0[1_A 1_B] = E_0[1_A E_0[1_B \mid X_n]].$$

But since $\{X_n\}$ is a Markov chain, the right member is equal to

$$E_0[E_0[1_A E[1_B \mid X_n] \mid X_n]] = E_0[E_0[1_A \mid X_n] E_0[1_B \mid X_n]]$$
$$= E_0[E_0[1_A 1_B \mid X_n]] = E_0[1_A 1_B],$$

which completes the proof.

The following definition is basic.

Definition 2.3. *The sequence* $X = \{X_n\}_{n \geqslant 0}$ *of random variables is called a homogeneous Markov chain with respect to the σ-algebras* $\mathscr{G}_n$ *with transition probability* P *if, for any integers* m, n *with* $m < n$ *and any function* $f \in \mathrm{b}\mathscr{E}$, *we have*

$$E_0[f(X_m) \mid \mathscr{G}_n] = P_{n-m} f(X_m) \quad P_0\text{-a.s.}$$

The probability measure ν defined by $\nu(A) = P_0[X_0 \in A]$ is called the *starting measure*. If $\mathscr{G}_n = \mathscr{F}_n$, we say more simply that X is a homogeneous Markov chain with transition probability P.

By the next proposition, a Markov chain in the sense of Definition 2.3 is a Markov chain in the sense of Definition 2.1.

Proposition 2.4. *The sequence* $\{X_n\}_{n \geqslant 0}$ *is a Markov chain with transition probability* P *if and only if for every finite collection of integers* $t_0 = 0 < t_1 \cdots < t_n$ *and functions* $f_0, \ldots, f_n$ *in* $\mathrm{b}\mathscr{E}$ *one has*

$$E_0 \left[\prod_{i=0}^{n} f_i(X_{t_i}) \right] = \int_E \nu(\mathrm{d}x_0) \, f_0(x_0) \int_E P_{t_1}(x_0, \mathrm{d}x_1) \, f_1(x_1) \cdots$$
$$\int_E P_{t_n - t_{n-1}}(x_{n-1}, \mathrm{d}x_n) \, f_n(x_n).$$

Proof. If $n = 1$, the above formula follows at once from Definition 2.3. Now, applying Definition 2.3, we get

$$E_0\left[\prod_{i=0}^{n} f_i(X_{t_i})\right] = E_0\left[\prod_{i=0}^{n-1} f_i(X_{t_i})\, E_0[f_n(X_{t_n}) \mid \mathscr{G}_{t_{n-1}}]\right]$$

$$= E_0\left[\prod_{i=0}^{n-1} f_i(X_{t_i})\, P_{t_n - t_{n-1}} f_n(X_{t_{n-1}})\right].$$

Since $f_{n-1}\, P_{t_n - t_{n-1}}\, f_n$ is still a function of $b\mathscr{E}$, the "only if" part follows by induction.

To obtain the "if" part, it suffices by the monotone class theorem, to prove that for every integer $t_0 = 0 < t_1 < \cdots < t_k \leqslant m < n$ and functions $f_0, f_1, \ldots, f_k, f$ in $b\mathscr{E}$ one has

$$E_0\left[\prod_{i=0}^{k} f_i(X_{t_i})\, f(X_n)\right] = E_0\left[\prod_{i=0}^{k} f_i(X_{t_i})\, P_{n-m} f(X_m)\right];$$

but this is an immediate consequence of the above formula.

Remark 2.5. It is easily seen that the condition in Definition 2.3 is satisfied provided it is satisfied for every pair of consecutive integers.

The main goal of this section is to show that with every transition probability we may associate a homogeneous Markov chain, which will be one of the main objects of our study. We begin with a few preliminaries.

Let P be a T.P. on E. Let $\varDelta$ be a point not in E and write $E_\varDelta = E \cup \{\varDelta\}$ and $\mathscr{E}_\varDelta = \sigma(\mathscr{E}, \{\varDelta\})$. We extend P to $(E_\varDelta, \mathscr{E}_\varDelta)$ by setting

$$P(x, \{\varDelta\}) = 1 - P(x, E) \quad \text{if } x \neq \varDelta, \qquad P(\varDelta, \{\varDelta\}) = 1.$$

If E is locally compact we choose as $\varDelta$ the point at infinity in the Alexandrov's compactification of E. We introduce the following convention: any numerical function f on E will *automatically be extended to $E_\varDelta$ by setting $f(\varDelta) = 0$*.

Heuristically speaking, P is the tool which permits us to describe the random path of a "particle" in E. Starting at x at time 0, the particle hits a random point x_1 at time 1 according to the probability measure $P(x, \cdot)$, then a random point x_2 at time 2 according to $P(x_1, \cdot)$ and so forth. If $P(x, E) < 1$, that means that the particle may disappear or "die" with positive probability; by convention it then arrives at the "fictitious" point $\varDelta$, where it stays for ever after. We assume however that $P(x, E) > 0$ for every x in E; that is, the particle does not die at once with probability one.

Definition 2.6. The point Δ is called the *cemetery*. We shall rather say "point at infinity" when E is locally compact. The space $(E, \mathscr{E})$ is called the *state space*.

We are now going to give a mathematical formulation of the above description. For every integer $n \geqslant 0$, let $(E_\Delta^n, \mathscr{E}_\Delta^n)$ be a copy of $(E_\Delta, \mathscr{E}_\Delta)$; we call $(\Omega, \mathscr{F})$ their product space, namely $\Omega = \prod_{n=0}^\infty E_\Delta^n$, and $\mathscr{F}$ is the σ-algebra generated by the semi-algebra $\mathscr{S}$ of *measurable rectangles* of Ω. We recall that a measurable rectangle is a set of the form

$$\prod_{n=0}^\infty A_n, \qquad A_n \in \mathscr{E}_\Delta^n,$$

where it is assumed that A_n is different from E_Δ^n for only finitely many n.

Definition 2.7. The space Ω is called the *canonical probability space*. We call X_n, $n \geqslant 0$, the coordinate mappings of Ω. Let $\omega = \{x_n, n \geqslant 0\}$ be a point in Ω; then $X_n(\omega) = x_n$; we also set $X_\infty(\omega) = \Delta$ for every ω in Ω. These mappings X_n are random variables defined on Ω with range in E, and are clearly measurable with respect to the σ-algebras $\mathscr{F}_n = \sigma(X_m, m \leqslant n)$. A point ω in Ω is referred to as a *trajectory* or a *path*.

We come to our main result.

Theorem 2.8. *For every x in E there exists a unique probability measure P_x on $(\Omega, \mathscr{F})$ such that for any finite collection $0 < n_1 < n_2 < \cdots < n_k$ of integers and every rectangle*

$$A = \prod_{i=0}^k A_{n_i} \times \prod_{n \neq n_i} E_\Delta^n,$$

$$P_x[A] = 1_{A_0}(x) \int_{A_{n_1}} P_{n_1}(x, dx_1) \int_{A_{n_2}} P_{n_2-n_1}(x_1, dx_2) \cdots$$

$$\int_{A_{n_{k-1}}} P_{n_{k-2}}(x_{k-2}, dx_{k-1}) \, P_{n_k-n_{k-1}}(x_{k-1}, A_{n_k}). \qquad (2.1)$$

Furthermore for every set $A \in \mathscr{F}$, the map $x \to P_x[A]$ is $\mathscr{E}_\Delta$-measurable.

Proof. Equation (2.1) defines clearly an additive set function on $\mathscr{S}$ which has a unique extension to an additive function on the Boolean algebra $\mathscr{A} = \bigcup_{n=0}^\infty \mathscr{F}_n$ and the restriction of this set function to each of the σ-algebras

$\mathscr{F}_n$ is a probability measure. To prove the theorem it suffices to show that it is σ-additive on $\mathscr{A}$.

We still call P_x the extended set function. By the properties of T.P.'s, it is plain that the map $x \to P_x[A]$ is measurable if A is in $\mathscr{A}$. Provided the first half of the statement is true, the family of sets A such that $x \to P_x[A]$ is measurable is closed under proper differences and increasing limits; the second half in the statement is then derived from the monotone class theorem.

We proceed to show the first half. To this end we set $\Omega^n = \prod_{m=n}^{\infty} E_{\Delta}^m$, and, for $A \in \mathscr{A}$ and $(x_0, x_1, \ldots, x_n)$ a finite collection of points in E_{Δ}, we write $A(x_0, x_1, \ldots, x_n)$ for the sets of points ω^{n+1} in Ω^{n+1} such that $(x_0, x_1, \ldots, x_n, \omega^{n+1})$ is in A. The space Ω^n being isomorphic to Ω, we may define a set function on the algebra generated by the rectangles of Ω^n in the same way as we have defined P_x. This set function will be denoted by P_x^n.

Let $\{A^j\}$ be a sequence in $\mathscr{A}$ decreasing to $\emptyset$ and suppose that $\lim_j P_x[A^j] > 0$. Since $A^j \in \mathscr{A}$, we have

$$P_x[A^j] = 1_{A_0^j}(x) \int_{E_{\Delta}^1} P(x, dx_1) \, P_{x_1}^1[A^j(x)],$$

where A_0^j is the projection of A^j on E^0. The assumption we have made implies then that x is in A_0^j for every j, and since $P(x, \cdot)$ is a probability measure, there exists a point $\bar{x}_1 \in E$ such that $\lim_j P_{\bar{x}_1}[A^j(x)] > 0$. We can repeat for $P_{\bar{x}_1}^1$ and $A^j(x)$ what has been said for P_x and A^j; it follows that $(x, \bar{x}_1)$ belongs to the projection of all the sets A^j on $E_{\Delta}^0 \times E_{\Delta}^1$, and that there exists a point $\bar{x}_2$ such that $\lim_j P_{\bar{x}_2}^2[A^j(x, \bar{x}_1)] > 0$.

Proceeding inductively, we find that for every n there is a point $\bar{x}_n$ in E_{Δ}^n such that $(x, \bar{x}_1, \ldots, \bar{x}_n)$ belongs, for every j, to the projection of A^j on $E_{\Delta}^0 \times E_{\Delta}^1 \times \cdots \times E_{\Delta}^n$. Now, for every j, there is an integer k such that the projection of A^j on E_{Δ}^p, $p > k$, is equal to E_{Δ}^p. As a result the point $\omega = (x, \bar{x}_1, \ldots, \bar{x}_n, \ldots)$ belongs to every A^j, which is a contradiction.

Definition 2.9. For every probability measure ν on $(E, \mathscr{E})$, we define a new probability measure P_ν on $(\Omega, \mathscr{F})$ by setting

$$P_\nu[A] = \int_E \nu(dx) \, P_x[A].$$

Indeed, the measurability in the preceding theorem gives sense to the above formula, which clearly defines a probability measure. For $\nu = \varepsilon_x$ we have $P_\nu = P_x$, and if A is the rectangle in Theorem 2.8, then since

$$A = \{\omega : X_0(\omega) \in A_0, \, X_{n_1}(\omega) \in A_{n_1}, \ldots, X_{n_k}(\omega) \in A_{n_k}\},$$

we have

$$P_\nu[A] = P_\nu[X_0 \in A_0, \, X_{n_1} \in A_1, \ldots, X_{n_k} \in A_{n_k}]$$

$$= \int_{A_0} \nu(\mathrm{d}x) \int_{A_{n_1}} P_{n_1}(x, \mathrm{d}x_1) \cdots$$

$$\int_{A_{n_{k-1}}} P_{n_{k-2}-n_{k-1}}(x_{k-2}, \mathrm{d}x_{k-1}) \, P_{n_k-n_{k-1}}(x_{k-1}, A_{n_k}). \tag{2.2}$$

By comparing this relation with that of Proposition 2.4, we can state:

Proposition 2.10. *For every probability measure P_ν the sequence $X = \{X_n\}_{n \geqslant 0}$ is a homogeneous Markov chain with transition probability P and starting measure ν. It is called the canonical Markov chain with transition probability P.*

Proof. By the usual argument we may replace the sets A_{n_i} in the above relation by functions f_{n_i}, so that X satisfies the condition of Proposition 2.4.

Definition 2.11. Let $q(\omega)$ be a property of ω; then q is said to hold *almost surely* (a.s.) *on* $\Lambda \in \mathscr{F}$, if the set of ω in Λ for which $q(\omega)$ fails to hold is contained in a set $\Lambda_0 \in \mathscr{F}$ such that for every $x \in E$, $P_x(\Lambda_0) = 0$. If $\Lambda = \Omega$ we simply say "almost surely".

We proceed with some more definitions and notations. Let Z be a positive numerical random variable on $(\Omega, \mathscr{F})$. Its mathematical expectation taken with respect to P_ν will be denoted $E_\nu[Z]$; if $\nu = \varepsilon_x$, then we write simply $E_x[Z]$. It is easily seen that the map $x \to E_x[Z]$ is in $\mathscr{E}$ and that

$$E_\nu[Z] = \int_E \nu(\mathrm{d}x) \, E_x[Z].$$

Furthermore if $f \in \mathscr{E}_+$, then $f(X_n)$ is a random variable on $(\Omega, \mathscr{F})$ and we have

$$E_x[f(X_n)] = P_n f(x) = \int_E P_n(x, \mathrm{d}y) \, f(y). \tag{2.3}$$

Indeed, for $f = 1_A$ this formula is a special case of eq. (2.1), and it may be extended to $\mathscr{E}_+$ by the usual argument.

Definition 2.12. The *shift operator* θ is the point transformation on Ω defined by

$$\theta(\{x_0, x_1, \ldots, x_n, \ldots\}) = \{x_1, x_2, \ldots, x_{n+1}, \ldots\}.$$

It is obvious that $\theta \in \mathscr{F}/\mathscr{F}$ and that $X_n(\theta(\omega)) = X_{n+1}(\omega)$. We write θ_p for the pth power of θ: $\theta_p = \theta \circ \theta \cdots \circ \theta$ p times. Clearly $X_n(\theta_p(\omega)) = X_{n+p}(\omega)$, which will also be written $X_n \circ \theta_p = X_{n+p}$. Since

$$\theta_p^{-1}\{X_n \in A\} = \{X_{n+p} \in A\},$$

it is easily seen that $\theta_p \in \sigma(X_n, n \geqslant p)/\mathscr{F}$.

The following proposition gives the handy form of the Markov property and will frequently be used in the sequel.

Proposition 2.13 (Markov property). *For every positive random variable Z on $(\Omega, \mathscr{F})$, every starting measure ν and integer n,*

$$E_\nu[Z \circ \theta_n \mid \mathscr{F}_n] = E_{X_n}[Z] \quad P_\nu\text{-a.s.}$$

Before we proceed to the proof let us remark that the right-hand side of the above relation is indeed a random variable because it is the composite mapping of the two measurable mappings $\omega \rightarrow X_n(\omega)$ and $x \rightarrow E_x[Z]$. We also notice that if $Z = 1_{\{X_m \in A\}}$, $A \in \mathscr{E}$, the above formula becomes

$$P_\nu[X_{n+m} \in A \mid \mathscr{F}_n] = P_{X_n}[X_m \in A] \quad P_\nu\text{-a.s.},$$

which is the formula of Definition 2.3.

Proof of 2.13. We must prove that for any $B \in \mathscr{F}_n$,

$$\int_B Z \circ \theta_n \, dP_\nu = \int_B E_{X_n}[Z] \, dP_\nu;$$

and by the usual extension argument it suffices to prove this relation for the case in which B is a rectangle, namely $B = \{X_{p_1} \in B_1, \ldots, X_{p_k} \in B_k\}$ with $B_i \in \mathscr{E}$, and in which $Z = 1_A$, where A is the rectangle used in Theorem 2.8. The result then follows immediately from eq. (2.2).

As much as P, our basic datum will henceforth be the canonical chain X associated with P. We shall be concerned with all probability measures P_ν, and shall use freely the Markov property of Proposition 2.13. Indeed, although the canonical chain is not the only chain with transition probability P, it has the following universal property which allows one to translate any problem on a chain Y to the analogous problem on the canonical chain X.

Proposition 2.14. *Let Y be a homogeneous Markov chain defined on the probability space $(W, \mathfrak{A}, Q)$ with transition probability P and starting measure $\nu(\cdot)$ $= Q[Y_0 \in \cdot\,]$. Then the canonical Markov chain associated with P is the image of Y by the mapping φ which sends $w \in W$ to the point*

$$\omega = \varphi(w) = (Y_0(w),\ Y_1(w), \ldots,\ Y_n(w), \ldots)$$

of $\Omega = E_\varDelta^N$. The image of Q by φ is equal to P_ν.

Proof. The mapping φ is measurable because the composite mappings of φ with the coordinate mappings X_n are equal to the random variables Y_n. It is then easily verified that $\varphi(Q) = P_\nu$.

Exercise 2.15. Prove that a real random variable Z is $\sigma(X_m, m \geqslant n)$-measurable if and only if $Z = Z' \circ \theta_n$ where $Z' \in \mathscr{F}$.

Exercise 2.16. A sequence $\{X_n\}_{n \geqslant 0}$ of random variables defined on $(\Omega, \mathscr{F}, P)$ is a Markov chain of order r if for every $B \in \mathscr{E}$ and integer n,

$$P[X_{n+1} \in B \mid \sigma(X_m, m \leqslant n)] = P[X_{n+1} \in B \mid \sigma(X_m, n - r + 1 \leqslant m \leqslant n)].$$

Prove that the sequence of random variables $Y_n = (X_{n+1}, \ldots, X_{n+r-1})$ with range in E^r is a Markov chain in the ordinary sense.

Exercise 2.17. (1) Suppose that for every pair $m \leqslant n$ of integers there is a T.P. called $P_{m,n}$ such that $P_{l,m} P_{m,n} = P_{l,n}$. Prove that one can associate with these T.P.'s a *non-homogeneous Markov chain*, that is, a sequence of random variables X_n defined on a space $(\Omega, \mathscr{F}, P)$ and such that for $f \in b\mathscr{E}$

$$E[f(X_n) \mid \sigma(X_k, k \leqslant m)] = P_{m,n}f(X_m) \quad \text{a.s.}$$

(2) In the situation of (1) the *space–time chain* $(X_n \times n)$ with range in $E \times \mathbf{N}$ is a homogeneous Markov chain. ((2) may be solved without previous solution of (1).)

Exercise 2.18 (Galton–Watson chain). This arises in the study of the growth of a population.

Let X be a Markov chain on $E = \mathbf{N}$ such that the conditional probability $P_v[X_{n+1} = x \mid \mathscr{F}_n]$ is equal to the sum of X_n independent equidistributed random variables of law $p = (p(x), x \in E)$. The T.P. is thus given by $P(x, y) = p^{*x}(y)$.

(1) Prove that for every n there exists a probability measure p_n on E such that $P_n(x, y) = p_n^{*x}(y)$.

[*Hint*: Begin by proving that the mapping φ from Ω^x into Ω defined by

$$X_n(\varphi(\omega_1, \ldots, \omega_x)) = X_n(\omega_1) + \cdots + X_n(\omega_x)$$

sends the product measure $P_1 \otimes P_1 \otimes \cdots \otimes P_1$ to P_x. This is the mathematical formulation of the following intuitive fact: the chain starting at x behaves as the sum of x independent chains starting at 1.]

(2) Prove that the generating functions $g_n(t) = \sum_{x \in E} t^x p_n(x)$ are given by the recurrence formula

$$g_{n+1}(t) = g_n(g(t)) = g(g_n(t)),$$

where g is the generating function of the measure p. Compute for P_1 the mean value and variance of X_n as functions of those of X_1 which are assumed to exist.

3. Stopping times. Strong Markov property

Definition 3.1. A *stopping time* of the canonical Markov chain X is a random variable defined on $(\Omega, \mathscr{F})$ with range in $\mathbf{N} \cup \{\infty\}$ and such that for every integer n the event $\{T = n\}$ is in $\mathscr{F}_n$. The family $\mathscr{F}_T$ of events $A \in \mathscr{F}$ such that for every n, $\{T = n\} \cap A \in \mathscr{F}_n$ is called the σ-algebra associated with T.

It is easily verified that $\mathscr{F}_T$ is indeed a sub-σ-algebra of $\mathscr{F}$. The constant random variables are stopping times, and if $T(\omega) = n$ for every $\omega \in \Omega$, then $\mathscr{F}_T = \mathscr{F}_n$. The stopping times thus appear as generalizations of the ordinary times. The following examples of stopping times are basic.

Definition 3.2. For $A \in \mathscr{E}$, we call first *hitting time* of A and first *return time* of A the random variables defined by

$$T_A(\omega) = \inf\{n \geqslant 0 \colon X_n(\omega) \in A\},$$

$$S_A(\omega) = \inf\{n > 0 \colon X_n(\omega) \in A\},$$

where in both cases the infimum of the empty set is understood to be $+\infty$.

It is readily checked that both variables are stopping times. For example

$$\{T_A = n\} = \bigcap_{m=0}^{n-1} \{X_m \in A^c\} \cap \{X_n \in A\} \in \mathscr{F}_n.$$

In the same way the random variable

$$\zeta(\omega) = \inf\{n \geqslant 0 \colon X_n(\omega) = \varDelta\}$$

is a stopping time called the death-time of X.

Definition 3.3. With each stopping time T we associate the following objects:
   (i) The random variable X_T is defined by setting

$$X_T(\omega) = X_n(\omega) \quad \text{if } T(\omega) = n, \qquad X_T(\omega) = \varDelta \quad \text{if } T(\omega) = +\infty.$$

It gives the position of the chain at time T, and the reader will easily check that $X_T \in \mathscr{F}_T/\mathscr{E}_\varDelta$.
   (ii) The point transformation θ_T on $\varOmega$ is defined by setting

$$\theta_T(\omega) = \theta_n(\omega) \quad \text{if } T(\omega) = n, \qquad \theta_T(\omega) = \omega_\varDelta \quad \text{if } T(\omega) = +\infty,$$

where $\omega_\varDelta$ is the trajectory $\{\varDelta, \varDelta, \ldots, \varDelta, \ldots\}$ of $\varOmega$. It is easily seen that $\theta_T \in \mathscr{F}/\mathscr{F}$ and that

$$X_n(\theta_T(\omega)) = X_{n+m}(\omega) \quad \text{on } \{T = m\}, \qquad X_n(\theta_T(\omega)) = \varDelta \quad \text{on } \{T = \infty\}.$$

Proposition 3.4. *Let S and T be two stopping times; then the mapping $S + T \circ \theta_S \colon \omega \to S(\omega) + T(\theta_S(\omega))$ is a stopping time.*

Proof. We have

$$\{S + T \circ \theta_S = n\} = \bigcup_{p \leqslant n} \{S = p\} \cap \{T \circ \theta_S = n - p\}.$$

The event $\{S = p\}$ is in $\mathscr{F}_p \subset \mathscr{F}_n$ and on $\{S = p\}$ we have $\theta_S = \theta_p$; hence

$$\{T \circ \theta_S = n - p\} = \{T \circ \theta_p = n - p\} = \theta_p^{-1}(\{T = n - p\}) \in \mathscr{F}_n$$

since $\{T = n - p\} \in \mathscr{F}_{n-p}$.

Intuitively one should think of stopping times as the first time some physical event occurs and of $\mathscr{F}_T$ as containing the information on the chain up to time T when this event occurs. The time $S + T \circ \theta_S$ is the first time where the "event T" occurs after the "event S" has occurred. For instance if $A \in \mathscr{E}$, $n + T_A \circ \theta_n$ is the first hitting time of A after time n; in particular $S_A = 1 + T_A \circ \theta_1$. If $A, B \in \mathscr{E}$, then $T_A + T_B \circ \theta_{T_A}$ is the first time the chain hits B after having hit A.

Despite its simplicity the following result is basic. It implies in particular that if one starts to observe the chain at a stopping time, the ensuing process is still a homogeneous Markov chain with the same T.P. (cf. Exercise 3.13).

Theorem 3.5 (Strong Markov property). *For every real positive random variable Z on $(\Omega, \mathscr{F})$, starting measure ν and stopping time T,*

$$E_\nu[Z \circ \theta_T \mid \mathscr{F}_T] = E_{X_T}[Z] \quad P_\nu\text{-a.s.}$$

By convention the two members vanish on $\{T = \infty\}$.

The right member is the composite mapping of $\omega \to X_T(\omega)$ and $x \to E_x[Z]$.

Proof. We have to show that for $A \in \mathscr{F}_T$,

$$\int_A Z \circ \theta_T \, dP_\nu = \int_A E_{X_T}[Z] \, dP_\nu,$$

or equivalently

$$\sum_{n \geqslant 0} \int_{A \cap \{T=n\}} Z \circ \theta_T \, dP_\nu = \sum_{n \geqslant 0} \int_{A \cap \{T=n\}} E_{X_T}[Z] \, dP_\nu.$$

It suffices therefore to prove that for every $n \geqslant 0$ and $B \in \mathscr{F}_n$,

$$\int_B Z \circ \theta_n \, dP_\nu = \int_B E_{X_n}[Z] \, dP_\nu,$$

but this is precisely the Markov property of Proposition 2.13.

Definition 3.6. With each stopping time T we associate a new T.P., denoted P_T, by setting for $B \in \mathscr{E}$,

$$P_T(x, B) = P_x[X_T \in B].$$

It is easily seen that if $f \in \mathscr{E}_+$, then

$$P_T f(x) = E_x[f(X_T)].$$

We recall that by our conventions $f(X_T) = 0$ on $\{T = \infty\}$. We further notice that if $T = n$ a.s., then $P_T = P_n$. Finally if $A \in \mathscr{E}$, we write P_A instead of P_{T_A}; this T.P. is called the *balayage operator* associated with A.

Before we state our next result, we introduce the following notation. Let $A \in \mathscr{E}$; define I_A to be the operator of multiplication by 1_A, $I_A f(x) = f(x)$ if $x \in A$, $I_A f(x) = 0$ if $x \notin A$. We may now give for P_A the following analytical expression.

Proposition 3.7. *For $A \in \mathscr{E}$,*

$$P_A = \sum_{n \geqslant 0} (I_{A^c} P)^n I_A.$$

Proof. Let $B \in \mathscr{E}$; using eq. (2.1), we have

$$P_A(x, B) = 1_{A \cap B}(x) + \sum_{n=1}^{\infty} P_x[X_0 \notin A, \ldots, X_{n-1} \notin A, X_n \in A \cap B]$$

$$= 1_{A \cap B}(x) + \sum_{n=1}^{\infty} 1_{A^c}(x) \int P(x, dx_1) \, 1_{A^c}(x_1) \int P(x_1, dx_2) \, 1_{A^c}(x_2) \cdots$$

$$\int P(x_{n-1}, dx_n) \, 1_{B \cap A}(x_n),$$

which is the desired result.

Clearly the measures $P_A(x, \cdot)$ vanish outside A. Furthermore if $x \in A$, then $P_A(x, \cdot) = \varepsilon_x$; indeed $x \in A$ implies $P_x[X_0 = x] = 1$, hence $T_A = 0$ P_x-a.s. and consequently $X_{T_A} = x$ P_x-a.s. In the same way, if $x \notin A$, then $T_A = S_A$ P_x-a.s. and $P_A(x, \cdot) = P_{S_A}(x, \cdot)$.

We close this section by applying the strong Markov property to compute the products of operators P_T. We first notice that if S and T are two stopping times then $X_T(\theta_S(\omega)) = X_{S+T\circ\theta_S}(\omega)$, which we write simply $X_T \circ \theta_S = X_{S+T\circ\theta_S}$.

Proposition 3.8. *Let S, T be two stopping times; then $P_S P_T = P_{S+T\circ\theta_S}$.*

Proof. Let $f \in b\mathscr{E}_+$. We have, applying Definition 3.6,

$$P_S P_T f(x) = E_x[P_T f(X_S)] = E_x[E_{X_S}[f(X_T)]]$$

$$= E_x[E_x[f(X_T \circ \theta_S) \mid \mathscr{F}_S]] = E_x[f(X_T \circ \theta_S)] = P_{S+T\circ\theta_S} f(x).$$

In particular, we get $P_{S_A} = PP_A$, which implies

$$P_{S_A} = P\left(\sum_{n \geqslant 0} (I_{A^c} P)^n I_A\right).$$

We set

$$\Pi_A = I_A P_{S_A} = I_A P\left(\sum_{n \geqslant 0} (I_{A^c} P)^n I_A\right) = I_A\left(\sum_{n \geqslant 0} (P I_{A^c})^n\right) P I_A.$$

The interpretation of the kernel Π_A is given in Exercise 3.12.

Exercise 3.9. Let $A, B \in \mathscr{E}$; can $T_{A \cup B}$ and $T_{A \cap B}$ be expressed as functions of T_A and T_B? Given $A \subset B$, compare T_A and T_B and prove that $P_B P_A = P_A$.

Exercise 3.10. Let S and T be two stopping times.
(1) Prove that $\inf(S, T)$ and $\sup(S, T)$ are stopping times. In particular $S \wedge n$ is a stopping time for every n.
(2) If $\Gamma \in \mathscr{F}_S$, then $\Gamma \cap \{S \leqslant T\} \in \mathscr{F}_T$. If $S \leqslant T$, then $\mathscr{F}_S \subset \mathscr{F}_T$.
(3) Prove that the event $\{S \leqslant T\}$ is in $\mathscr{F}_S \cap \mathscr{F}_T$;
(4) Prove that $S + T$ is a stopping time.

Exercise 3.11. (1) Let $A \in \mathscr{E}$; prove that $T_A = n + T_A \circ \theta_n$ on $\{T_A \geqslant n\}$. Let $A, B \in \mathscr{E}$; has $T_A + T_B \circ \theta_{T_A}$ the same property as T_A?
(2) Let T be a stopping time such that $T = n + T \circ \theta_n$ on $\{T \geqslant n\}$. Let Y be the sequence of random variables defined by

$$Y_n(\omega) = X_n(\omega) \quad \text{if } T(\omega) > n, \qquad Y_n(\omega) = \Delta \quad \text{if } T(\omega) \leqslant n.$$

Prove that Y is a homogeneous Markov chain with respect to the σ-algebras $\mathscr{F}_{T \wedge n}$ for every probability measure P_x on $(\Omega, \mathscr{F})$. When $T = T_A$ we can take A^c as its state space; prove then that its T.P. is equal to $I_{A^c} P I_{A^c}$. The chain Y is said to be obtained by *killing* X at time T_A.

Exercise 3.12. Let $A \in \mathscr{E}$ and define inductively the times

$$T_1 = S_A, \; T_2 = T_1 + S_A \circ \theta_{T_1}, \ldots, \; T_n = T_{n-1} + S_A \circ \theta_{T_{n-1}}, \ldots.$$

(1) Prove that the times T_n are the successive times at which the chain returns in A.
(2) Prove that the sequence $\{Y_n = X_{T_n}\}$ is a homogeneous Markov chain with respect to the σ-algebras $\mathscr{F}_{T_n}$ with T.P. Π_A. This chain is called the chain *induced* on A or the *trace chain* on A.

Exercise 3.13. Let T be a finite stopping time. Prove that the sequence $Y = \{X_{T+n}\}_{n \geqslant 0}$ is a homogeneous Markov chain with transition probability P with respect to the σ-algebras $\mathscr{F}_{T+n}$. What can be said if T is not finite?

Exercise 3.14. *Stopped chains.* If T is a stopping time of X prove that the sequence $Y = \{X_{T \wedge n}\}_{n \geqslant 0}$ is a homogeneous Markov chain if and only if $T = T_A$ for a set $A \in \mathscr{E}$. In that case write down the T.P. of the chain Y.

Exercise 3.15. Let T be a stopping time and G a real function on $\Omega \times \Omega$ measurable with respect to $\mathscr{F}_T \otimes \mathscr{F}$. Prove that for any ν,

$$E_\nu[G(\omega, \theta_T(\omega)) \mid \mathscr{F}_T] = \int_\Omega P_{X_T}(\omega)\, (d\omega')\, G(\omega, \omega') \quad P_\nu\text{-a.s.}$$

for $\omega, \omega' \in \Omega$.

[*Hint*: Begin with $G(\omega, \omega') = \varphi(\omega)\, \psi(\omega')$, where $\varphi \in \mathscr{F}_T$.]

Exercise 3.16. Let T be a stopping time and S a random variable $\mathscr{F}_T$-measurable and $\geqslant T$ a.s. Prove that, for $f \in \mathscr{E}_+$,

$$E_\nu[f \circ X_S \mid \mathscr{F}_T]\,(\omega) = P_{S(\omega)-T(\omega)}(X_T, f) \quad P_\nu\text{-a.s.}$$

[*Hint*: Use the preceding exercise with $G(\omega, \omega') = f(X_{S(\omega)}(\omega'))$.]

Exercise 3.17. A random variable L defined on $(\Omega, \mathscr{F})$, with range in $\mathbf{N} \cup \{\infty\}$, is called a *death time* if $L \circ \theta = (L-1)^+$, that is,

$$L \circ \theta = L - 1 \quad \text{if } L \geqslant 1, \qquad L \circ \theta = 0 \quad \text{if } L = 0.$$

(1) Let $A \in \mathscr{E}$; prove that the last hitting time of A, namely

$$L_A = \sup\{n \geqslant 0, X_n \in A\},$$

where the supremum of the empty set is taken equal to zero, is a death time. The death time of the chain is a death time.

(2) Prove that $X_L \circ \theta = X_L$ on $\{0 < L\}$ if L is a death time.

(3) If L and L' are death times, then $L \vee L'$ and $L \wedge L'$ are death times; $(L-n)^+$ is a death time for every n.

4. Random walks on groups and homogeneous spaces

In this section we define an important family of Markov chains, which will occur frequently in the sequel both for their intrinsic interest and to provide examples about general results.

In the sequel G is an LCCB group and we call $\mathscr{G}$ the σ-algebra of its Borel sets. The elements of G will be denoted $g, g', h, \ldots$ and the inverse of g by g^{-1}. The unit element is denoted e.

Definition 4.1. A *right (left) random walk on* G is a Markov chain with state space $(G, \mathscr{G})$ and transition probability $\varepsilon_g * \mu$ ($\mu * \varepsilon_g$), where μ is a probability measure on $(G, \mathscr{G})$ which is called the *law* of the random walk.

For the right random walk we have therefore $P(g, A) = \varepsilon_g * \mu(A)$. For $h \in G$ we set $hA = \{hg : g \in A\}$; we then have $P(hg, hA) = P(g, A)$. *The right random walk is invariant under left translations.* Of course on an abelian group there is only one random walk of law μ.

Proposition 4.2. *Let X be the right random walk of law μ; then for every P_ν the random variables $Z_n = X_{n-1}^{-1} X_n$, $n \geqslant 1$, are independent and equidistributed with law μ.*

Proof. Let f_i, $i = 1, 2, \ldots, p$ be a finite collection of bounded Borel functions. We have

$$E_\nu \left[\prod_{i=1}^{p} f_i(Z_i) \right] = E_\nu \left[\prod_{i=1}^{p-1} f_i(Z_i) \, E_\nu[f_p(X_{p-1}^{-1} X_p) \mid \mathscr{F}_p] \right]$$

$$= E_\nu \left[\prod_{i=1}^{p-1} f_i(Z_i) \, E_{X_{p-1}}[f_p(X_0^{-1} X_1)] \right].$$

For every g in G we have $E_g[f(X_0^{-1} X_1)] = \mu(f)$, so that we get inductively

$$E_\nu \left[\prod_{i=1}^{p} f_i(Z_i) \right] = \prod_{i=1}^{p} \mu(f_i) = \prod_{i=1}^{p} E_\nu[f_i(Z_i)],$$

which is the desired result.

Remarks 4.3. The random variable X_n is thus a.s. equal to the product $X_0 Z_1 \cdots Z_n$, where the Z_i are independent with law μ. In particular X_n is P_e-a.s. equal to the product of n independent equidistributed random variables. Of course there is a left-handed version of these results and the left random walk may be written $Z_n Z_{n-1} \cdots Z_1 X_0$. The invariance by translation is also obvious from this relation.

We assume now that G operates on the left on an LCCB space M; let $\mathscr{M}$ be the σ-algebra of Borel subsets of M. We may associate with μ a T.P. on $(M, \mathscr{M})$ by setting (cf. Example 1.4 (ii)), for $x \in M$, $A \in \mathscr{M}$,

$$P(x, A) = \int_G 1_A(gx)\, \mu(\mathrm{d}g).$$

We are going to show an interesting way of constructing a Markov chain with transition probability P.

Let X be the left canonical random walk of law μ on $\mathbf{G}$. We set $\bar{\Omega} = \mathbf{M} \times \Omega$, $\overline{\mathscr{F}} = \mathscr{M} \otimes \mathscr{F}$, $\overline{\mathscr{F}}_n = \mathscr{M} \otimes \mathscr{F}_n$, and if ν is a probability measure on $(\mathbf{M}, \mathscr{M})$ we call $\bar{P}_\nu$ the probability measure $\nu \otimes P_e$ on $(\bar{\Omega}, \overline{\mathscr{F}})$. Next, for $\bar{\omega} = (x, \omega)$ we set $Y_0(\bar{\omega}) = x$ and

$$Y_n(\bar{\omega}) = X_n(\omega)\, Y_0(\bar{\omega}) = X_n(\omega)\, x.$$

Proposition 4.4. *The sequence $\{Y_n\}_{n \geqslant 0}$ is a homogeneous Markov chain with respect to the σ-algebras $\overline{\mathscr{F}}_n$ for any probability measure $\bar{P}_\nu$. Its transition probability is equal to P.*

Proof. The σ-algebra $\overline{\mathscr{F}}_n$ is generated by the rectangles $\Lambda \times \Gamma$ where $\Lambda \in \mathscr{M}$ and $\Gamma \in \mathscr{F}_n$. For A in $\mathscr{M}$ we have

$$\int_{\Lambda \times \Gamma} 1_A(Y_{m+n})\, \mathrm{d}\bar{P}_\nu = \int_\Lambda \nu(\mathrm{d}x) \int_\Gamma 1_A(X_{m+n}(\omega)\, x)\, \mathrm{d}P_e(\omega)$$

$$= \int_\Lambda \nu(\mathrm{d}x) \int_\Gamma E_e[1_A(X_{m+n}x) \mid \mathscr{F}_n]\, \mathrm{d}P_e$$

$$= \int_\Lambda \nu(\mathrm{d}x) \int_\Gamma (\mu^m * \varepsilon_{X_n})\, (\tilde{A})\, \mathrm{d}P_e,$$

where $\tilde{A} = \{g : gx \in A\}$; but $(\mu^m * \varepsilon_{X_n})\, (\tilde{A}) = (\mu^m * \varepsilon_{X_n}x)\, (A)$, so that finally

$$\int_{\Lambda \times \Gamma} 1_A(Y_{m+n})\, \mathrm{d}\bar{P}_\nu = \int_{\Lambda \times \Gamma} (\mu^m * \varepsilon_{Y_n})\, (A)\, \mathrm{d}\bar{P}_\nu,$$

which is the desired conclusion.

Remark 4.5. The chain Y thus constructed is not the canonical chain associated with P, but it is sometimes useful to know that one can construct a chain associated with P in the above way, for instance when one must deal simultaneously with the random walks on $\mathbf{G}$ and on $\mathbf{M}$.

In the preceding discussion one could not use the right random walk instead of the left random walk unless $\mathbf{G}$ operates on $\mathbf{M}$ on the right. We shall, however, show that under an additional hypothesis one may associate with right random walks some interesting random walks on (left) homogeneous spaces of G. We begin with a result of more general scope.

Let X be a Markov chain on $(E, \mathscr{E})$ and σ a measurable mapping from $(E, \mathscr{E})$ onto a space $(E', \mathscr{E}')$ such that, for every $A' \in \mathscr{E}'$,

$$P(x, \sigma^{-1}(A')) = P(x', \sigma^{-1}(A') \quad \text{if } \sigma(x) = \sigma(x'), \tag{4.1}$$

and moreover such that for $A \in \mathscr{E}$, $\sigma(A) \in \mathscr{E}'$. We set

$$X'_n = \sigma(X_n), \qquad P'(x', A) = P(\sigma^{-1}(x'), \sigma^{-1}(A)),$$

where $\sigma^{-1}(x')$ is any point in $\sigma^{-1}(\{x'\})$. Thanks to the second property of σ, it may be checked that P' is a T.P. on E', and we have

Proposition 4.6. *The sequence* $\{X'_n\}_{n \geqslant 0}$ *is a homogeneous Markov chain on* $(E', \mathscr{E}')$ *with transition probability* P'.

Proof. Let $A' \in \mathscr{E}'$ and P_ν be a probability measure on the space Ω of the chain X; we have

$$P_\nu[X'_{m+n} \in A' \mid \mathscr{F}_n] = P_\nu[\sigma(X_{m+n}) \in A' \mid \mathscr{F}_n] = P_\nu[X_{m+n} \in \sigma^{-1}(A') \mid \mathscr{F}_n]$$

$$= P_n[X_m, \sigma^{-1}(A')] = P'_n[X'_m, A'],$$

since it is easily seen from eq. (4.1) that

$$P'_n(x', A') = P_n(\sigma^{-1}(x'), \sigma^{-1}(A')).$$

Remark and Examples 4.7. Here also the chain X'_n is not the canonical chain associated with P', since the random variables X'_n are defined on the space Ω of the chain X. This proposition allows us to construct new chains from already known ones. Let us call *symmetric* a random walk such that $\mu = \hat{\mu}$ where $\hat{\mu}$ is the image of μ by the mapping $x \to x^{-1}$. Let X be a symmetric random walk on $\mathbf{R}$ or $\mathbf{Z}$. Then we may apply the above result with the map $\sigma : x \to |x|$. We then say that X' is obtained from X by reflection at the point 0.

Now let G be a group and K a compact sub-group of G; let σ denote the canonical, continuous and open mapping $G \to G/K$. If $x \in G/K$, $\sigma^{-1}(x)$ is of the form gK and the T.P. of the right random walk of law μ on G satisfies the conditions of Proposition 4.6 if μ is K-invariant, that is to say that $\varepsilon_k * \mu = \mu$ for every $k \in K$ or equivalently that $\mu = m_K * \mu'$, where m_K is the normalized Haar measure for K and μ' any probability measure on G. The image of the right random walk on G by σ is then a homogeneous Markov chain on G/K. When G is a semi-simple Lie group with finite centre and K a maximal compact sub-group, we thus obtain random walks on the Riemannian symmetric space G/K.

We could have taken the image of the left random walk by σ, but the well-known equivariance properties of σ would then imply that

$$\sigma(Z_n Z_{n-1} \cdots Z_1 X_0) = Z_n Z_{n-1} \cdots Z_1 \sigma(X_0)$$

and we would be in the general situation of Proposition 4.4.

Exercise 4.8. A *sub-random walk* is a Markov chain on a group G with T.P. $\varepsilon_x * \mu$ (or $\mu * \varepsilon_x$) but with $\mu(G) < 1$.

Prove, using the same notation as in Proposition 4.2, that the random variables of any finite collection $Z_{n_1}, \ldots, Z_{n_k}$ are independent on the set $\{\zeta > n_k\}$.

Exercise 4.9. (1) Let X be a right random walk of law μ and T a stopping time. Prove, after restricting the probability space to $\Omega_T = \{T < \infty\}$, that the variables $X_T^{-1} X_{T+n}$ are independent of $\mathscr{F}_T$ and that $Y = X_{T+n}$ is still a right random walk of law μ.

[*Hint*: See Exercise 3.13.]

(2) We assume that the underlying group is $\mathbf{R}$ or $\mathbf{Z}$ and we define inductively the following sequence of random variables

$$T_1(\omega) = \inf\{n \geqslant 1 : X_n(\omega) > 0\},$$

$$T_p(\omega) = \inf\{n > T_{p-1} : X_n(\omega) > X_{T_{p-1}}(\omega)\},$$

where the infimum of the empty set is taken equal to $+\infty$. Prove that the variables T_p are stopping times and that the sequences $\{T_n\}$ and $\{X_{T_n}\}$ are sub-random walks. Under which condition are they true random walks?

Exercise 4.10. Let X be a random walk of law μ on G and T_n the nth return time (cf. Exercise 3.12) to a closed subgroup H. Prove that $Y = \{X_{T_n}\}$ is a sub-random walk on H. Give its law as a function of μ and 1_H. Under which condition is it a true random walk?

Exercise 4.11. Let G be a LCCB group which is the semi-direct product of two groups H and K. Every element g in G may be written uniquely as a pair

(h, k), and using the additive notation in K we have $(h, k) (h', k') = (hh', hk' + k)$. (Example: G is the group of rigid motions of the euclidean plane, H is the group of rotations and K the group of translations.) Let $X_n = (H_n, K_n)$ be a left random walk on G; then H_n is a random walk on H and K_n the Markov chain induced (cf. Proposition 4.4) by X_n on K. (We recall that K is an invariant subgroup of G and therefore that G operates on K in a natural way.)

Exercise 4.12. One can study the random walks on the spaces $(W, \mathscr{A}, P)$ equal to the infinite product $(G, \mathscr{G}, \mu)^{\mathbf{N}}$. We let $\{Z_n\}_{n \geqslant 0}$ be the coordinate mappings, which are clearly independent and equidistributed.

(1) The probability measure P_g on $(\Omega, \mathscr{F})$ is the image of P by the mapping from W to Ω

$$(g_1, g_2, \ldots, g_n, \ldots) \to (g, gg_1, gg_1g_2, \ldots, gg_1, g_n, \ldots)$$

(2) Prove that P is invariant under finite permutations of the coordinates in W.

(3) An event $A \in \mathscr{A}$ is said to be symmetric if it is invariant under finite permutations of coordinates. Prove that the family of symmetric events is a σ-algebra and that if A is symmetric then either $P(A) = 0$ or $P(A) = 1$. This is the so-called *zero-or-one law for symmetric events*. Finally prove that the events in $\bigcap_{n=1}^{\infty} \sigma(Z_m, m \geqslant n)$ are symmetric.

[*Hint*: To prove the zero-or-one law, approximate sets in $\mathscr{A}$ by rectangles C depending on the first n coordinates and use the permutation σ exchanging 1 and $n + 1$, 2 and $n + 2, \ldots, n$ and $2n$. Then calling $C\sigma$ the image of C by σ prove that $P(C \cap C\sigma) = P(C) = P(C)^2$.]

5. Analytical properties of integral kernels

This section should be omitted at first reading. Its purpose is to collect some results which will be useful later and which will then be referred to. Since these results deal mainly with compactness, we recall:

Definition 5.1. A linear and continuous operator from a Banach space into another Banach space is said to be *compact* if it maps bounded sets onto relatively compact ones. A kernel on $(E, \mathscr{E})$ is said to be *compact* if it maps the unit ball $\mathscr{U}$ of $b\mathscr{E}$ into a relatively compact set in $b\mathscr{E}$. A compact kernel is thus a bounded kernel.

Let us also recall that an operator with finite-dimensional range is compact and that every compact operator is the uniform limit (cf. ch. 6, Definition 3.1) of operators with finite dimensional range. Finally the adjoint of a compact operator is itself compact. We characterize below the compact kernels.

Proposition 5.2. *If $(E, \mathscr{E})$ is separable, a compact kernel is an integral kernel.*

Proof. Let N be a compact kernel; its adjoint N^* is a compact endomorphism of $b\mathscr{E}^*$. But since $b\mathscr{M}(\mathscr{E})$ is closed in $b\mathscr{E}^*$ and invariant by N, the operator N^*, which is equal to N operating on the left, is a compact endomorphism of $b\mathscr{M}(\mathscr{E})$. As a result the set $\{N(x, \cdot): x \in E\}$ is relatively compact in $b\mathscr{M}(\mathscr{E})$, and consequently there is a probability measure λ on $\mathscr{E}$ such that for every x in E one has $N(x, \cdot) \ll \lambda$. The proposition then follows from the following lemma.

Lemma 5.3. *If $(E, \mathscr{E})$ is separable, for every probability measure λ on $\mathscr{E}$ and every proper kernel N on $(E, \mathscr{E})$ there exists a function $(x, y) \to n(x, y)$ which is $\mathscr{E} \otimes \mathscr{E}$-measurable and such that N is the sum of the integral kernel with basis λ associated with n and of a kernel N^1 such that all measures $N^1(x, \cdot)$ are singular with respect to λ.*

In other words, the Lebesgue decomposition of N with respect to λ may be written

$$N(x, \mathrm{d}y) = n(x, y)\, \lambda(\mathrm{d}y) + N^1(x, \mathrm{d}y).$$

The function n is called the *density* (unique up to equivalence) of N with respect to λ.

Proof. By hypothesis there exists a sequence of finite partitions $\mathscr{P}^n$ of E such that $\mathscr{P}^{n+1}$ is a refinement of $\mathscr{P}^n$ and that $\mathscr{E}$ is generated by $\bigcup_0^\infty \mathscr{P}^n$. A point y in E belongs to one and only one set in $\mathscr{P}^n$, which we call E_y^n. Let ν be a probability measure on $\mathscr{E}$; the functions f_n defined by setting

$$f_n(y) = \nu(E_y^n)/\lambda(E_y^n) \quad \text{if } \lambda(E_y^n) > 0,$$

$$f_n(y) = 0 \qquad\qquad \text{if } \lambda(E_y^n) = 0,$$

form a martingale relative to the σ-algebras $\sigma(\mathscr{P}^n)$ and the probability measure λ. Consequently, as $n \to \infty$, $f_n \to f_\infty$ λ-a.s. Let f be a density of ν with respect to λ; we have $f_n = E_\lambda[f \mid \mathscr{P}^n]$, hence, passing to the limit,

$$f_\infty = E_\lambda\left[f \mid \sigma\left(\bigcup_{n=0}^{\infty} \mathscr{P}^n\right)\right] = E_\lambda[f \mid \mathscr{E}] = f \quad \lambda\text{-a.s.}$$

The sequence f_n thus converges a.s. to a density of ν with respect to λ.

Let now N be a bounded kernel; we apply the above discussion to the probability measures $N(x, \cdot)/N(x, E) = P(x, \cdot)$. Since the functions

$$1_S\, P(x, E_y^n)/\lambda(E_y^n),$$

where $S = \{y: \lambda(E_y^n) > 0\}$, are $\mathscr{E} \otimes \mathscr{E}$-measurable, their limit is $\mathscr{E} \otimes \mathscr{E}$-measurable and provides the desired function n. If N is merely proper we begin by multiplying it on the right by a strictly positive function such that Nf is bounded (cf. ch. 2, Proposition 1.15).

Remark. For fixed x, $n(x, \cdot)$ is defined up to equivalence. The lemma shows that we can pick $n(x, \cdot)$ within its equivalence class in such a way that n is $\mathscr{E} \otimes \mathscr{E}$-measurable.

Corollary 5.4. *If $(E, \mathscr{E})$ is separable, then every proper kernel N such that $N(x, \cdot) \ll \lambda$ for every x in E is an integral kernel.*

The following results will go in the converse direction. We start with a preliminary result which is a generalization of Egoroff's theorem.

Proposition 5.5. *Let H be a set of finite functions in $\mathscr{E}$, compact and metrizable for the topology of pointwise convergence; for every $\varepsilon > 0$ there exists a set $F \in \mathscr{E}$ such that $\lambda(F^c) < \varepsilon$ and $I_F(H)$ is compact for the topology of uniform convergence.*

Proof. By hypothesis there exists a sequence $\{x_n\}_{n \geqslant 0}$ of points in E which separates H and a countable subset H_1 of H which is dense in H for the topology of pointwise convergence. We set

$$h_n = \sup\{(f - g): f, g \in H \quad \text{and} \quad |f(x_k) - g(x_k)| < 2^{-n} \text{ for } k \leqslant n\}.$$

Since H_1 is dense in H, the supremum may be obtained by considering only the functions of H_1; as a result h_n is in $\mathscr{E}$. Each function h_n is finite and moreover $h_{n+1} \leqslant h_n$ and $\inf_n h_n = 0$.

For every sequence $\{g_p\} \subset H$ which converges pointwise to $g \in H$, we have the following property: for every n there exists a p_0 such that $p \geqslant p_0$ implies $|g - g_p| \leqslant h_n$. It follows that for a set $F \in \mathscr{E}$, such that $\{1_F h_n\}$ converges uniformly to zero, the set $1_F H$ is compact for the topology of uniform convergence. The desired result then follows from Egoroff's theorem.

Lemma 5.6. *Let N be an integral kernel with basis λ; the image of the unit ball $\mathcal{U}$ of $b\mathcal{E}$ by N is compact and metrizable for the topology of pointwise convergence.*

Proof. The image $N(\mathcal{U})$ is equal to the image by N of the unit ball in $L^\infty(\lambda)$, which is compact and metrizable for the weak* topology $\sigma(L^\infty(\lambda), L^1(\lambda))$. Since N is a continuous operator with respect to this topology and the topology of pointwise convergence on E we get the desired result.

We are now ready to state

Theorem 5.7. *Let N be an integral kernel with basis λ on a separable space $(E, \mathcal{E})$ and such that $N1$ is finite; then there exists an increasing sequence of sets A_n in $\mathcal{E}$ such that:*
   (i) *for every $\varepsilon > 0$ there is an integer n such that $\lambda(A_n^c) < \varepsilon$;*
   (ii) *the kernels $I_{A_n} N$ are compact.*

Proof. As $N1$ is finite, the set $N(\mathcal{U})$ is a set of finite functions compact and metrizable for the topology of pointwise convergence. By Proposition 5.4 there exists a sequence $\{A_n\}$ of sets in $\mathcal{E}$ with the required properties and such that the sets $1_{A_n} N(\mathcal{U})$ are compact for the topology of uniform convergence – hence such that the operators $I_{A_n} N$ are compact.

The preceding results are useful in many situations. In this book we shall use them to prove quasi-compactness properties. We are now going to state in a topological setting some properties which may be used to the same end.

We assume below that E is an LCCB space and $\mathcal{E}$ the σ-algebra of Borel sets.

Definition 5.8. A sub-markovian kernel N on $(E, \mathcal{E})$ is said to be
   (i) *Feller* if the map $x \to \varepsilon_x N$ from E to $b\mathcal{M}(\mathcal{E})$ is continuous for the strict topology on $b\mathcal{M}(\mathcal{E})$, in other words if $Nf \in C(E)$ whenever $f \in C(E)$;
   (ii) *strong Feller* if the same map is continuous for the weak-star topology $\sigma(b\mathcal{M}(\mathcal{E}), b\mathcal{E})$, in other words if $Nf \in C(E)$ whenever $f \in b\mathcal{E}$;
   (iii) *strong Feller in the strict sense* if the same map is continuous for the norm topology on $b\mathcal{M}(\mathcal{E})$.

Plainly each of these conditions is more stringent than the previous one. The convolution kernels provide examples of Feller kernels, and even of

strong Feller kernels, whenever the relevant measure is absolutely continuous. Examples of kernels strongly Feller in the strict sense will be obtained
as by-products of the following results.

Proposition 5.9. *The following two conditions are equivalent:*
  (i) *the kernel N is strong Feller in the strict sense;*
  (ii) *the image by N of bounded sets of $C(E)$ are compact for the topology of
  uniform convergence on compact sets.*

Proof. If f is in the unit ball of $C(E)$ then for every pair (x, y) in $E \times E$,

$$|Nf(x) - Nf(y)| \leqslant \|N(x, \cdot) - N(y, \cdot)\|;$$

thus functions Nf, f in the unit ball of $C(E)$, are equi-uniformly continuous on
compact sets and (ii) follows from (i).
  The converse follows at once from the relation

$$\|N(x, \cdot) - N(y, \cdot)\| = \sup\{|Nf(x) - Nf(y)| : f \in C(E), \|f\| \leqslant 1\}$$

and the equi-continuity on compact sets of the functions $Nf(f \in C(E), \|f\| < 1)$.

Remark. The image by N of the bounded sets of $b\mathscr{E}$ are also compact for
the topology of uniform convergence on compact sets.

Theorem 5.10. *The product of two strong Feller kernels is strong Feller in the
strict sense.*

Proof. The theorem follows immediately from the preceding proposition and
the next two lemmas, in which N is a strong Feller kernel.

Lemma 5.11. *From every sequence $\{g_n\}$ of functions in the unit ball $\mathscr{U}$ of $b\mathscr{E}$,
one can extract a sub-sequence $\{g_n'\}$ such that $\{Ng_n'\}$ is pointwise convergent.*

Proof. Let $\{x_n\}$ be a countable dense subset of E, and set $\lambda = \sum_n 2^{-n} N(x_n, \cdot)$.
The measures $N(x, \cdot)$ are all absolutely continuous with respect to λ. Indeed
if f is λ-negligible, the continuous function Nf vanishes at all points x_n, hence
everywhere.
  Let now $\{g_n'\}$ be a subsequence of $\{g_n\}$ convergent in the sense of
$\sigma(L^\infty(\lambda), L^1(\lambda))$. (We indulge in the usual confusion between functions and
their equivalence classes.) Then the sequence $\{Ng_n'\}$ where

$$Ng_n'(x) = \langle N(x, \cdot\,), g_n' \rangle$$

is convergent for every x in E.

Lemma 5.12. *Let $\{g_n\}$ be a sequence of functions in $\mathcal{U}$ converging pointwise to a function g; then the sequence $\{Ng_n\}$ converges to Ng uniformly on every compact set.*

Proof. It suffices to prove the lemma for the case $g = 0$. Set $h_n = \sup_{m \geqslant n}|g_n|$; as $|Ng_n| \leqslant Nh_n$ it suffices to show that $\{Nh_n\}$ converges to zero uniformly on compact sets. Since the functions Nh_n are continuous and decrease to zero we conclude the proof by applying Dini's lemma.

As an application, let us give the following result. The reader may refer to ch. 2 §4 for the definition of a resolvent.

Proposition 5.13. *If the kernels $\{V_\alpha\}_{\alpha > 0}$ of a submarkovian resolvent are strong Feller, then they are strong Feller in the strict sense.*

Proof. Let $\beta > \alpha$; the map $x \to \varepsilon_x V_\alpha V_\beta$ is continuous for the norm topology by Theorem 5.10, and the maps $x \to \varepsilon_x V_\beta$ converge uniformly to zero whenever $\beta \to \infty$, since $\|\varepsilon_x V_\beta\| < \beta^{-1}$. The result thus follows from the relation

$$V_\alpha = (\beta - \alpha)V_\alpha V_\beta + V_\beta.$$

Exercise 5.14. If E is an LCCB space, $N1$ is continuous, and $N(C_K(E)) \subset C(E)$, then N is Feller.

Exercise 5.15. If G is a group, prove that the convolution kernels $\varepsilon_x * \mu$ on G are Feller. If μ is absolutely continuous with respect to the Haar measure, then $\varepsilon_x * \mu$ is strong Feller. Prove by an example that it is not always strong Feller in the strict sense.

CHAPTER 2

POTENTIAL THEORY

Except in a short section devoted to resolvents, our basic data will be a transition probability P on $(E, \mathcal{E})$ and the associated canonical Markov chain.

1. Superharmonic functions and the maximum principle

Definition 1.1. The Poisson equation with second member g is the equation

$$(I - P) f = g.$$

A finite function of $\mathcal{E}$ will be called *harmonic* if it is a solution of the Poisson equation without second member $(g = 0)$. A function f in $\mathcal{E}_+$ is called *superharmonic* if $f \geqslant Pf$ everywhere on E.

The positive harmonic functions are superharmonic. The following characterization involves the canonical chain X and hints at the probabilistic significance of superharmonic functions.

Proposition 1.2. *A function f is superharmonic (bounded harmonic) if and only if the sequence $\{f(X_n)\}$ of random variables is a supermartingale (bounded martingale) with respect to the σ-algebras $\mathcal{F}_n$ for any probability measure P_ν.*

Proof. For $m \geqslant n$ and f superharmonic, the Markov property implies that

$$E_\nu[f(X_m) \mid \mathcal{F}_n] = E_\nu[f(X_{m-n} \circ \theta_n) \mid \mathcal{F}_n]$$

$$= E_{X_n}[f(X_{m-n})] = P_{m-n} f(X_n) \leqslant f(X_n), \quad P_\nu\text{-a.s.}$$

Conversely, integrating the inequality $f(X_0) \geqslant E_x[f(X_1) \mid \mathcal{F}_0]$ with respect to P_x yields $f(x) \geqslant Pf(x)$.

Examples 1.3. The function 1 is always superharmonic; it is harmonic if P is markovian. If X is a right random walk of law μ on a group G, the function

f is harmonic if and only if

$$f(g) = \int_G f(gh)\, \mu(\mathrm{d}h).$$

Other examples will be found in the exercises. Let us mention without proof that the harmonic functions for random walks on symmetric spaces are harmonic in the classical sense, that is they are solutions of Laplace equations on these spaces. In particular, the classical harmonic functions in the unit disc are the harmonic functions of suitable Markov chains.

Proposition 1.4. *The set of superharmonic functions is a left lattice and a convex cone. If $\{f_n\}_{n\geqslant 0}$ is a sequence of superharmonic functions, then $\underline{\lim}_n f_n$ is superharmonic.*

The set of harmonic functions is a vector space. The set of bounded harmonic functions is a Banach subspace of $\mathrm{b}\mathscr{E}$.

Proof. Given that f, g are superharmonic and a, b are in $\mathbf{R}_+$, the reader can easily check that $af + bg$ and $f \wedge g$ are superharmonic. The other properties in the statement are also straightforward.

The subject of potential theory, which we are about to develop in this and the next section, is the study of the cone of superharmonic functions, which will be henceforth denoted by $\mathscr{S}$.

Definition 1.5. The *potential kernel* of P, or of X, is the kernel

$$G = \sum_{n=0}^{\infty} P_n = I + P + P_2 + \cdots.$$

The reader can easily check that G is indeed a kernel, but will observe that the measures $G(x, \cdot)$ are not always σ-finite. (Take $P = I$ for instance, but less trivial examples will be seen later on.)

We recall (ch. 1, Definition 1.1) that the kernel G is said to be *proper* if E is the increasing limit of a sequence E_n of sets in $\mathscr{E}$ such that the functions $G(\cdot, E_n)$ are bounded. The probabilistic significance of this condition will be seen in due course.

The kernel G satisfies the identity

$$G = I + PG = I + GP. \tag{1.1}$$

On the other hand, using ch. 1, eq. (2.3), we may write, for $A \in \mathscr{E}$,

$$G(x, A) = E_x \left[\sum_{n=0}^{\infty} 1_{\{X_n \in A\}} \right].$$ (1.2)

Let f be in $\mathscr{E}$; if the function Gf is defined it will be called the *potential of the function* f. If $f = 1_A$, then $Gf(x) = G(x, A)$ is called the potential of the set A, and by eq. (1.2) appears as the mean number of times the chain started at x hits the set A. One sees easily that the potentials of positive functions are superharmonic and we have

Theorem 1.6 (Riesz decomposition theorem). *A finite superharmonic function f has a unique representation as a sum $f = Gg + h$, where Gg is a potential and h a harmonic function.*

Proof. By hypothesis the sequence of function $P_n f$ decreases, and thus admits a positive limit $h = \lim_n P_n f$. We have

$$Ph = P \left[\lim_n P_n f \right] = \lim_n P_{n+1} f = h;$$

hence h is harmonic.

Next, $g = f - Pf$ is a positive function, and

$$\sum_0^N P_n g = f - P_{N+1} f;$$

passing to the limit as N tends to infinity yields $Gg = f - h$, which is the desired representation.

Suppose that f has another representation of the same kind, namely $f = Gg' + h'$. For every n, we then have

$$P_n Gg + h = P_n Gg' + h';$$

but $P_n Gg = \sum_n^\infty P_k g$ converges to zero as n tends to infinity, since Gg is a finite function, and therefore $h = h'$. It follows that $Gg = Gg'$, and applying $I - P$ through to the left of this equality we get $g = g'$.

Remark 1.7. If $g \in \mathscr{E}_+$ and Gg is finite, then it is a solution of the Poisson equation

$$(I - P) f = g.$$

If f is another finite solution, it is a superharmonic function which can be written $f = Gg + h$, where $h = \lim_n P_n f$ is harmonic and positive. Thus Gg

appears as the *smallest positive solution of the Poisson equation with second member g.*

Corollary 1.8. *A superharmonic function dominated by a finite potential is a potential. A harmonic function dominated by a finite potential vanishes identically.*

Proof. By the Riesz decomposition theorem it suffices to show the second sentence in the statement. Let h be harmonic and $h \leqslant Gg < \infty$; for every n we have $h = P_n h \leqslant P_n Gg$ and since this sequence converges to zero as n tends to infinity, the proof is complete.

Theorem 1.9. *If the kernel G is proper every superharmonic function is the increasing limit of a sequence of finite potentials.*

Proof. Let us resume the usual notation and set $g_n = G(n \, 1_{E_n})$; the sequence g_n is a sequence of finite potentials increasing everywhere to $+\infty$. If f is superharmonic, the functions $f \wedge g_n$ are finite potentials and increase to f.

In ch. 1, §3 we saw how one can associate with X other Markov chains, in particular by killing X at time T_A for $A \in \mathscr{E}$. The T.P. of this new chain is $I_{A^c} P I_{A^c}$; we shall denote by G^A its potential kernel, so we have

$$G^A = \sum_{n=0}^{\infty} I_{A^c}(PI_{A^c})^n = \sum_{n=0}^{\infty} (I_{A^c}P)^n \, I_{A^c}.$$

By reasoning in the same way as in ch. 1, Proposition 3.7 the reader can prove without difficulty that

$$G^A f(x) = E_x \left[\sum_{n < T_A} f(X_n) \right];$$

for $f = 1_B$, this is precisely the mean number of times that X hits B before hitting A.

The following result generalizes the formula $G = I + PG$.

Proposition 1.10. $G = G^A + P_A G$.

Proof. Let g be in $\mathscr{E}_+$; by applying the strong Markov property, we get

$$P_A G \, g(x) = E_x[G \, g(X_{T_A})] = E_x \left[\sum_{n=0}^{\infty} P_n \, g(X_{T_A}) \right]$$

$$= E_x \left[E_{X_{T_A}} \left[\sum_{n=0}^{\infty} g(X_n) \right] \right] = E_x \left[\sum_{n=0}^{\infty} g(X_{n+T_A}) \right]$$

$$= E_x \left[\sum_{n=T_A}^{\infty} g(X_n) \right].$$

Since

$$E_x \left[\sum_{n=0}^{\infty} g(X_n) \right] = E_x \left[\sum_{n<T_A} g(X_n) \right] + E_x \left[\sum_{n=T_A}^{\infty} g(X_n) \right],$$

we have the desired result.

Remark. This formula may be shown by using the expressions of G, G^A, P_A as functions of P and I_A.

Corollary 1.11. *If g vanishes outside A, then $P_A G g = G g$.*

Proof. Since $G^A I_A = 0$, this follows immediately from Proposition 1.10.

We are going to use Proposition 1.10 to prove a very important result.

Theorem 1.12 (complete maximum principle). *Let (f, g) be a pair of functions in $\mathscr{E}_+$, and let a be a constant $\geqslant 0$ such that*

$$G f(x) \leqslant G g(x) + a$$

for $x \in \{f > 0\}$. Then $Gf \leqslant Gg + a$ everywhere.

Proof. Set $A = \{f > 0\}$. If $Gf \leqslant Gg + a$ on A, since the measures $P_A(x, \cdot)$ vanish outside A, we have

$$P_A Gf \leqslant P_A Gg + a P_A I$$

everywhere, and by Proposition 1.10,

$$Gf - G^A f \leqslant Gg + a.$$

Since $G^A f = 0$ by definition of G^A, the proof is complete.

Remark. In the above statement we may merely assume that $Gf = Gf \pm Gf^-$ is meaningful instead of $f \in \mathscr{E}_+$. Since $G^A f$ is then $\leqslant 0$, we still have $P_A Gf - G^A f \geqslant Gf$. We even get in the conclusion $Gf \leqslant Gg + a - f^-$ everywhere.

Corollary 1.13. *The kernel G satisfies the following reinforced maximum principle: for every $a \geqslant 0$ and every pair (f, g) of functions in $\mathscr{E}_+$ such that*

$$Gf(x) \leqslant a + Gg(x) - g(x) \quad \text{for all } x \in \{f > 0\},$$

we have $Gf \leqslant a + Gg - g$ everywhere.

Proof. Since $Gg - g = GPg$, the corollary follows easily from the complete maximum principle.

For our later needs we shall lay down the following.

Definition 1.14. A kernel G (not necessarily the potential kernel of a Markov chain) is said to satisfy the *complete maximum principle* (*reinforced maximum principle*) if it satisfies the condition of Theorem 1.12 (1.13).

If, in Theorem 1.12, we replace $Gg + a$ by Gg (by a) we say that G satisfies the *domination principle* (the *maximum principle*).

Clearly a kernel which satisfies the complete principle also satisfies the two last principles. We shall see later that a kernel which satisfies the reinforced principle satisfies the complete principle (see Exercise 2.19).

We now give a first application of the maximum principles by showing that for the potential kernel of a Markov chain one can replace "bounded" by "finite" in the definition of "proper".

Proposition 1.15. *A positive kernel N is proper if and only if there is a function f strictly positive everywhere such that Nf is bounded.*

The potential kernel G of a Markov chain is proper if and only if there is a function f strictly positive such that Gf is finite or equivalently if and only if E is the union of a sequence E_n of sets in such that the potentials $G(\cdot, E_n)$ are finite.

Proof. For $f > 0$, the sets $E_N = \{f > 1/n\}$ increase to E and $N(\cdot, E_n) \leqslant nNf(\cdot)$. Conversely, if $N(\cdot, E_n) \leqslant M_n$, the function $f = \sum_1^\infty M_n^{-1} 2^{-n} 1_{E_n}$ is strictly positive and Nf is bounded.

In the same way, the existence of $f > 0$ with $Gf < \infty$ implies the existence of sets E_n with finite potentials $G(\cdot, E_n)$. Set

$$H_{nm} = \{x \in E_n : G(x, E_n) \leqslant m\};$$

the space E is the union of the sets H_{nm}, and since $H_{nm} \subset E_n$, we have

$$G(\,\cdot\,, H_{nm}) \leqslant G(\,\cdot\,, E_n) \leqslant m$$

on H_{nm} and therefore everywhere, by the maximum principle. The kernel G is thus proper, and by the first half of the proof there exists a function $f > 0$ such that Gf is bounded; this completes the proof.

Exercise 1.16. Let X be the chain of translation on integers $(P(x, \cdot\,) = \varepsilon_{x+1}(\,\cdot\,)$, $x \in \mathbf{Z})$. Compute the kernel G and characterize the harmonic functions and potentials.

Exercise 1.17. Extend the Riesz decomposition theorem to the case where the superharmonic function takes infinite values.

Exercise 1.18. A function h is said to be *harmonic outside* A if $f(x) = Pf(x)$ for all $x \in A^c$. Prove that Gg is harmonic outside $\{g > 0\}$.

Exercise 1.19. If the kernel G is bounded $(G(x, E) \leqslant M < \infty$ for all $x \in E)$ every bounded superharmonic function is a potential.

Exercise 1.20. A set $A \subset E$ is said to be *absorbing* if $P(x, A) = 1$ for all x in A. If Gg is a bounded potential, the set $\{Gg = 0\}$ is absorbing and the set $\{Gg > 0\}$ is the union of a sequence of sets with bounded potentials.

Exercise 1.21. *Principle of lower envelope.* The lower envelope of a sequence of finite potentials is a potential.

Exercise 1.22. (1) *Principle of unicity of charges.* If (f, g) are in $\mathscr{E}_+$ and $Gf = Gg < \infty$, then $f = g$.

(2) If f and g are two positive functions vanishing outside A and if $Gf = Gg$ on A, then $f = g$.

Exercise 1.23. Let p_m be the Poisson distribution of parameter m. We define inductively a sequence of random variables: X_1 is a random variable of law p_1, X_2 is a random variable of law $p_{X_1}, \ldots, X_n$ is a random variable of law $p_{X_{n-1}}, \ldots$. Prove that the point 0 is reached with probability 1.

[*Hint*: This is an example of a Galton–Watson chain (ch. 1 §2.18) for which the function $f(n) = n$ is harmonic.]

Exercise 1.24. Assume that E is the set of non-negative integers and that P is given by

$$P(x, x + 1) = p_x, \qquad P(x, x - 1) = q_x, \qquad P(x, x) = r_x,$$

with $q_0 = 0$ and $p_x + q_x + r_x = 1$ for all x in E. Find all the harmonic functions.

Exercise 1.25. If G satisfies the complete maximum principle, then for every positive real α the kernel $I + \alpha G$ satisfies the reinforced maximum principle.

Exercise 1.26. Let $f \in \mathscr{S}$ and set $E_f = \{0 < f < \infty\}$. Prove that, by setting

$$P^f(x, A) = \frac{1}{f(x)} \int_A P(x, \mathrm{d}y) \, f(y),$$

one defines a transition probability on $(E_f, E_f \cap \mathscr{E})$. Prove that a function g is P^f-superharmonic if and only if there is a P-superharmonic function u such that $u = fg$.

Exercise 1.27. Let f, g be two superharmonic functions; we say that $f < g$ for the proper order of the cone $\mathscr{S}$ if $g - f \in \mathscr{S}$. Prove that $\mathscr{S}$ is a lattice for its proper order.

[*Hint*: Prove first that the least upper bound of two harmonic functions h and h' is

$$\mathrm{l.u.b.}(h, h') = \lim_n P_n[h \vee h'];$$

then if $f = Gg + h$, $f' = Gg' + h'$, prove that

$$\mathrm{l.u.b.}(f, f') = G[g \vee g'] + \mathrm{l.u.b.}(h, h').]$$

2. Reduced functions

This section is devoted to the notion of reduced functions and to some applications. We give two different proofs of the balayage theorem, the first one to hint at the probabilistic aspect of the theorem, the second one of more analytical and general character. We introduce thereafter a family of kernels which will be very important in the sequel.

In Theorems 2.1–2.3 we assume the kernel G to be proper.

Theorem 2.1 (balayage theorem). *Let f be superharmonic and A a set in $\mathscr{E}$. The function $P_A f$ is the smallest superharmonic function which dominates f on A. It is called the reduced function of f on A.*

Proof. We first prove that $P_A f \leqslant f$. If f is a finite potential, namely $f = Gg$, then by Proposition 1.10

$$P_A f = Gg - G^A g.$$

Hence $P_A f \leqslant Gg = f$, and G being proper, Theorem 1.9 allows us to proceed to the general case.

We next show that $P_A f$ is superharmonic. If $x \notin A$, then $T_A \geqslant 1$ P_x-a.s., and therefore, by ch. 1, Proposition 3.8,

$$P P_A f(x) = P_{1 + T_A \circ \theta_1} f(x) = P_A f(x)$$

(that is, $P_A f$ is harmonic outside A); if $x \in A$, then $P_A f(x) = f(x)$, and since $P_A f \leqslant f$ everywhere, we have

$$P P_A f(x) \leqslant P f(x) \leqslant f(x) = P_A f(x),$$

which proves the above statement.

Finally let $h \in \mathscr{S}$ and $h \geqslant f$ on A; by the first part of the proof, and since $P_A(x, \cdot)$ vanishes outside A, we have

$$h \geqslant P_A h \geqslant P_A f.$$

The proof is thus complete.

Remark. If f is a potential, $P_A f$ is also a potential, by Corollary 1.8. It is the potential of a function vanishing outside A which is given in Exercise 2.16.

Let $g \in \mathscr{E}_+$ and define inductively a sequence $\{g_n\}_{n \geqslant 0}$ of functions in $\mathscr{E}_+$, by setting

$$g_0 = g, \qquad g_n = g_{n-1} \vee P g_{n-1}, \quad n \geqslant 1;$$

this sequence is clearly increasing, hence converges pointwise to a limit $Rg \geqslant 0$.

Theorem 2.2. *The function Rg is the smallest superharmonic function which dominates g. Moreover, $PRg = Rg$ on $\{g < Rg\}$ and $Rg = g$ if and only if g is superharmonic.*

Proof. Passing to the limit in the definition of g_n as a function of g_{n-1} yields that $Rg = Rg \vee PRg$, which proves that Rg is superharmonic. Obviously, $Rg \geqslant g$, and for $h \in \mathscr{S}$ with $h \geqslant g$, we have $h \geqslant Ph \geqslant Pg$; hence $h \geqslant g \vee Pg = g_1$, and, inductively, $h \geqslant g_n$ for every n. It follows that $h \geqslant Rg$, which gives the first conclusion in the statement.

We may also consider the sequence $\{g'_n\}$ defined inductively by

$$g'_0 = g, \qquad g'_n = g \vee Pg'_{n-1}, \quad n \geqslant 1;$$

this sequence also increases and thus converges to a limit $R'g \leqslant Rg$. Passing to the limit we get also $R'g = g \vee R'g$; thus $R'g$ is superharmonic, and since it dominates g we get $Rg = R'g$. Consequently $Rg = g \vee PRg$, which implies that $PRg = Rg$ on $\{g < Rg\}$.

Remark. If f is superharmonic and $A \in \mathscr{E}$, we get $P_A f$ by applying to $g = 1_A f$ one of the above schemes. Indeed

$$g \vee Pg = 1_A f \vee P 1_A f = I_{A^c} P I_A f + 1_A(f \vee P I_A f),$$

and since $PI_A f \leqslant Pf \leqslant f$, we have $g \vee Pg = I_{A^c} P I_A f + 1_A f$. It follows inductively that

$$g'_n = I_A f + \sum_{0 < p \leqslant n} (I_{A^c} P)^p I_A f,$$

and consequently that $Rg = P_A f$.

The above results allow us to return to the maximum principle and prove

Theorem 2.3. *A function $f \in \mathscr{E}_+$ is superharmonic if and only if it satisfies the following property: for every function $g \in \mathscr{E}_+$ the inequality $Gg \leqslant f$ holds everywhere whenever it holds on $\{g > 0\}$.*

Proof. Set $A = \{g > 0\}$; from the inequality $Gg \leqslant f$ on A we get

$$P_A G g \leqslant P_A f \leqslant f$$

everywhere, and we may conclude the proof as in Theorem 1.12.

Conversely, begin with a function f majorized by a finite potential; then the reduced function Rf is also majorized by this potential; hence it is a potential, namely, $Rf = Gk$, where $k = Rf - P(Rf)$. But since $Rf = P(Rf)$ on $\{f < Rf\}$, we have $f = Gk$ on $\{k > 0\}$; hence, by the maximum property, $f \geqslant Gk$ everywhere. It follows that $f = Rf$; that is, f is superharmonic.

Next suppose f arbitrary and let Gg be a finite potential. The function $f \wedge Gg$ is majorized by a finite potential and satisfies the property of the statement because f and Gg do so. Thus $f \wedge Gg$ is superharmonic. The kernel G being proper, we may apply this to the functions $f \wedge Gg_n$, where Gg_n is a sequence of finite potentials converging everywhere to $+\infty$.

Remarks. (1) The functions $a + Gg$ being superharmonic, the above property implies the complete maximum principle.

(2) Exercise 4.13 gives another proof of the sufficiency.

(3) Theorem 2.3 gives a characterization of superharmonic functions which will be useful later on.

Definition 2.4. Let A be in $\mathscr{E}$; the superharmonic function $P_A 1$ is called the *equilibrium potential* of A.

This superharmonic function is actually a potential only in some "classical" cases, as is seen from the following result, which specifies its Riesz decomposition.

Proposition 2.5. *For any set A in $\mathscr{E}$, we have*

$$P_A 1 = G g_A + h_A,$$

where g_A is the probability that the chain never returns to A ($g_A(x) = 0$ for $x \notin A$, and $g_A(x) = P_x[S_A = \infty]$ for $x \in A$), and h_A is the probability that the chain hits A infinitely many times.

Proof. By definition, $P_A 1(x) = P_x[T_A < \infty]$. By the Riesz decomposition theorem, 1.6, we have $P_A 1(x) = G g_A(x) + h_A(x)$, where h_A is harmonic and equal to $\lim_n P_n P_A 1(x)$. But by ch. 1, Proposition 3.8,

$$P_n P_A 1(x) = P_x[n + T_A \circ \theta_n < \infty] = P_x\left[\bigcup_{m=n}^{\infty} \{X_m \in A\} \right].$$

Consequently,

$$h_A(x) = P_x\left[\bigcap_{n=0}^{\infty} \bigcup_{m=n}^{\infty} \{X_m \in A\} \right] = P_x\left[\overline{\lim_{n \to \infty}} \{X_n \in A\} \right],$$

which is the probability that X hits A infinitely many times.

By Theorem 1.6, we have also

$$g_A(x) = P_A 1(x) - P P_A 1(x) = P_x[T_A < \infty] - P_x[S_A < \infty].$$

By ch. 1, Proposition 3.8 it follows that g_A vanishes on A^c, and is equal to $1 - P_x[S_A < \infty] = P_x[S_A = \infty]$ on A.

Definition 2.6. A set A in $\mathscr{E}$ will be called *transient* if $P_A 1$ is a potential, hence if and only if the set A is almost surely hit only finitely many times.

Proposition 2.7. *If the potential $G(\cdot, A)$ is everywhere finite, the set A is transient.*

Proof. Since $G(x, A) = E_x[\sum_0^\infty 1_{\{X_n \in A\}}]$, the hypothesis implies that the sum is finite P_x-a.s., for all x in E, hence that $h_A = 0$.

This result permits us to understand the probabilistic significance of the condition "G is a proper kernel"; it means that E is the union of an increasing sequence of transient sets.

In the course of the proof of the balayage theorem, we saw that $P P_A f = P_{S_A} f \leqslant f$; in other words, the superharmonic functions are also superharmonic for the chain induced on A (ch. 1, Exercise 3.12). We are going to generalize this result. We recall that the unit ball of $b\mathscr{E}$ is denoted by $\mathscr{U}$; thus $\mathscr{U}_+$ is the set of measurable functions h such that $0 \leqslant h \leqslant 1$.

Definition 2.8. With each function h of $\mathscr{U}_+$ we associate the kernel

$$U_h = \sum_{n \geqslant 0} (PI_{1-h})^n P = \sum_{n \geqslant 0} P(I_{1-h}P)^n$$

where the kernel I_f is defined by $I_f g = fg$ or $I_f(x, \cdot) = f(x)\varepsilon_x$. When $h = 1_A$ we write U_A instead of U_h, and if $h = c \in [0, 1]$ we write U_c instead of U_h.

By reasoning in a way similar to ch. 1, Proposition 3.7, it is easily seen that, for $f \in \mathscr{E}_+$,

$$U_h f(x) = E_x\left[\sum_{n \geqslant 1} (1 - h(X_1))\, (1 - h(X_2)) \cdots (1 - h(X_{n-1}))\, f(X_n)\right],$$

$$U_A f(x) = E_x\left[\sum_{n=1}^{S_A} f(X_n)\right].$$

These kernels will be very important in the sequel, for the following reasons. On the one hand, all useful kernels may be easily expressed as functions of the U_h's; for instance

$$\Pi_A = I_A U_A I_A, \qquad P_A = I_A + I_{A^c}U_A I_A, \qquad P = U_1, \qquad G = I + U_0.$$

On the other hand, these kernels are very easy to handle, thanks to the following.

Proposition 2.9 (resolvent equation). *For $h, k \in \mathscr{E}_+$ and $h \leqslant k$,*

$$U_h = \sum_{n \geqslant 0} (U_k I_{k-h})^n\, U_k = \sum_{n \geqslant 0} U_k (I_{k-h} U_k)^n,$$

which implies

$$U_h = U_k + U_h I_{k-h} U_k = U_k + U_k I_{k-h} U_h.$$

Proof. This is an immediate consequence of ch. 1, Exercise 1.13, which we solve rapidly below.

For every integer n,

$$(N(A + B))^n N = \sum_{\substack{k,n_0,\ldots,n_k \\ k+n_0+\ldots+n_k=n}} \{((NA)^{n_0}N) B ((NA)^{n_1}N) B \cdots B ((NA)^{n_k}N)\}$$

by summing over n and interchanging the order of summations, which is possible since all the kernels are positive, we obtain

$$\sum_{n \geqslant 0} (N(A + B))^n N = \sum_{k \geqslant 0} \sum_{n_0,\ldots,n_k \in \mathbf{N}^{k+1}} ((NA)^{n_0}N) B ((NA)^{n_k}N)$$

$$= \sum_{k \geqslant 0} (SB)^k S.$$

Remark. This result says that one may compute U_h as a function of U_k in the same way as as a function of $P = U_1$. We notice also that $U_h \geqslant U_k$.

Proposition 2.10. *If $f \in \mathscr{S}$ and h, k are functions in $\mathscr{U}_+$ such that $h \leqslant k$, then*

$$U_h I_h f \leqslant U_k I_k f \leqslant f.$$

In particular $U_h(h) \leqslant 1$ for all h in $\mathscr{U}_+$ and $U_h(h)$ increases with h.

Proof. Let us first assume that $U_k I_k f \leqslant f$, which implies that

$$U_k I_h f + (U_k I_{k-h}) U_k I_k f \leqslant U_k I_k f \leqslant f.$$

This is what results, for $p = 1$, from the inequality

$$\sum_{n < p} (U_k I_{k-h})^n U_k I_h f + (U_k I_{k-h})^p U_k I_k f \leqslant U_k I_k f \leqslant f. \tag{2.1}$$

Assume eq. (2.1) to be true up to p, and multiply the left and the right terms to the left by $U_k I_{k-h}$; then adding through $U_k I_h f$ yields

$$U_k I_h f + \sum_{n < p} (U_k I_{k-h})^{n+1} U_k I_h f + (U_k I_{k-h})^{p+1} U_k I_k f \leqslant$$

$$\leqslant U_k I_h f + U_k I_{k-h} f = U_k I_k f \leqslant f.$$

Thus eq. (2.1) is true for all p. If we let p tend to infinity in eq. (2.1), it follows by the resolvent equation of Proposition 2.9, that

$$U_h I_h f \leqslant U_k I_k f \leqslant f.$$

Now if $k = 1$, then $U_k I_k f = Pf \leqslant f$, and by the preceding discussion $U_h I_h f \leqslant f$ for all $h \in \mathcal{U}_+$. It follows that the hypothesis with which we started the proof always holds, and consequently the proof is complete.

If we had started with f harmonic and positive, since the term $\lim(U_k I_{k-h})^p U_k I_k f$ is not bound to vanish (cf. below), we would still only get an inequality in the above result. In the same way $P_A f = f$ is not always true, as seen from the example of the function 1 when $P1 = 1$ and A is transient. We have, however:

Lemma 2.11. *If h is harmonic and positive, and if $U_A I_{A^c} h < \infty$, then $P_A h = P_{S_A} h = h$.*

Proof. The resolvent equation, $U_A = P + U_A I_{A^c} P$, yields

$$U_A h = h + U_A I_{A^c} h,$$

and by substracting $U_A I_{A^c} h$ from both members we get

$$P_{S_A} h = U_A I_A h = h,$$

and also $P_A h = I_A h + I_{A^c} U_A I_A h = h$.

We shall now use the reduced functions to give a characterization of potentials. We assume G to be proper.

Proposition 2.12. *A finite superharmonic function f is a potential if and only if $\lim_n P_{A_n} f = 0$ for every decreasing sequence $\{A_n\}_{n \geqslant 0}$ of sets in $\mathscr{E}$ such that $\bigcap A_n = \emptyset$.*

Proof. Let f be a potential; since $T_{A_n} \leqslant T_{A_{n+1}}$ a.s., the proof of Theorem 2.1 shows that the sequence $g_n = P_{A_n} f$ decreases; let g denote its limit. Since by Theorem 2.1, $Pg_n = g_n$ on A_n^c, an application of Lebesgue's theorem yields $Pg = g$. By Corollary 1.8, it follows that g vanishes identically.

Conversely, we suppose that f is not a potential and we call h the harmonic part of its Riesz decomposition. Let E_n be an increasing sequence of sets such that $E = \bigcup E_n$ and $G(x, E_n) < \infty$ for every integer n and all x in E. Then set $A_n^c = E_n \cap \{h \leqslant n\}$; we have $U_{A_n} I_{A_n^c} h \leqslant U_0 I_{A_n^c} h \leqslant n\, G\, 1_{E_n} < \infty$. Therefore $P_{A_n} h = h$ for every n, and it follows that $\lim_n P_{A_n} f \geqslant \lim_n P_{A_n} h = h \neq 0$ although $\bigcap A_n = \emptyset$.

Exercise 2.13. Let f be a finite superharmonic function. For every x in E, the set function L defined on $\mathcal{E}$ by $L(A) = P_A f(x)$ is strongly sub-additive, that is

$$L(A \cup B) + L(A \cap B) \leqslant L(A) + L(B).$$

Exercise 2.14. Let S and T be two stopping times such that $S \leqslant T$ and f a superharmonic function; prove that $P_S f \geqslant P_T f$. If $\{S_n\}$ is a sequence of stopping times decreasing to the stopping time S, then

$$P_S f = \lim_n P_{S_n} f.$$

In particular, if $\{A_n\}$ is an increasing sequence of sets with union A, then $\lim_n P_{A_n} 1 = P_A 1$. What can be said if A_n is decreasing?

Exercise 2.15. If A is transient prove that $P_A = G(I_A - \Pi_A)$ and that if $f \in \mathcal{S}$ then $P_A f$ is a potential.

Exercise 2.16. For $A \in \mathcal{E}$, we define a kernel H_A by setting for $f \in \mathcal{E}_+$

$$H_A f(x) = 1_A(x)\, E_x \left[\sum_{n=0}^{S_A - 1} f(X_n) \right].$$

(1) Prove that

$$H_A = I_A \sum_{n \geqslant 0} (P I_{A^c})^n = I_A + I_A U_A I_{A^c}.$$

In particular $H_A f$ vanishes outside A.

(2) Prove that $G H_A = G - G^A = P_A G$ (cf. Proposition 1.10), and derive that if Gg is a potential, then $P_A Gg$ is the potential of the function $H_A g$ which vanishes outside A (the reader will see in the next section other interpretations of H_A).

Exercise 2.17 (Dirichlet's problem). Let $A \in \mathcal{E}$ and $f \in \mathcal{E}_+$; prove that $P_A f$ is the smallest function equal to f on A and harmonic outside A.

Exercise 2.18. For $h \in \mathcal{U}_+$, show that

$$U_h(h)\,(x) = 1 - E_x\left[\prod_{n=1}^{\infty}(1 - h(X_n))\right].$$

If P is markovian and $\inf_{x \in E} h(x) > 0$, then $U_h(h) = 1$. The result may fail to be true if one of the two conditions is not verified; give examples.

Exercise 2.19. Let N be a kernel on $(E, \mathscr{E})$ satisfying the reinforced maximum principle and let $\mathscr{B}$ be the space of bounded functions f such that $N|f|$ is bounded.

(1) If $h \in \mathscr{B}$ is such that $Nh \geqslant 0$, then $Nh \geqslant h$. Derive that $Nf = Nf'$ with $f, f' \in \mathscr{B}$ implies $f = f'$.

(2) Prove that N satisfies the complete maximum principle for the functions in $\mathscr{B}_+$. (This exercise is solved in ch. 10.)

Exercise 2.20. Prove that the kernel U_0 satisfies the complete maximum principle if it is proper, and derive (cf. Exercise 1.25) that G satisfies the reinforced maximum principle.

Exercise 2.21. (1) Let L be a death time (ch. 1, Exercise 3.17). Prove that $\varphi(x) = P_x[L > 0]$ is superharmonic. Express its Riesz decomposition. Under what conditions is φ a potential? In particular if $L = L_A$, what condition must A satisfy in order that φ be a potential?

(2) For every probability measure P_ν on Ω, the sequence $\{Y_n\}_{n \geqslant 0}$ defined by

$$Y_n(\omega) = X_n(\omega) \quad \text{if } n < L(\omega),$$

$$Y_n(\omega) = \Delta \quad \quad \text{if } n \geqslant L(\omega),$$

is a homogeneous Markov chain with transition probability P^φ (notation of Exercise 1.26) and initial measure $\varphi\,\nu$. (Notice that this measure may have a total mass less than one.)

3. Invariant and excessive measures

In the last two sections, P was viewed as operating on the right on functions. We are now going to let it operate on the left on measures and sketch a potential theory relative to measures. We thereafter introduce the important notion of Markov chains in duality.

Definition 3.1. A σ-finite measure m is said to be *invariant* by P, or P-invariant, if $mP = m$. We shall also say that m is invariant for the chain X, or simply invariant if there is no risk of confusion.

Examples. The left (right) Haar measure on a group G is invariant for the left (right) random walks on G. If P is the T.P. defined in ch. 1, Example 1.4(iii), the measure m is P-invariant if and only if $\theta(m) = m$, namely if m is invariant with respect to θ.

3.2. The probabilistic significance of an invariant measure is the following: even if the positive measure m is unbounded, one can define a measure P_m on $(\Omega, \mathscr{F})$ by setting

$$P_m[\Gamma] = \int_E P_x[\Gamma] \, \mathrm{d}m(x).$$

If the measure m is invariant, the chain X is then *stationary* for the measure P_m: for all integers $n_1, n_2, \ldots, n_k$ and n and sets $A_1, \ldots, A_k \in \mathscr{E}$,

$$P_m[X_{n_1} \in A_1, \ldots, X_{n_k} \in A_k] = P_m[X_{n+n_1} \in A_1, \ldots, X_{n+n_k} \in A_k],$$

which may also be expressed by saying that P_m is invariant with respect to the shift operator θ.

Definition 3.3. A positive σ-finite measure m is said to be *P-excessive* if $mP \leqslant m$. We also say that m is excessive for X, or simply excessive when there is no fear of mistake.

Examples. Let ν be a positive measure such that the measure νG is σ-finite; we then say that ν is a charge and νG is an excessive measure called the *potential measure* of the charge ν. If G is proper, all bounded measures are charges.

    If m is excessive (invariant) then αm, where $\alpha \in \mathbf{R}_+$, is still excessive (invariant). In the sequel, when we state that an excessive (invariant) measure is unique, we mean unique up to multiplication. Moreover the sum of two excessive (invariant) measures is an excessive (invariant) measure; thus the set of excessive (invariant) measures is a convex cone. As for superharmonic functions, one can state a Riesz decomposition theorem.

Proposition 3.4. *Every excessive measure may be uniquely written as the sum of an invariant measure and of a potential measure.*

Proof. If $f \in b\mathscr{E}_+$, the sequence of numbers $mP_n(f)$ decreases to a limit $v(f)$ which defines an invariant measure, as is easily seen. The proof then follows the same pattern as for functions.

As in the case of functions, we shall see that the restriction to a set A of an excessive measure is excessive for the chain induced on A, namely $mP \leqslant m$ implies $(1_A m) \Pi_A \leqslant 1_A m$, or equivalently $mI_A U_A I_A \leqslant mI_A$. This is shown by the following.

Proposition 3.5. *If m is excessive and h, k are in $\mathscr{U}_+$ and such that $h \leqslant k$, then*

$$mI_h U_h \leqslant mI_k U_k \leqslant m.$$

The proof is the same as for Proposition 2.10 with right multiplication instead of left multiplications. As in the case of functions, if m is invariant, $1_A m$ is not bound to be Π_A-invariant (cf. Exercise 3.12). In the next chapter, we shall find sufficient conditions implying this result.

Let us now prove the result analogous to Theorem 2.1.

Theorem 3.6 (balayage theorem). *Let m be an excessive measure. The measure mH_A, where $H_A = I_A + I_A U_A I_{A^c}$, is the smallest excessive measure which dominates m on A.*

Proof. Clearly $mH_A = m$ on A, and by Proposition 3.5, $mH_A \leqslant m$; moreover, by the resolvent equation of Proposition 2.9, we have

$$mH_A P = mI_A P + mI_A U_A I_{A^c} P$$

$$= mI_A P + mI_A(U_A - P) = mI_A U_A.$$

But Proposition 3.5 implies that

$$mI_A U_A = mI_A U_A I_A + mI_A U_A I_{A^c} \leqslant mI_A + mI_A U_A I_{A^c},$$

so that $mH_A P \leqslant mH_A$, which proves that mH_A is excessive.

Finally if m' is excessive and $m'I_A \geqslant mI_A$, then $m' \geqslant m'H_A \geqslant mH_A$ and the proof is completed.

The kernel H_A was introduced and studied in Exercise 2.16. It is called the *co-balayage operator* relative to A, because it acts with respect to measures as P_A acts with respect to functions, as one can see by comparing on the one hand Theorems 2.1 and 3.6 and on the other hand Exercises 2.16

and 3.14. This duality between the operators P_A and H_A appears in an even more striking form under the "duality hypothesis" that we are going to introduce now.

Definition 3.7. Two kernels N and $\hat{N}$ on $(E, \mathscr{E})$ are said to be *in duality* relative to the positive σ-finite measure m, if for every pair (f, g) of functions in $\mathscr{E}_+$,

$$\int_E Nf\, g \,\mathrm{d}m = \int_E f\, \hat{N}g \,\mathrm{d}m,$$

which will also be written $\langle Nf, g \rangle_m = \langle f, \hat{N}g \rangle_m$, or even $\langle Nf, g \rangle = \langle f, \hat{N}g \rangle$ when the relevant measure m cannot be mistaken.

Two Markov chains X and $\hat{X}$ are said to be in duality relative to m if their T.P.'s are in duality relative to m. One of the two chains is said to be the *dual* or *reversed* chain of the other one. The objects defined in terms of $\hat{X}$ will be designated by the symbol ^ and the prefix "co-". For example, a function co-superharmonic is a function which is superharmonic for $\hat{P}$, the T.P. of $\hat{X}$, and the set of co-superharmonic functions is denoted by $\hat{\mathscr{S}}$.

Some easy remarks and examples are collected in Exercise 3.16. In particular, by making $g = 1$ ($f = 1$) in the definition it is seen that m is excessive (co-excessive). More generally, we must emphasize the relationship between superharmonic functions and co-excessive measures.

The reader will notice that, without any special hypothesis, there may be several T.P.'s in duality with a given T.P. Their relationship is settled in the following.

Lemma 3.8. *If $(E, \mathscr{E})$ is separable and if each of the two transition probabilities $\hat{P}$ and $\hat{P}'$ is in duality with P relative to m, then there is an m-negligible set N such that $\hat{P}(x, \cdot) = \hat{P}'(x, \cdot)$ for all x in N^c.*

Proof. The duality hypothesis implies at once that for every $f \in b\mathscr{E}_+$, we have $\hat{P}f = \hat{P}'f$ m-a.e. We can therefore find an m-negligible set N such that if x is in N^c, then $\hat{P}(x, A_n) = \hat{P}'(x, A_n)$ for every set A_n in a countable algebra generating $\mathscr{E}$, hence $\hat{P}(x, \cdot) = \hat{P}'(x, \cdot)$.

Definition 3.9. Any T.P. which is in duality with P relative to m is called a *modification* of $\hat{P}$.

Proposition 3.10. *Let X and $\hat{X}$ be in duality relative to m; then for every $h \in \mathcal{U}_+$ the kernels U_h and $\hat{U}_h$ are in duality relative to m.*

Proof. One must prove that, for $f, g \in b\mathscr{E}_+$,

$$\int_E \left(\sum_{n \geqslant 0} (PI_{1-h})^n Pf \right) g \, dm = \int_E f \left(\sum_{n \geqslant 0} (\hat{P}I_{1-h})^n \hat{P}g \right) dm,$$

but this follows from repeated applications of the formula

$$\int_E (PI_{1-h}) Pf \, g \, dm = \int_E f \, (\hat{P}I_{1-h}) \hat{P}g \, dm,$$

which in turn is an obvious consequence of the duality formula of Definition 3.7.

Corollary 3.11. *For $A \in \mathscr{E}$, the kernels H_A and $\hat{P}_A$ and the transition probabilities Π_A and $\hat{\Pi}_A$ are in duality.*

Proof. Since the operator I_A is its own dual, the corollary follows at once from Proposition 3.10 and the expression of the kernels as functions of U_A. For example,

$$\langle H_A f, g \rangle_m = \langle I_A f, g \rangle_m + \langle I_A U_A I_{A^c} f, g \rangle_m$$

$$= \langle f, I_A g \rangle_m + \langle f, I_{A^c} \hat{U}_A I_A g \rangle_m = \langle f, \hat{P}_A g \rangle_m.$$

Exercise 3.12. Prove by an example that in Proposition 3.5, one may have $m\Pi_A < 1_A m$, even if m is invariant.

[*Hint*: One can use the chain of translation on integers.]

Exercise 3.13 (Principle of unicity of charges). If ν and λ are two charges such that $\nu G = \lambda G$, then $\nu = \lambda$.

Exercise 3.14. If ν is a charge, the measure $\nu' = \nu P_A$ is the unique measure carried by A and such that: (i) $\nu'G = \nu G$ on A, (ii) $\nu'G \leqslant \nu G$ everywhere.

Exercise 3.15 (Capacities). (1) For $A \in \mathscr{E}$, prove that

$$(I - P_{S_A}) GI_A = I_A.$$

(2) Let m be an excessive measure for P and f, g two functions in $\mathscr{E}_+$ vanishing outside A and such that $Gf \leqslant Gg$ on A. Prove that

$$\int f \, dm \leqslant \int g \, dm.$$

(3) Prove that for $A, B \in \mathscr{E}$, we have

$$P_{A \cup B} 1 + P_{A \cap B} 1 \leqslant P_A 1 + P_B 1,$$

and derive that the set of transient sets is closed under finite unions and intersections. Can this result be sharpened?

(4) We call *capacity* of the transient set A the number

$$C(A) = \int_A P_x[S_A = \infty] \, m(dx).$$

Prove that $C(A) \leqslant C(B)$ if $A \subset B$, and that for any pair (A, B) of transient sets we have

$$C(A \cup B) + C(A \cap B) \leqslant C(A) + C(B).$$

(5) Let $\mathscr{L}$ be the subset of $\mathscr{E}_+$ of functions g vanishing outside A and such that $Gg \leqslant 1$ on A. Prove that

$$C(A) = \sup_{g \in \mathscr{L}} \int_A g \, dm.$$

(6) Assume furthermore that X is in duality with $\hat{X}$ relative to m, which is then also co-excessive, and prove that if A is transient for both chains then $C(A) = \hat{C}(A)$.

Exercise 3.16. Let P and $\hat{P}$ be two T.P.'s in duality relative to the measure m.

(1) Prove that m is both excessive and co-excessive. If E is countable and $\mathscr{E}$ discrete, then the empty set is the only set of m-measure zero; the duality hypothesis is equivalent to the requirement that

$$m(x) P(x, y) = m(y) \hat{P}(y, x)$$

for every pair (x, y) of points in E.

(2) A right (left) random walk of law μ on a group G in duality relative to the right (left) Haar measure on G with the right (left) random walk of law $\hat{\mu}$, where $\hat{\mu}$ is the image of μ by the map $x \to x^{-1}$.

(3) If $f \in \mathscr{S}$, the measure $f\,m$ is co-excessive. If f is harmonic, the measure $f\,m$ is co-invariant.

Exercise 3.17. (1) If m is P-excessive then P maps the functions m-a.e. bounded into functions m-a.e. bounded, and thus induces a positive contraction on $L^\infty(E, \mathscr{E}, m)$.

[*Hint*: Use the weaker condition $mP \ll m$. Solution in ch. 4, Proposition 1.3.]

(2) Solve the same problem with $L^1(m)$ instead of $L^\infty(m)$. By using Holder's inequality for the measures $P(x, \cdot\,)$, prove that for every $p \in [1, \infty]$ the transition probability P induces on $L^p(m)$ a positive contraction (one may also use the Riesz convexity theorem). If P and $\hat{P}$ are in duality relative to m, the operators induced by P on $L^1(m)$ and by $\hat{P}$ on $L^\infty(m)$ are adjoint operators.

Exercise 3.18. Let P and $\hat{P}$ be in duality relative to m and let f be finite and P-superharmonic. Then, with the notation of Exercise 1.26, P^f is in duality with $\hat{P}$ relative to $f\,m$.

Exercise 3.19. (1) If P is in duality with itself with respect to m, that is if

$$\int Pf\,g\,\mathrm{d}m = \int f\,Pg\,\mathrm{d}m$$

for every pair (f, g) of functions in $\mathscr{E}_+$, then P induces on $L^2(m)$ a self-adjoint operator of norm less than one (see Exercise 3.17 above). There exists therefore a resolution of the identity $E(\mathrm{d}\lambda)$ in $L^2(m)$ such that

$$P_n = \int_{-1}^{+1} \lambda^n\,E(\mathrm{d}\lambda).$$

In particular, if E is countable,

$$m(x)\,P_n(x, y) = \int_{-1}^{+1} \lambda^n\,\mu_{x,y}(\mathrm{d}\lambda),$$

where $\mu_{x,y}$ is the measure defined by $\mu_{x,y}([-1, \lambda[) = \langle E[-1, \lambda[y, x\rangle$. (In the last formula x and y stand for the elements $1_{\{x\}}$ and $1_{\{y\}}$ of $L^2(m)$.)

(2) The space E still being countable, it is assumed that $G(x, y) < \infty$ for every pair (x, y) of points in E. Prove that the infinite matrix

$$\Gamma(x, y) = m(x)\,G(x, y) = m(y)\,G(y, x)$$

is positive definite. Derive that the space $\mathscr{V}$ of functions with finite supports may be endowed with a structure of pre-Hilbert space, by setting

$$(f, g) = \sum_{x,y} \Gamma(x, y)\,f(x)\,g(y) = \langle f, Gg\rangle_m.$$

Let $\mathscr{V}_A$ be the subspace of $\mathscr{V}$ of functions with support in A; prove that the orthogonal projector proj_A on $\mathscr{V}_A$ satisfies the relation

$$\mathrm{proj}_A f = P_A f = (f\,m)\,H_A/m,$$

where the last term is the Radon–Nikodym derivative of $(f\,m)\,H_A$ with respect to m.

(3) If $g_A(x) = 1_A(x)\,P_x[S_A = \infty]$ set $C(A) = m(g_A)$. (See Exercise 3.15(4).) Prove that on the set of functions g of $\mathscr{V}_A$ such that $m(g) = 1$, the quantity (g, g) reaches its infimum $C(A)^{-1}$ for the unique function $g_A/C(A)$.

Exercise 3.20. (1) Let M be a homogeneous space of a group G admitting a measure ν invariant by G, that is $\varepsilon_g * \nu = \nu$ for all $g \in G$. Prove that ν is invariant for all random walks induced on M. If M is compact, every random walk on M induced by a random walk of law μ on G has at least one invariant probability measure [*Hint*: A cluster point of the sequence $n^{-1} \sum_{m=1}^{m=n} \mu^m * \nu'$, where ν' is any probability measure on M] and the set of invariant probability measures is a vaguely compact convex set.

(2) If ν is an invariant probability measure for the induced random walk, then for every function $\varphi \in L^\infty(\nu)$, the function

$$f(g) = \int_M \varphi(gx)\,\nu(dx)$$

is μ-harmonic.

Exercise 3.21 (Continuation of Exercise 1.24). (1) Prove that there exists one and only one excessive measure m such that P is in duality with itself with respect to m. Compute this measure and find under which condition it is an invariant measure.

(2) Using the notation and results of Exercise 3.19, prove that there are polynomial functions $Q_k(\lambda)$ and a unique measure μ such that for every pair (k, l) of integers,

$$\mu_{k,l}(d\lambda) = Q_k(\lambda)\,Q_l(\lambda)\,\mu(d\lambda),$$

and therefore

$$m(k)\,P_n(k, l) = \int_{-1}^{+1} Q_k(\lambda)\,Q_l(\lambda)\,\mu(d\lambda).$$

Exercise 3.22. If E is an LCCB and P maps the functions of C_K into continuous functions, every limit for the vague topology of excessive measures is an excessive measure.

4. Resolvents

In this section we digress from our main subject to introduce another situation which also gives rise to a potential theory and which is related to Markov processes with continuous time parameters. Some results relevant to this situation may be obtained by mere translation of results about transition probabilities. Numerous exercises in the following chapters will be designed to this end.

Definition 4.1. A *sub-markovian resolvent* on $(E, \mathscr{E})$ is a family $\{V_\alpha, \alpha > 0\}$ of positive kernels such that
  (i) $\alpha V_\alpha(x, E) \leqslant 1$ for each x in E and $\alpha > 0$;
  (ii) $V_\alpha - V_\beta = (\beta - \alpha) V_\alpha V_\beta = (\beta - \alpha) V_\beta V_\alpha$ for $\alpha, \beta > 0$.
Equation (ii) is called the *resolvent equation*. The reader will notice its resemblance to the equation of Proposition 2.9 and should also refer to Exercise 4.12.

For $f \in \mathscr{E}_+$, it follows from the resolvent equation that the map $\alpha \to V_\alpha f$ is decreasing and that we may thus define

$$V_0 f = \sup_\alpha V_\alpha f = \lim_{\alpha \to 0} V_\alpha f. \qquad (4.1)$$

If (f_n) is an increasing sequence of functions with limit f, by interchange of increasing limits we get immediately

$$V_0 f = \lim_n V_0 f_n;$$

this shows that V_0 is a positive kernel on $(E, \mathscr{E})$ which satisfies the identities

$$V_0 = V_\alpha + \alpha V_0 V_\alpha = V_\alpha + \alpha V_\alpha V_0. \qquad (4.2)$$

In the remainder of this section we consider only *proper resolvents*, that is, resolvents such that V_0 is a proper kernel.

For each $\alpha > 0$, the kernel $P^\alpha = \alpha V_\alpha$ is a T.P. on E. We shall call X^α the canonical Markov chain associated with P^α.

Definition 4.2. A function f in $\mathscr{E}_+$ is called *supermedian (invariant)* for the resolvent $\{V_\alpha\}$ if it is superharmonic (harmonic) for every chain X^α, in other words if

$$\alpha V_\alpha f \leqslant f \, (\alpha V_\alpha f = f) \quad \text{for each } \alpha > 0.$$

Proposition 4.3. *If $f \in \mathscr{E}_+$, then $V_0 f$ is supermedian. If $V_0 f$ is finite and if h is positive, invariant and smaller than f, then h vanishes identically.*

Proof. The first sentence is an obvious consequence of eq. (4.2). If $h \leqslant V_0 f$, then eq. (4.2) again yields

$$h = \alpha V_\alpha h \leqslant \alpha V_\alpha V_0 f = V_0 f - V_\alpha f$$

for every $\alpha > 0$. As α tends to zero, $V_0 f - V_\alpha f$ converges to zero and consequently $h = 0$.

Proposition 4.4. *The potential kernel G^α of X^α is equal to $I + \alpha V_0$.*

Proof. Since $I + \alpha V_0$ is a proper kernel, it suffices to show that

$$\alpha V_0 f = \sum_{n=1}^{n=\infty} (\alpha V_\alpha)^n f$$

for every $f \in \mathscr{E}_+$ such that $V_0 f$ is finite. By applying k times the identity of eq. (4.2), we get

$$\alpha V_0 f = \sum_{n=1}^{n=k-1} (\alpha V_\alpha)^n f + (\alpha V_\alpha)^k V_0 f;$$

if k tends to infinity, the term $(\alpha V_\alpha)^k V_0 f$ decreases to an invariant function which is smaller than $V_0 f$, and hence vanishes identically. The proof is then easily completed.

Remark. The kernels G^α are thus also proper kernels.

Theorem 4.5. *The kernel V_0 satisfies the complete maximum principle; more precisely, if $f \in \mathscr{E}_+$ and g is supermedian, the inequality $V_0 f \leqslant g$ holds everywhere if it holds on $\{f > 0\}$.*

Proof. Suppose that $V_0 f(x) \leqslant g(x)$ for $x \in \{f > 0\}$. If, for every integer n, we set $f_n = f \wedge n$, we have

$$V_0 f_n(x) \leqslant g(x), \qquad x \in \{f > 0\},$$

and consequently, for every $\alpha > 0$ and $x \in \{f > 0\}$,

$$G^\alpha f_n(x) = f_n(x) + \alpha V_0 f(x) \leqslant \alpha g(x) + n.$$

By Theorem 2.3, applied to the chain X^α, we get

$$G^\alpha f_n = f_n + \alpha V_0 f_n \leqslant \alpha g + n \quad \text{everywhere,}$$

and, since α may be taken arbitrarily large, it follows that $V_0 f_n \leqslant g$ everywhere. The proof is now easily completed by letting n tend to infinity.

We close this section with a characterization of supermedian functions similar to Theorem 2.3 (see also Exercise 4.13).

Proposition 4.6. *A function $g \in \mathscr{E}_+$ is supermedian if and only if for every function $f \in \mathscr{E}_+$ such that $V_0 f$ is finite, the inequality $V_0 f \leqslant g$ holds everywhere if it holds on $\{f > 0\}$.*

Proof. The necessity is shown in the preceding theorem. Conversely, let f be a function in $\mathscr{E}_+$ such that $V_0 f$ is bounded, and set $g_n = g \wedge n f$, $h_n = \alpha(g_n - \alpha V_\alpha g_n)$. We have $V_0 h_n = \alpha V_\alpha g_n$, and therefore

$$g \geqslant \alpha V_\alpha g_n = V_0 h_n \quad \text{on } \{g - \alpha V_\alpha g_n > 0\},$$

hence a fortiori on $\{g_n - \alpha V_\alpha g_n > 0\} = \{h_n > 0\}$. The hypothesis then implies that for every n, $g \geqslant \alpha V_\alpha g_n$ everywhere, and by passing to the limit, we obtain $g \geqslant \alpha V_\alpha g$. Since this is true for all α, the function g is supermedian.

Exercise 4.7. Let $\{V_\alpha, \alpha > 0\}$ be a resolvent and β a real number > 0. Prove that the family of kernels $V'_\alpha = V_{\alpha+\beta}$ is a proper resolvent.

Exercise 4.8 (Resolvent of linear brownian motion). Prove that the family of convolution kernels V_α defined on $\mathbf{R}$ by the densities

$$v_\alpha(x, y) = (2\alpha)^{-1/2} \exp\{-(2\alpha)^{-1/2} |y - x|\}$$

is a resolvent.

Exercise 4.9. The integral kernels defined on $\mathbf{R}$ by the densities

$$v_\alpha(x, y) = v^{-1} \exp\{-\alpha(y - x)/v\} \quad \text{if } y > x,$$

$$= 0 \qquad\qquad\qquad \text{if } y \leqslant x,$$

form a proper resolvent.

Exercise 4.10. If h is a positive finite function such that $V_\beta h$ is finite for all $\beta > 0$ and if there is an α such that $\alpha V_\alpha h = h$, then h is invariant.

Exercise 4.11. If $f \in \mathscr{E}_+$, then for every x in E the function $\alpha \to V_\alpha f(x)$ is decreasing, right continuous and continuous on every open interval on which it is finite.

Exercise 4.12. (1) Let $\{V_\alpha, \alpha > 0\}$ be a resolvent and h a function in $b\mathscr{E}_+$. Pick $\alpha > \|h\|$ and define

$$V_h = \sum_{n \geqslant 0} (V_\alpha I_{\alpha - h})^n V_\alpha.$$

Prove that V_h does not depend on α and that for $h \leqslant k$ we have

$$V_h = \sum_{n \geqslant 0} (V_k I_{k-h})^n \, V_k = \sum_{n \geqslant 0} V_k (I_{k-h} V_k)^n,$$

and

$$V_h = V_k + V_k I_{k-h} V_h = V_k + V_h I_{k-h} V_k.$$

These equations contain the resolvent equation, since for $h = \beta$ we have $V_h = V_\beta$.

[*Hint*: Use the chains X^α for which $V_h = \alpha^{-1} U_{h\alpha-1}$; in particular for $h \leqslant 1$, we have $V_h = U_h$, where this kernel is computed for X^1.]

(2) The family of kernels $\tilde{V}_\alpha = V_{\alpha h} I_h$ is a resolvent.

Exercise 4.13. (1) Let P be a T.P. on $(E, \mathscr{E})$. Prove that one defines a resolvent by setting

$$V_\alpha = (1 + \alpha)^{-1} \sum_{n \geqslant 0} ((1 + \alpha)^{-1} P)^n.$$

Prove that $V_0 = G$.

(2) Assume that G is a proper kernel, and prove that a function is superharmonic for P if and only if it is supermedian for V_α. Then derive Proposition 2.3 from Proposition 4.6.

Exercise 4.14. Consider a proper resolvent $\{V_\alpha, \alpha > 0\}$.

(1) Prove that, if $\alpha < \beta$, the superharmonic functions for X^β are superharmonic for X^α.

(2) Let f be supermedian, and for $A \in \mathscr{E}$ let $P_A^\alpha f$ be the reduced function of f relative to X^α. Prove that the following limit

$$R_A f = \lim_{\alpha \to \infty} P_A^\alpha f$$

exists, and defines the smallest supermedian function which dominates f on A.

(3) Prove that $R_A f \leqslant f$, $R_A f = f$ on A and if f, g are supermedian and $f \leqslant g$ on A, then $R_A f \leqslant R_A g$. If $\{f_n\}$ is an increasing sequence of supermedian functions with limit f, then $R_A f = \lim R_A f_n$.

(4) If h is a positive function vanishing outside A, then $R_A V_0 h = V_0 h$. The operator $R_A V_0$ is given by a kernel. Is the same thing true for the operator R_A?

(5) If f, g are supermedian, then $R_A(f + g) = R_A f + R_A g$.

(6) If $\{A_n\}$ is an increasing sequence of sets with union A, then $R_A f = \lim_n R_{A_n} f$.

Exercise 4.15 (excessive functions). (1) If f is supermedian, the function $\alpha \to \alpha V_\alpha f(x)$ is increasing for each x in E. We call f *excessive* for the given resolvent if in addition $\lim_{\alpha \to \infty} \alpha V_\alpha f = f$. Prove that the potentials $V_0 g, g \in \mathscr{E}_+$, are excessive functions.

(2) Let f be supermedian and set $f^* = \lim_{\alpha \to \infty} \alpha V_\alpha f$. Show that f^* is an excessive function and that $f^* \leqslant f$. Show that the set $K = \{f^* < f\}$ on which f^* differs from f is of *potential zero*, that is $V_\alpha(\cdot, K) = 0$ for one (hence for all) $\alpha > 0$. Show that f^* is the greatest excessive function bounded above by f.

(3) Let f be a supermedian function and define, with the notation of Exercise 4.14, $(R_A f)^* = \lim_{\alpha \to \infty} \alpha V_\alpha R_A f$. Prove that $(R_A f)^*$ is excessive and that it is the smallest supermedian function which majorizes f on A up to a set of potential zero.

Exercise 4.16. A σ-finite positive measure m is *invariant* (*supermedian*) for a resolvent $\{V_\alpha\}$ if $\alpha m V_\alpha = m$ ($\alpha m V_\alpha \leqslant m$) for all $\alpha > 0$. It is *excessive* if it is supermedian and if in addition $\lim_{\alpha \to 0} \alpha m V_\alpha = m$.

(1) Work out for supermedian measures results similar to those in Exercise 4.14. For A in $\mathscr{E}$ and m supermedian, set

$$mL_A = \lim_{\alpha \to \infty} mH_A^\alpha.$$

(2) Prove that the operator $V_0 L_A$ is given by a kernel and that $V_0 L_A = R_A V_0$. (Compare with Exercise 2.16.)

Exercise 4.17. If E is locally compact and if $\lim_{\alpha \to \infty} \alpha V_\alpha(x, \cdot) = \varepsilon_x$ in the vague topology, show that the supermedian Radon measures are excessive measures.

CHAPTER 3

TRANSIENCE AND RECURRENCE

In this chapter we describe the basic classification of Markov chains according to their asymptotic behaviour. We start with countable state space where the situation is particularly nice and then proceed to more general state spaces.

1. Discrete Markov chains

Definition 1.1. A Markov chain will be called *discrete* if the state space E is countable and $\mathscr{E}$ is the discrete σ-algebra on E.

In this section, we shall deal only with discrete chains, and shall use the notational device of ch. 1, §1.4, namely, we shall not distinguish between the point x and the set $\{x\}$; when μ is a measure we write $\mu(y)$ in place of $\mu(\{y\})$, and in particular $P(x, y)$ for $P(x, \{y\})$.

Remark. If E is an uncountable set and $\mathscr{E}$ is the discrete σ-algebra, then for every T.P. on $(E, \mathscr{E})$, every point $x \in E$ is contained in the countable absorbing set $\bigcup_0^\infty \{y: P_n(x, y) > 0\}$. It suffices therefore to study countable state spaces, justifying the above terminology. In the same way, in the case of random walks on a discrete group, the identity is contained in a countable absorbing subgroup. In the sequel, the term *discrete group* will therefore be understood to mean countable and discrete.

Proposition 1.2. *For every x in E there are only two possibilities*:
  (i) $P_x[\overline{\lim}_n\{X_n = x\}] = 0$,
  (ii) $P_x[\overline{\lim}_n\{X_n = x\}] = 1$.

Proof. Let $S_x(\omega) = \inf\{n > 0: X_n(\omega) = x\}$, and define inductively

$$S_1 = S_x, \ldots, S_n = S_{n-1} + S_x \circ \theta_{S_{n-1}}, \ldots;$$

we have $S_n = \inf\{p > S_{n-1}: X_p = x\}$, and the S_n are the successive random

65

times where X is in x. Set $\varphi(\,\cdot\,) = P.[S_x < \infty]$; the strong Markov property implies that

$$P_x[S_n < \infty] = P_x[S_{n-1} + S_x \circ \theta_{S_{n-1}} < \infty]$$
$$= E_x[P_x[\{S_{n-1} < \infty\} \cap \{S_x \circ \theta_{S_{n-1}} < \infty\} \mid \mathscr{F}_{S_{n-1}}]]$$
$$= E_x[1_{\{S_{n-1} < \infty\}}\, \varphi(X_{S_{n-1}})];$$

and since $X_{S_{n-1}} = x$ on the event $\{S_{n-1} < \infty\}$ we get

$$P_x[S_n < \infty] = P_x[S_{n-1} < \infty]\, P_x[S_x < \infty].$$

It follows inductively that $P_x[S_n < \infty] = (P_x[S_x < \infty])^n$. If $P_x[S_x < \infty] = 1$, then $P_x[S_n < \infty] = 1$ for every n and we are in case (ii). Otherwise $P_x[S_x < \infty] = a < 1$, so that

$$\sum_{1}^{\infty} P_x[S_n < \infty] = a(1 - a)^{-1} < \infty,$$

and the Borel–Cantelli lemma implies that we are in case (i).

Definition 1.3. In case (i) of Proposition 1.2 the state x will be called *transient*; in case (ii) it will be called *recurrent*.

Proposition 1.4. *The state x is recurrent if and only if $G(x, x) = +\infty$.*

Proof. Let $N = \sum_{n=0}^{\infty} 1_{\{X_n = x\}}$ be the random number of passages through x. Clearly $\{N \geqslant k\} = \{S_k < \infty\}$, and

$$G(x, x) = E_x[N] = 1 + \sum_{n=1}^{\infty} P_x[S_n < \infty].$$

If x is recurrent, it is obvious that $G(x, x) = +\infty$, whereas if x is transient, then $G(x, x) = (1 - a)^{-1} < \infty$.

Definition 1.5. We shall say that y is a *consequent* of x if there is an integer k such that $P_k(x, y) > 0$.

Proposition 1.6. *If x is recurrent and y is a consequent of x then y is recurrent and x is a consequent of y. Moreover $G(x, y) = G(y, x) = +\infty$.*

Proof. By the maximum principle of ch. 2, Proposition 1.12, we have

$$G(y, y) \geqslant G(x, y) \geqslant \sum_{n=0}^{\infty} P_n(x, x)\, P_k(x, y) = \infty.$$

The state y is thus recurrent. If x is not a consequent of y then $P_y[S_x < \infty] = 0$, and by the strong Markov property $S_y + S_x \circ \theta_{S_y} = \infty$ P_x-a.s. But since y is a consequent of x there is an integer n such that $P_x[S_y \leqslant n] > 0$, and on the event $\{S_y \leqslant n\}$ we have $n + S_x \circ \theta_n \geqslant S_y + S_x \circ \theta_{S_y} = \infty$, which contradicts the fact that x is recurrent.

Theorem 1.7. *There is a unique partition $(C_i, i \in I)$ of the set of recurrent states such that each C_i is an absorbing set and for every pair (x, y) of states within the same class C_i, $P_x[\overline{\lim}\{X_n = y\}] = 1$. Moreover $G(x, y) = + \infty$ or 0 according to whether x and y are in the same class or not.*

Proof. By Proposition 1.6 the relation $x \sim y$ if x is a consequent of y is an equivalence relation on the set of recurrent states. The classes C_i are the equivalence classes for this relation. All the statements are then obvious from the previous results.

Definition 1.8. The chain X will be called *transient* if all the states are transient. In that case $G(x, y) < \infty$ for every pair of states in E. If C is a class of recurrent states, then for the study of X with respect to the probability measures P_x, $x \in C$, we can restrict the state space to C. The chain X will be called *irreducible recurrent* if all the states are recurrent and if there is only one equivalence class. We then have $G(x, y) = \infty$ identically.

We shall end this section by studying irreducible recurrent chains. The following proposition, which will be generalized later, shows that the main concern of the potential theory of ch. 2 is with transient chains. In the recurrent case, we will have to give another definition of potential theory.

Proposition 1.9. *If X is irreducible recurrent the superharmonic and bounded harmonic functions are constant.*

Proof. If f is superharmonic, $f(X_n)$ is a positive supermartingale which converges a.s. But for x and y in E, $f(x)$ and $f(y)$ are limit points of $f(X_n)$ and therefore $f(x) = f(y)$. The same argument works for the bounded harmonic functions.

Theorem 1.10. *If X is irreducible recurrent, there exists a unique (up to multiplication) excessive measure m and this measure is invariant. If x is any point in E, we may define m by*

$$m(y) = H_{\{x\}}(x, y) = U_{\{x\}}(x, y).$$

Proof. Pick a point x in E and set

$$m(y) = E_x\left[\sum_{n<S_x} 1_y(X_n)\right] = H_{\{x\}}(x, y).$$

For every y in E, $0 < m(y) < \infty$; indeed, there is a strictly positive probability of entering y before returning to x, and on the other hand the chain killed at S_x is clearly transient.

Now by the Markov property

$$mP(y) = \sum_z m(z)\, P(z, y) = E_x\left[\sum_{n<S_x} P(X_n, y)\right]$$

$$= E_x\left[\sum_{n<S_x} E_{X_n}[1_y(X_1)]\right] = E_x\left[\sum_{n<S_x} 1_y(X_1 \circ \theta_n)\right]$$

$$= E_x\left[\sum_{n<S_x} 1_y(X_{n+1})\right] = E_x\left[\sum_{n=1}^{S_x} 1_y(X_n)\right] = U_{\{x\}}(x, y).$$

But for $n = 0$, we have $1_y(X_n) = 0$ P_x-a.s. if $y \neq x$, and $1_y(X_n) = 1$ P_x-a.s. if $y = x$, and on $\{S_x = n\}$ we have also $1_y(X_n) = 0$ if $y \neq x$ and $1_y(X_n) = 1$ if $y = x$; consequently

$$E_x\left[\sum_{n=1}^{S_x} 1_y(X_n)\right] = E_x\left[\sum_{n<S_x} 1_y(X_n)\right],$$

that is exactly $H_{\{x\}}(x, y) = U_{\{x\}}(x, y)$, and it follows that $mP = m$.

To prove that m is the only excessive measure for P we set $\hat{P}(x, y) = m(y)\, P(y, x)/m(x)$. The reader will easily check that $\hat{P}$ is a T.P. in duality with P with respect to m, and that the corresponding chain is irreducible recurrent.

If μ is an excessive measure for P, then $f(\,\cdot\,) = \mu(\,\cdot\,)/m(\,\cdot\,)$ is superharmonic for $\hat{P}$, so that the result follows from Proposition 1.9.

Remark. The empty set is the only set of m-measure zero.

Corollary 1.11. *If X is irreducible recurrent, either $E_x[S_x] < \infty$ for every x in E and the invariant measure m is bounded or $E_x[S_x] = \infty$ for every x in E and the invariant measure m is unbounded.*

Proof. By Theorem 1.10, we have

$$m(E) = \sum_{y \in E} m(y) = U_{\{x\}}(x, E) = E_x[S_x];$$

since x is arbitrary we get the desired result.

Remark. The transition probability $\hat{P}$ defined in the proof of Theorem 1.10 is the only one to be in duality with P. For an irreducible recurrent chain we may therefore speak freely of its dual chain, which exists and is unique. The two chains play totally symmetric roles, in particular m is invariant for $\hat{P}$ as well as for P.

The theory of recurrence we have been sketching here cannot be carried over in an obvious way to general state spaces. The sequel of this chapter aims at giving some of the possible extensions. Other viewpoints will be developed in the next chapter.

Exercise 1.12. When the space E is finite, it is customary to represent the T.P. as a square matrix with entry $P(x, y)$ on row x and column y. Prove that P_n is then given by the nth power of the matrix P.

Classify the states and describe the asymptotic behaviour of the chains with T.P.'s given by the following matrices:

$$
\begin{bmatrix}
1 & 0 & 0 & 0 \\
\frac{1}{4} & \frac{1}{2} & \frac{1}{4} & 0 \\
0 & 0 & \frac{1}{2} & \frac{1}{2} \\
0 & 0 & \frac{1}{2} & \frac{1}{2}
\end{bmatrix},
\quad
\begin{bmatrix}
\frac{1}{2} & 0 & 0 & 0 \\
\frac{1}{2} & \frac{1}{2} & 0 & 0 \\
0 & \frac{1}{2} & \frac{1}{2} & 0 \\
0 & 0 & \frac{1}{2} & \frac{1}{2}
\end{bmatrix},
\quad
\begin{bmatrix}
\frac{1}{3} & \frac{1}{3} & \frac{1}{3} \\
\frac{1}{3} & \frac{1}{3} & \frac{1}{3} \\
\frac{1}{3} & \frac{1}{3} & \frac{1}{3}
\end{bmatrix}.
$$

In the case of countable state space it is also sometimes useful to write P as an infinite matrix.

Exercise 1.13. Let E be finite and $P(x, E) = 1$ for all x in E. Prove that there is at least one recurrent point. If there are N points in E and if y is a consequent of x prove that $P_x[S_y < N - 1] > 0$.

Exercise 1.14. Resume the notation of Proposition 1.2.

(1) For $s \in [0, 1[$, set

$$
g(s) = \sum_{n=0}^{\infty} P_n(x, x)\, s^n, \qquad h(s) = \sum_{n=1}^{\infty} P_x[S_x = n]\, s^n.
$$

Compute g as a function of h and derive an alternative proof of Proposition 1.4.

(2) Suppose that x is recurrent and prove that for any integer-valued and $\mathscr{F}_{S_x}$-measurable random variable Z, the sequence of random variables $Z \circ \theta_{S_n}$ is independent and equidistributed with respect to P_x. This is true in particular for $S_n - S_{n-1}$.

(3) Assume further that X is the random walk on $\mathbf{Z}$ with law μ defined by $\mu(1) = p, \mu(-1) = 1 - p$. Under what condition is the state 0 recurrent?

Exercise 1.15. Another proof of Proposition 1.9. Derive from the equality

$$\left(\sum_{m < n} P_m \right) (f - Pf) = f - P_{m+1}f$$

that every superharmonic function is harmonic. Then prove that if a harmonic function vanishes at one point in E it vanishes identically, and apply this result to $f - (f \wedge k)$ for every choice of the constant k.

Exercise 1.16. Let E be the set of positive integers and define a T.P. on E by $P(n, n + 1) = p_n, P(n, 0) = 1 - p_n$. Under what condition is it irreducible recurrent? Compute the invariant measure for that case.

Exercise 1.17. Prove the following converse to Proposition 1.9: if all superharmonic functions are constant, then X is irreducible recurrent.

Exercise 1.18. Continuation of ch. 2, Exercise 3.21. Assume $p_x > 0$ and $q_x > 0$ for all x in E. Prove that the chain is either transient or irreducible recurrent and that the latter case occurs if and only if

$$\int_{-1}^{+1} (1 - \lambda)^{-1} \, d\mu(\lambda) = +\infty.$$

Exercise 1.19 (Galton–Watson chain; continuation of ch. 1, Exercise 2.18).

(1) Call σ the smallest solution of the equation $\check{p}(s) = s$ in the interval $]0, 1]$. Prove that $\sigma = 1$ if $E_1[X_1] \leqslant 1$ and $\sigma < 1$ if $E_1[X_1] > 1$.

(2) Assume that $0 < p(0) < 1$, the other cases offering neither interest nor difficulty. Show that 0 is an absorbing (hence recurrent) state and that

$$P_x \left[\varliminf_n \{X_n = 0\} \right] = \sigma^x.$$

Interpret this probability with respect to the relevant population. Prove that all the other states are transient and describe the asymptotic behaviour of the chain according to the value of σ. See ch. 2, Exercise 1.23 for a particular case.

2. Irreducible chains and Harris chains

We now return to a general state space $(E, \mathscr{E})$, but we assume henceforth that it is separable.

Definition 2.1. The chain X is said to be *ν-irreducible* if there exists a probability measure ν on $\mathscr{E}$ absolutely continuous with respect to $U_c(x, \cdot)$ for all $x \in E$ and $c \in]0, 1[$.

Clearly if the above condition is satisfied for a measure ν', it is satisfied for a probability measure ν equivalent to ν'; it is satisfied for all numbers $c \in]0, 1[$ as soon as it is satisfied for one of them. This property can also be spelled out as: if $A \in \mathscr{E}$ and $\nu(A) > 0$, then for all x in E there is an integer n such that $P_n(x, A) > 0$.

The purpose of this section is to show that for a ν-irreducible chain either the potential kernel is proper or the chain is recurrent (in a strong sense to be defined later).

Following ch. 1, §5.3 we shall call $p_c(x, y)$ an $\mathscr{E} \otimes \mathscr{E}$-measurable version of the density of $U_c(x, \cdot)$ with respect to ν. The irreducibility of X implies that for all x in E, $p_c(x, \cdot)$ is > 0 ν-a.s.; then $p_c(x, \cdot) + 1_{\{p_c=0\}}(x, \cdot)$ is still a density for $U_c(x, \cdot)$ and is strictly positive everywhere. We shall therefore take p_c to be strictly positive in the sequel.

Lemma 2.2. *For $c \in]0, 1[$, there exist two strictly positive measurable functions a_c and b_c such that*
$$U_c \geqslant a_c \otimes b_c \nu.$$

Proof. Let $c < c' < 1$; by the resolvent equation of ch. 2, Proposition 2.9,
$$U_c \geqslant (c' - c) \, U_c U_{c'} \geqslant (c' - c) \, qv,$$
where
$$q(x, y) = \int_E p_c(x, z) \, p_{c'}(z, y) \, \nu(dz).$$

It suffices thus to show that $q(x, y) \geqslant a_c(x) \, b_c(y)$ for suitable functions a_c and b_c.

Since p_c is $\mathscr{E} \otimes \mathscr{E}$-measurable and > 0, the functions $f_k(\cdot)$ $= \nu(\{z : p_c(\cdot, z) \geqslant 1/k\})$ are measurable and increase to 1 as k tends to infinity. There is therefore a smallest integer $k(x) \geqslant 1$ such that
$$\nu(\{z : p_c(x, z) \geqslant 1/k\}) \geqslant \tfrac{3}{4}.$$

Since

$$\{x: k(x) = p\} = \{x: f_{p-1}(x) < \tfrac{3}{4}\} \cap \{x: f_p(x) \geqslant \tfrac{3}{4}\}$$

the map $x \to k(x)$ is measurable, and setting $a(x) = 1/k(x)$, we have

$$\nu(\{z: p_{c'}(x, z) \geqslant a(x)\}) \geqslant \tfrac{3}{4}$$

for every x in E. In the same way we can find a function b such that, for every y in E,

$$\nu(\{z: p_c(z, y) \geqslant b(y)\}) \geqslant \tfrac{3}{4}.$$

We then have

$$q(x, y) \geqslant a(x)\, b(y)\, \nu(\{z: p_c(x, z) \geqslant a(x),\ p_{c'}(z, y) \geqslant b(y)\}) \geqslant \tfrac{1}{2} a(x)\, b(y).$$

It suffices thus to set $a_c = \tfrac{1}{2}(c' - c)\, a$ and $b_c = b$ to get the desired result.

Proposition 2.3. *There is a function $h_0 \in \mathcal{U}_+$, strictly positive and strictly less than* 1, *and a positive measure m_0 equivalent to ν such that*

$$U_{h_0} \geqslant U_{h_0}(h_0) \otimes m_0.$$

Proof. Since the preceding lemma is still true if we replace a_c by $\inf(\tfrac{1}{2}c, a_c)$, we may assume that $c \geqslant 2a_c$. Let $h_0 = a_c$; the resolvent equation then implies

$$U_{h_0} \geqslant U_{h_0} I_{c-h_0} U_c \geqslant \tfrac{1}{2} c U_{h_0} U_c \geqslant \tfrac{1}{2} c U_{h_0}(h_0 \otimes b_c \nu),$$

and it remains to set $m_0 = \tfrac{1}{2} c b_c \nu$ to complete the proof.

Before we proceed to the main results of this section we need another lemma. We recall that a T.P. is said to be markovian if $P(x, E) = 1$ for all x in E. We call B the Banach space of bounded measures ν such that $\nu(E) = 0$.

Lemma 2.4. *The Banach space B is left invariant by any markovian transition probability Q. If the norm Δ of Q as an endomorphism of B is strictly less than one, there exists a unique Q-invariant probability measure Π on $(E, \mathcal{E})$, and for every x in E*

$$\|Q^n(x, \cdot) - \Pi(\cdot)\| \leqslant 2\Delta^n.$$

Proof. The first sentence of the lemma is straightforward. Let ν be any probability measure on $\mathcal{E}$ and k any integer. The measure $\nu - \nu Q^k$ is in B and its norm is at most equal to 2; thus

$$\|\nu Q^n - \nu Q^{k+n}\| = \|(\nu - \nu Q^k)\, Q^n\| \leqslant 2\varDelta^n$$

which shows that the sequence $\{\nu Q^n\}$ is a Cauchy sequence in the space of bounded measures. It has therefore a limit $\varPi$ which is plainly Q-invariant and such that

$$\|\nu Q^n - \varPi\| \leqslant 2\varDelta^n.$$

If ν' is another probability measure on $\mathscr{E}$, we have

$$\|\nu' Q^n - \varPi\| = \|(\nu' - \varPi)\, Q^n\| \leqslant 2\varDelta^n;$$

it follows that if ν' is invariant, then $\nu' = \varPi$, hence $\varPi$ is the only Q-invariant probability measure. Moreover, letting $\nu' = \varepsilon_x$, we obtain the last conclusion in the statement.

We recall the following:

Definition 2.5. A set F in $\mathscr{E}$ is said to be *absorbing* for X if $P(x, F) = 1$ for every x in F, or equivalently, if 1_{F^c} is a superharmonic function.

Starting from a point x in an absorbing set F, the chain stays in F P_x-a.s. It is therefore natural to restrict P to F and so obtain a T.P. on the space $(F, F \cap \mathscr{E})$. The classes of recurrent states of discrete chains provide examples of absorbing sets.

Theorem 2.6. *For a ν-irreducible chain X, there are only two possibilities:*
(i) *the potential kernel is a proper kernel;*
(ii) *there is an absorbing set F such that $\nu(F^c) = 0$ and a strictly positive function $h_0 \in \mathscr{U}_+$, such that for every x in F*

$$U_{h_0}(h_0)\, (x) = 1 \quad and \quad U_{h_0}(x, \cdot) \geqslant m_0(\cdot).$$

Proof. Let h_0 be the function of Proposition 2.3. According as $U_{h_0}(h_0) = 1$ ν-a.s. or not, we will get the second or the first possibility.

(1) Suppose that $1 - U_{h_0}(h_0)$ is not ν-negligible, which implies that $\langle h_0 m_0, 1 - U_{h_0}(h_0)\rangle = c > 0$. Since $U_{h_0} \geqslant U_{h_0}(h_0) \otimes m_0$, we have

$$(U_{h_0} I_{h_0})^2\, 1 = U_{h_0}(h_0) - U_{h_0} I_{h_0}(1 - U_{h_0}(h_0)) \leqslant (1 - c)\, U_{h_0}(h_0),$$

and inductively

$$(U_{h_0} I_{h_0})^n\, 1 \leqslant (1 - c)^{n-1}\, U_{h_0}(h_0).$$

Now by ch. 2, Proposition 2.9,

$$Gh_0 = h_0 + \sum_{n \geq 0} (U_{h_0} I_{h_0})^n U_{h_0}(h_0),$$

so that Gh_0 is a bounded function, and it follows from ch. 2, Proposition 1.15 that (i) holds.

(2) If, on the other hand, $U_{h_0}(h_0) = 1$ ν-a.s., the set $F = \{U_{h_0}(h_0) = 1\}$ is such that $\nu(F^c) = 0$, and we claim that it is an absorbing set. The resolvent equation $U_{h_0} = P + PI_{1-h_0}U_{h_0}$ implies

$$1 - U_{h_0}(h_0)\,(x) \geq P((1 - h_0)\,(1 - U_{h_0}(h_0)))\,(x);$$

for x in F the first member of this inequality vanishes, hence $P(x, \cdot)$ vanishes outside the set $\{(1 - h_0)\,(1 - U_{h_0}(h_0)) = 0\}$, which is equal to F, since $h_0 < 1$ on E. On the other hand, $P(x, E) = 1$, because $U_{h_0}(h_0)\,(x) = 1$ and consequently $P(x, F) = 1$. The set F is thus an absorbing set, and by Proposition 2.3 the proof is complete.

In case (i) the space E is the union of an increasing sequence of transient sets. We are now going to show that in the case (ii) the chain is recurrent. For this purpose we restrict ourselves to the absorbing set F, or equivalently we shall assume that $U_{h_0}(h_0) = 1$ everywhere on E and $U_{h_0} \geq 1 \otimes m_0$. We then get

Theorem 2.7. *There exists a positive, σ-finite, P-invariant measure m such that $m \gg \nu$ and such that $m(A) > 0$ implies*

$$P_x\left[\sum_{n=1}^{\infty} 1_A(X_n) = \infty\right] = 1$$

for every x in E. More generally, we have $U_h(h) = 1$ for every $h \in \mathcal{U}_+$ such that $m(h) > 0$.

Proof. Let λ be a measure in the space B of Lemma 2.4; we have $\lambda U_{h_0} I_{h_0} = \lambda(U_{h_0} I_{h_0} - 1 \otimes h_0 m_0)$, and the norm of the operator $U_{h_0} I_{h_0}$ on B is therefore less than or equal to $1 - m_0(h_0) < 1$. By Lemma 2.4, there exists therefore a probability measure Π that is invariant by $U_{h_0} I_{h_0}$, hence such that $\Pi = \Pi U_{h_0} I_{h_0} \geq h_0 m_0$.

Next set $m = (1/h_0)\,\Pi$; the measure m is positive and σ-finite, since h_0 is strictly positive and $m \geq m_0$, which implies $m \gg \nu$. Finally for $g \in b\mathcal{E}_+$, using the resolvent equation $U_{h_0} = P + U_{h_0} I_{1-h_0} P$, we get

ELSEVIER
EXCERPTA MEDICA
NORTH-HOLLAND

Associated Scientific Publishers

P.O. BOX 211
AMSTERDAM
THE NETHERLANDS

Please add my name to your mailing list.

On this card, please mark the numbers which correspond to your specific field(s) of interest, and return to us. Information on new publications of direct importance to you will then be forwarded.

MATHEMATICS

- 5760 ☐ Logic & Foundations
- 5705 ☐ Discrete Mathematics
- 5710 ☐ Algebra
- 5740 ☐ Topology, Geometry
- 5720 ☐ Analysis
- 5790 ☐ Probability & Statistics
- 5780 ☐ Numerical Analysis and Computation
- 57A0 ☐ Applied Mathematics & Mechanics
- 5781 ☐ Operations Research, Programming, Systems and Control

INFORMATION PROCESSING

- 57A5 ☐ Mathematics of Computation
- 6A60 ☐ Software
- 6830 ☐ Hardware
  - Applications:
- 57B0 ☐ Science & Engineering
- 6A70 ☐ Management
- 6A40 ☐ Artificial Intelligence

Name (please print or type) .... title ....

Institute or company ....

Full address ....

....

....

$$\langle m, Pg \rangle = \langle \Pi, h_0^{-1} Pg \rangle = \langle \Pi U_{h_0} I_{h_0}, h_0^{-1} Pg \rangle$$

$$= \langle \Pi, U_{h_0} Pg \rangle = \langle \Pi, U_{h_0} g - Pg + U_{h_0} I_{h_0} Pg \rangle$$

$$= \langle \Pi, U_{h_0} g \rangle = \langle \Pi, h_0^{-1} g \rangle = \langle m, g \rangle,$$

which proves that m is P-invariant.

We proceed to prove the last conclusion in the statement. If h is not m-negligible, then $h' = h \wedge h_0$ is also non-negligible, and since $U_h(h)$ increases with h (ch. 2, Proposition 2.10), we have $U_{h'}(h') \leqslant U_h(h) \leqslant 1$. It suffices, therefore, to prove the desired result for $h \leqslant h_0$. We then have

$$U_h(h) = U_{h_0}(h) + U_{h_0}((h_0 - h) U_h(h));$$

on the other hand the equality $U_{h_0}(h_0) = 1$ may be written

$$1 = U_{h_0}(h) + U_{h_0}(h_0 - h).$$

Substracting termwise these two inequalities and setting $g = 1 - U_h(h)$ we get

$$g = U_{h_0}((h_0 - h) g).$$

Consequently $g \leqslant (U_{h_0} I_{h_0}) g \leqslant \cdots \leqslant (U_{h_0} I_{h_0})^n g \leqslant \cdots$, and by Lemma 2.4 we get $g \leqslant \Pi(g)$ everywhere on E. It follows that $g \leqslant U_{h_0}(h_0 - h) \Pi(g)$, and integrating with respect to Π yields

$$\Pi(g) \leqslant \Pi(g) \langle \Pi, U_{h_0}(h_0 - h) \rangle = (1 - m(h)) \Pi(g).$$

If $m(h) > 0$, then $\Pi(g) = 0$ and $g = 0$ everywhere.

If A is a set such that $m(A) > 0$, we thus have $U_A(1_A) = P.[S_A < \infty] = 1$ everywhere on E. Setting $S_n = S_{n-1} + S_A \circ \theta_{S_{n-1}}$, the strong Markov property implies obviously that $P.[S_n < \infty] = 1$ everywhere on E, and that is the desired result.

Definition 2.8. The chain X will be said to be *recurrent in the sense of Harris* if there exists a positive, σ-finite, invariant measure m such that $m(A) > 0$ implies

$$P_x \left[\sum_{n=1}^{\infty} 1_A(X_n) = \infty \right] = 1$$

for all x in E. We shall also say more simply that X is a *Harris chain* or that X is *Harris*. The T.P. of a Harris chain will also be said to be Harris.

A Harris chain is clearly irreducible, and conversely we have just shown that an irreducible chain such that the potential kernel is not proper is recurrent in the sense of Harris up to a negligible set. The irreducible recurrent discrete chains are Harris chains, and we shall study other important examples later on.

One of the main subjects of this book will be the study of Harris chains. We start here with a few preliminary results.

The condition in Definition 2.8 is equivalent to $U_A(1_A) = 1$ everywhere on E provided $m(A) > 0$. Actually it is equivalent to a less stringent condition.

Proposition 2.9. *The following three statements are equivalent:*

(i) *X is recurrent in the sense of Harris with respect to the invariant measure m;*

(ii) *there is a strictly positive function $h_0 \in \mathcal{U}_+$ and a non-zero measure m_0, such that $U_{h_0}(h_0) = 1$ on E and $U_{h_0} \geq 1 \otimes m_0$;*

(iii) *there is a non-zero positive measure m_1 such that*

$$P.[S_A < \infty] = U_A(1_A) = 1$$

everywhere on E provided $m_1(A) > 0$.

The measures m_0 and m_1 are then absolutely continuous with respect to m.

Proof. Clearly (i) implies (iii), and we saw that (ii) implies (i). It remains to show that (iii) implies (ii).

If (iii) is satisfied, X is clearly m_1-irreducible. Thus, by Proposition 2.3, there is a strictly positive function $h_0 \in \mathcal{U}_+$ and a measure m_0 equivalent to m_1 such that $U_{h_0} \geq U_{h_0}(h_0) \otimes m_0$. We must show that $U_{h_0}(h_0) = 1$. Since h_0 is strictly positive there is a number $\alpha \in]0, 1[$ such that the set $A = \{h_0 \geq \alpha\}$ is of positive m_1-measure. Since $h_0 \geq \alpha 1_A$, we have $U_{h_0}(h_0) \geq U_{\alpha 1_A}(\alpha 1_A)$; but the resolvent equation (ch. 2, Proposition 2.9), applied to the kernels U_A and $U_{\alpha 1_A}$, yields

$$U_{\alpha 1_A} = \sum_{n \geq 0} (1 - \alpha)^n (U_A I_A)^n U_A,$$

and it follows that

$$U_{\alpha 1_A}(\alpha 1_A) = \alpha \sum_{n \geq 0} (1 - \alpha)^n (U_A I_A)^{n+1} 1 = \alpha \sum_{n \geq 0} (1 - \alpha)^n = 1,$$

which completes the proof.

Proposition 2.10. *If X is Harris, the measure m is the only σ-finite P-excessive measure (up to multiplication by a positive scalar).*

Proof. Let λ be a σ-finite excessive measure and h_0 the function of the preceding proof. The measure $h_0\lambda$ is σ-finite, and ch. 2, Proposition 3.5 implies that

$$h_0\lambda \geqslant (h_0\lambda)\, U_{h_0}I_{h_0} \geqslant \cdots (h_0\lambda)\, (U_{h_0}I_{h_0})^n \geqslant \cdots,$$

and passing to the limit yields, by Fatou's lemma,

$$h_0\lambda \geqslant \lambda(h_0)\, (h_0 m).$$

This implies $\lambda(h_0) < \infty$; otherwise $h_0\lambda$ would not be σ-finite. Now, since $m(h_0) = 1$, the measures on both sides of this inequality have the same total variation, hence they are equal, and the proof is complete.

We shall now improve ch. 2, Proposition 3.5, and prove that, for Harris chains, $1_A\, m$ is actually invariant by Π_A when A is not negligible.

Proposition 2.11. *If $f \in \mathscr{U}_+$ and $m(f) > 0$, then the measure $f\, m$ is invariant by $U_f I_f$, and it is the only excessive measure for this kernel. Moreover $m = (fm)\, U_f$, and for $A \in \mathscr{E}$, $m(A) > 0$, we have $mH_A = m$.*

Proof. Set $E_f = \{f > 0\}$; the kernel $Q = I_{E_f} U_f I_f$ is a T.P. on $(E_f, E_f \cap \mathscr{E})$. Let $A \in \mathscr{E}$ be such that $(fm)\,(A) > 0$; by ch. 2, Proposition 2.9,

$$\sum_{n>0} Q^n\, 1_A = 1_{E_f}\, U_0(f 1_A) = \sum_{n>0} I_{E_f}\, P_n(f 1_A),$$

and since X is Harris we get $\sum_{n>0} Q^n\, 1_A = +\infty$. The transition probability Q is (fm)-irreducible, and the canonical Markov chain associated with Q is recurrent in the sense of Harris on an absorbing set of full (fm)-measure. Since, by ch. 2, Proposition 3.5, the measure (fm) is Q-excessive, it follows from Proposition 2.10 that it is Q-invariant and that it is the only Q-excessive measure.

Now, by the resolvent equation, we have

$$(fm)\, U_f P = (fm)\, U_f - (fm)\, P + (fm)\, U_f I_f P;$$

since $(fm)\, P \leqslant mP = m$, the measure $(fm)\, P$ is σ-finite, and by the above discussion the two last summands cancel. The measure $(fm)\, U_f$ is therefore P-invariant, and consequently there is a number k such that $km = (fm)\, U_f$. If f is integrable, multiplying to the right by f immediately gives $k = 1$. If f is not integrable, let g be an integrable function smaller than f. By the above discussion $(gm)\, U_g = m$; applying (gm) to the left of both sides of the equality $U_g = U_f + U_g(f - g) U_f$ gives

$$(gm) U_g = (gm) U_f + (fm) U_f - (gm) U_f.$$

Since $U_g \geqslant U_f$, the measure $(gm) U_f$ is σ-finite, and by cancellation we obtain

$$(fm) U_f = (gm) U_g = m.$$

Finally, if $A \in \mathscr{E}$ and $m(A) > 0$, the preceding equality yields $m I_A U_A I_{A^c} = 1_{A^c} m$; hence $m H_A = m$.

Remark 2.12. That $m H_A = m$ may be derived from ch. 2, Theorem 3.6, and the fact that m is the only excessive measure. This result contains Theorem 1.10 concerning discrete chains.

We shall end this section by a further study of irreducibility. These results will not be used in the sequel.

Definition 2.13. Let ν be a probability measure on $\mathscr{E}$. The chain X will be said ν-*essentially irreducible* if for every $F \in \mathscr{E}$ such that $\nu(F) > 0$ we have

$$\sum_0^\infty P_n(\cdot, F) > 0 \quad \nu\text{-a.s.}$$

This condition is obviously weaker than irreducibility. We remark that if we replace ν by $\nu' = \sum_0^\infty 2^{-n-1} \nu P_n$, then $\nu' P \ll \nu'$ and the chain is still ν'-essentially irreducible. The significance of the latter condition will be seen at the beginning of the next chapter.

Theorem 2.14. *For a ν-essentially irreducible chain X such that $\nu P \ll \nu$, there are only two possibilities*:

(i) *there is an absorbing set E_1 such that $\nu(E_1^c) = 0$ and the restriction of X to E_1 is ν-irreducible*;

(ii) *there is an absorbing set E_2 such that $\nu(E_2^c) = 0$ and for all x in E_2, the measures ν and $\sum_0^\infty 2^{-n} P_n(x, \cdot)$ are mutually singular.*

Proof. Pick $c \in \,]0, 1[$ and set

$$A = \{x \in E : \nu \ll U_c(x, \cdot)\};$$

we claim that A is in $\mathscr{E}$. Let $\mathscr{G}$ be a denumerable algebra of sets generating $\mathscr{E}$ and put

$$\mathcal{G}_n = \{G \in \mathcal{G} : \nu(G) \geqslant 1/n\};$$

then ν is not absolutely continuous with respect to $U_c(x, \cdot)$ if and only if there is an integer $n > 0$ such that, for all $\delta > 0$, there is a $G \in \mathcal{G}$ such that $U_c(x, G) \leqslant \delta$ and $\nu(G) \geqslant 1/n$. Consequently,

$$A^c = \bigcup_n \left\{ x : \inf_{G \in \mathcal{G}_n} U_c(x, G) = 0 \right\},$$

and since each $\mathcal{G}_n$ is countable the set A is in $\mathcal{E}$.

Plainly A does not depend on the choice of c within $]0, 1[$. We proceed to show that $A^c = \{x : \nu \perp U_c(x, \cdot)\}$. Let x be a point in E such that $U_c(x, \cdot)$ is not singular with respect to ν; if $\nu(F) > 0$ the resolvent equation and the ν-essential irreducibility imply that, for $c' < c$,

$$U_{c'}(x, F) \geqslant (c - c') \int U_c(x, dy) \, U_{c'}(y, F) > 0.$$

Thus $\nu \ll U_{c'}(x, \cdot)$, and x is in A.

Let x be a point in E such that $U_0(x, A) > 0$. For every F in $\mathcal{E}$ such that $\nu(F) > 0$, we have $U_c(\cdot, F) > 0$ on A, and consequently

$$U_0(x, F) \geqslant c \int_A U_0(x, dy) \, U_c(y, F) > 0;$$

it follows that $\nu \ll U_0(x, \cdot)$, hence that x is in A. Thus $U_0(\cdot, A) = 0$ on A^c and A^c is an absorbing set. Moreover, we have either $\nu(A) = 0$ or $\nu(A^c) = 0$; indeed, if $\nu(A) > 0$, by hypothesis $U_0(\cdot, A) > 0$ ν-a.s., and since $U_0(\cdot, A) = 0$ on A^c, we get $\nu(A^c) = 0$.

Thus either $\nu(A) = 0$ and (ii) is verified for $E_2 = A^c$, or $\nu(A^c) = 0$ and we shall show that (i) is verified for $E_1 = \{x : U_0(x, A^c) = 0\}$. Since $\nu P \ll \nu$ we have $\nu U_0 \ll \nu$; hence $\nu U_0(A^c) = 0$, which proves that $\nu(E_1^c) = 0$. Moreover, the inequality $P U_0 \leqslant U_0$ leads easily to the fact that E_1 is absorbing. Finally, since A^c is absorbing, we have $U_0(\cdot, A^c) > 0$ on A^c; hence $E_1 \subset A$ and therefore $\nu \ll U_c(x, \cdot)$ for all x in E_1.

In the last section, we saw that an irreducible recurrent discrete chain always has a dual chain which is also irreducible recurrent. The above theorem will be applied to show, in the case of Harris chains, a preliminary result in this direction; the main result will be completed in the next chapter. Another proof yielding more, but relying on more elaborate notions, will be given in ch. 8.

We begin with a preliminary lemma. Let m be a positive σ-finite measure and N a positive kernel on $(E, \mathscr{E})$. We define a σ-finite measure Π_N on $\mathscr{E} \otimes \mathscr{E}$ by setting

$$\Pi_N(A \times B) = \int_A m(\mathrm{d}x) \, N(x, B).$$

Lemma 2.15. *The density $\bar{\omega}$ of Π_N with respect to $m \otimes m$ is equal $m \otimes m$-a.e. to the density n of N with respect to m.*

Proof. Clearly $\Pi_N \geqslant n(m \otimes m)$, hence $\bar{\omega} \geqslant n$ $m \otimes m$-a.e. If this inequality were not an equality there would exist a positive non-negligible function φ on $E \times E$ such that

$$\Pi_{N^1} \geqslant \varphi(m \otimes m),$$

where N^1 is the singular part of N (ch. 1, §5); hence for all A

$$N^1(\,\cdot\,, A) \geqslant \int \varphi(\,\cdot\,, y) \, 1_A(y) \, m(\mathrm{d}y) \quad m\text{-a.e.}$$

Letting A run through a denumerable algebra of sets generating $\mathscr{E}$, we obtain that for almost all x,

$$N^1(x, \mathrm{d}y) \geqslant \varphi(x, y) \, m(\mathrm{d}y)$$

which contradicts the definition of N^1.

Theorem 2.16. *If P and $\hat{P}$ are two T.P.'s in duality with respect to the measure m, and if P is Harris, then there is modification of $\hat{P}$ which is also Harris.*

Proof. Since P is Harris, the measure m is the invariant measure for P. Let p_c be a strictly positive density for U_c with respect to m and $\hat{p}_c$ a version of the density of $\hat{U}_c$. The duality formula of ch. 2, §3 between U_c and $\hat{U}_c$ implies immediately that $\Pi_{U_c} = \Pi_{\hat{U}_c}$, hence that $\hat{p}_c = p_c$ $m \otimes m$-a.e.

It is then evident that $\hat{P}$ is m-essentially irreducible, and we are not in the situation (ii) of Theorem 2.14. Thus there is an absorbing set E_1 such that $m(E_1^c) = 0$ and such that the restriction of $\hat{P}$ to E_1 is m-irreducible. We may therefore apply Theorems 2.6 and 2.7. If the kernel $\hat{G}$ were proper, we could find a function $h > 0$ such that $\hat{G}h$ were bounded, hence also a function $g > 0$ such that

$$\langle Gg, h \rangle = \langle g, \hat{G}h \rangle < \infty.$$

The potential Gg would be finite m-a.e., which would contradict the fact that P is Harris. There exists therefore a set E_1' such that $m(E_1'^c) = 0$ and the restriction of $\hat{P}$ to E_1' is Harris. It remains to set $\hat{P}'(x, \cdot) = \hat{P}(x, \cdot)$ for $x \in E_1'$, and $\hat{P}'(x, \cdot) = 1 \otimes fm$ with $f \in L_+^1(m)$, for $x \in E_1'^c$, to get the desired modification.

Exercise 2.17. Prove that there is no measure for which the chain of translation on $\mathbf{Z}$ $(P(x, \cdot) = \varepsilon_{x+1}(\cdot))$ is irreducible.

Exercise 2.18. If X is Harris, prove that superharmonic functions are constant m-a.e. and bounded harmonic functions are constant (solution in the next section).

Exercise 2.19. (1) Using the notation of ch. 1, Lemma 5.3, prove that for any T.P. on a separable state space and any probability measure ν such that $\nu P \ll \nu$,

$$P_{n+m}^1(x, \cdot) \leqslant \int_E P_n^1(x, dy) \, P_m^1(y, \cdot),$$

and derive that $g(x) = \lim_n P_n^1(x, E)$ exists for all x in E.

(2) If X is Harris and if m and ν are not mutually singular, then $g(x) = 0$ for all x in E.

[*Hint*: Show that $1 - g$ is superharmonic and use Exercise 2.18.]

Exercise 2.20. (1) If X is irreducible and if there is a bounded invariant measure, then we have the situation (ii) of Theorem 2.6. Give an example to show that we can have (i) with a non-bounded invariant measure.

[*Hint*: See §4.]

(2) Prove that in the situation (i) a measure is invariant if and only if it can be written $\lambda + \lambda I_{h_0} U_{h_0}$, where λ is a positive measure such that $\langle \lambda, h_0 U_0(h_0) \rangle < \infty$ and $\lambda I_{1-h_0} P = \lambda$.

Exercise 2.21. Give an example in which the set $\{U_{h_0}(h_0) < 1\}$ of Theorem 2.7 is not empty although $P1 = 1$.

[*Hint*: Use a discrete irreducible recurrent chain on the space E and take as new space the sum of E and $\mathbf{N}$. Define P such that $P(n, n+1) = q_n$ and $P(n, E) = 1 - q_n$, and choose the q_n's suitably.]

Exercise 2.22. Resume the notation of ch. 2, Exercise 4.12 and for $h = 1_A$ write $V_h = V_A$.

(1) The resolvent $\{V_\alpha\}$ is said to be (*recurrent in the sense of*) *Harris* if there is a positive measure m_1 such that $V_A(1_A) = 1$ everywhere on E provided

$m_1(A) > 0$. Prove that $\{V_\alpha\}$ is Harris if and only if X^1 is Harris and that X^α is then Harris for each $\alpha > 0$. If $\{V_\alpha\}$ is Harris, there exists an invariant measure m for $\{V_\alpha\}$ and m has the same property as m_1.

(2) The resolvent $\{V_\alpha\}$ is said to be v-*irreducible* if there is a probability measure v on $(E, \mathscr{E})$ such that $v \ll V_\alpha(x, \cdot)$ for all x in E. Prove that Theorems 2.6 and 2.7 extend to the present situation.

Exercise 2.23. Proposition 2.10 cannot be extended to signed measures. For instance, the measure of density x with respect to the Lebesgue measure dx is invariant for the chain X^1 of the resolvent of Brownian motion; see ch. 2, Exercise 4.8. (However, the reader should be cautious, because this measure is a Radon measure, which is not defined for all Borel subsets of **R**.)

3. Invariant events. Transient and recurrent sets

We resume the study of general chains, for which we state the following important definition.

Definition 3.1. An event $\Gamma \in \mathscr{F}$ is called *invariant* if $\theta^{-1}(\Gamma) = \Gamma$. The class of invariant events is a σ-algebra denoted $\mathscr{I}$. A random variable Z is $\mathscr{I}$-measurable if and only if $Z \circ \theta = Z$; such a random variable is called *invariant*. Two invariant random variables Z and Z' are said to be *equivalent* if $P_v[Z \neq Z'] = 0$ for every probability measure v.

Proposition 3.2. *If P is markovian, the formula*

$$h(x) = E_x[Z]$$

sets up a one-to-one correspondence between equivalence classes of bounded invariant random variables and bounded harmonic functions. Moreover

$$\lim_n h(X_n) = Z \quad a.s.$$

Proof. If Z is invariant, the function $h(\cdot) = E_{\cdot}[Z]$ is harmonic, as is seen by a straightforward application of the Markov property. Conversely, if h is bounded and harmonic, then $h(X_n)$ is a bounded martingale which converges a.s. to a random variable Z, obviously invariant. By Lebesgue's theorem, we have

$$h(x) = E_x[Z]$$

for every x in E. The correspondence is clearly one-to-one.

If P is not markovian, the function $E.[Z]$ is superharmonic but not harmonic at points x such that $P_x[\zeta = 1] > 0$.

Definition 3.3. For $A \in \mathscr{E}$, set

$$R(A) = \left\{\omega: \overline{\lim_{n \to \infty}} \, 1_A(X_n(\omega)) = 1\right\} = \bigcap_{n=0}^{\infty} \{n + S_A \circ \theta_n < \infty\}.$$

The event $R(A)$ is the set of trajectories ω which hit A infinitely often; clearly $R(A)$ is an invariant event. If A is a transient set, then $P.[R(A)] = 0$ everywhere on E. Consequently we have:

Definition 3.4. A set $A \in \mathscr{E}$ is called *recurrent* if $P.[R(A)] = 1$ everywhere on E.

A set may be neither recurrent nor transient, but we have, assuming henceforth that P is markovian:

Proposition 3.5. *The three following statements are equivalent*:
   (i) *The bounded harmonic functions are constant*;
   (ii) *The σ-algebra $\mathscr{I}$ is trivial (up to equivalence)*;
   (iii) *Every set is either recurrent or transient.*

Proof. The equivalence of (i) and (ii) is an immediate consequence of Proposition 3.2. Since, in addition, $R(A)$ is in $\mathscr{I}$, these conditions imply (iii). It remains to show that (iii) implies (ii).
   Let $\Gamma \in \mathscr{I}$ and put $A = \{x: P_x[\Gamma] > a\}$, where $a \in]0, 1[$. We know that $1_\Gamma = \lim_n P_{X_n}[\Gamma]$ a.s.; if A is recurrent, then $\Gamma = \Omega$ a.s., and if A is transient, then $\Gamma = \emptyset$ a.s.

The situation where these equivalent conditions hold is very interesting. It occurs for large classes of random walks as will be seen in ch. 5. It occurs for Harris chains by the following proposition, which is dual to Proposition 2.10 and subsumes Proposition 1.9. A much stronger result will be shown in ch. 6 §2.

Proposition 3.6. *Let X be Harris, then the superharmonic functions are constant m-a.e. and the bounded harmonic functions are constant.*

Proof. If the superharmonic function f is not constant m-a.e. we can find two numbers $a < b$ such that $m(\{f < a\}) > 0$ and $m(\{f > b\}) > 0$. The sequence $f(X_n)$ is a positive supermartingale which converges a.s. to a random variable Z. Since by hypothesis X hits infinitely often the sets $\{f < a\}$ and $\{f > b\}$, we have $Z < a$ a.s. and $Z > b$ a.s., which is a contradiction.

For a bounded harmonic function, the same argument proves that $f(X_n)$ converges a.s. to a constant C. But since in addition the convergence holds in $L^1(P_x)$ for every x in E, we get that $f = C$.

For Harris chains every set is thus either recurrent or transient; we want a criterion to decide which one a particular set is.

Lemma 3.7. *Let $A \in \mathscr{E}$; the supermartingale $P_{X_n}[S_A < \infty]$ converges a.s. to* $1_{R(A)}$ *as n tends to infinity.*

Proof. For every v we have P_v-a.s.

$$P_{X_n}[S_A < \infty] = E_v[1_{\{S_A \circ \theta_n < \infty\}} \mid \mathscr{F}_n]$$
$$= E_v[1_{\{n+S_A \circ \theta_n < \infty\}} \mid \mathscr{F}_n];$$

the sequence of sets $\{n + S_A \circ \theta_n < \infty\}$ decreases to $R(A)$ as n tends to infinity, hence by ch. 0, Proposition 2.2 the above expression converges to $E_v[1_{R(A)} \mid \mathscr{F}]$ P_v-a.s.; as $R(A) \in \mathscr{F}$, the proof is complete.

Proposition 3.8. *Let X be recurrent in the sense of Harris; then the following statements are equivalent:*

(i) *The set A is transient;*

(ii) $P.[S_A < \infty] = 0$ *m-a.e.;*

(iii) $m(A) = 0$.

Proof. That (i) implies (iii) is clear. Conversely, assume that $m(A) = 0$; then for every k,

$$E_m\left[\sum_1^k 1_A(X_n)\right] = km(A) = 0,$$

but if A were recurrent the left member would tend to infinity with k, which is impossible; thus (iii) implies (i).

If A is recurrent we have $P.[S_A < \infty] = 1$ everywhere; thus (ii) implies (i). Assume conversely that

$$m(\{x : P_x[S_A < \infty] > 0\}) > 0;$$

then there is a real $a > 0$ such that

$$m(\{x : P_x[S_A < \infty] > a\}) > 0.$$

Since X is Harris we get therefore

$$\overline{\lim_{n \to \infty}} \, P_{X_n}[S_A < \infty] \geqslant a > 0 \quad \text{a.s.,}$$

and by Lemma 3.7 we have $1_{R(A)} > 0$ a.s. Hence $P_x[R(A)] = 1$ for all x in E. The set A is thus recurrent, and (i) implies (ii).

Corollary 3.9. *A set A is recurrent if and only if $P_x[S_A < \infty] = 1$ for all x in E; it is transient if and only if $P_m[S_A < \infty] = 0$.*

Proof. Obvious.

Corollary 3.10. *Every transient set A is contained in a transient set B such that B^c is absorbing.*

Proof. Pick a $c \in \,]0, 1[$ and set $B = \{x : c \, U_c(x, A) > 0\}$. Then B^c is absorbing by the Markov property and $m(B) = 0$, since if this were not so we would have $cm \, U_c(A) = m(A) > 0$.

Exercise 3.11. Prove that if a set A is not transient, then there exists at least one point $x \in E$ such that $P_x[R(A)] = 1$.

Exercise 3.12. (1) Pick $a \in \,]0, 1[$ and set $A = \{x : P_x[\Gamma] > a\}$, where Γ is an invariant event. Prove that $\Gamma = \lim\{X_n \in A\}$ a.s.

(2) A set $A \in \mathscr{E}$ is called *regular* if $\lim\{X_n \in A\}$ exists almost surely. Prove that the collection Σ of regular sets is a sub-algebra of $\mathscr{E}$. Transient sets are regular, and the class of transient sets is an ideal in Σ.

(3) Two regular sets A and A' are said to be equivalent if $A \, \triangle \, A'$ is transient. If A and A' are equivalent, then $P_x[R(A)] = P_x[R(A')]$ for all x in E. [*Hint*: Prove that $R(A) \, \triangle \, R(A') \subset R(A \, \triangle \, A')$.]

(4) Prove that the Boolean algebras of equivalence classes of regular sets and invariant events are isomorphic.

[*Hint*: Associate with A the event $\lim\{X_n \in A\}$.]

(5) Prove that if $f \in b\mathscr{E}$ is such that $\lim f(X_n)$ exists a.s. if and only if f is the uniform limit of simple functions on Σ. This exercise is solved in ch. 7 §1.

Exercise 3.13. Using the notation and hypothesis of Exercise 2.19(1), let N_x^n be a set of ν-measure zero such that $P_n^1(x, (N_x^n)^c) = 0$. Further set $N_x = \bigcup_n N_x^n$.

(1) Prove that, for $n < m$,

$$\{X_m \in N_x\} \subset \{X_n \in N_x\} \quad P_x\text{-a.s.,}$$

and give an interpretation of this result. Prove that $g(x) = P_x[R(N_x)]$.

(2) If $\Gamma \in \mathscr{I}$ and $P_v[\Gamma] = 0$, then $P_x[\Gamma] = P_x[\Gamma \cap R(N_x)]$.

(3) Derive from the above questions that if $vP \ll v$, then the following two statements are equivalent: (i) $g(x) = 0$, (ii) $P_x \ll P_v$ on $\mathscr{I}$ (solution in ch. 7 §1). Compare this result with Exercise 2.21(2). If v is arbitrary it is possible that $P_x \ll P_v$ and even $P_x \sim P_v$ on $\mathscr{I}$ with $g(x) > 0$.

Exercise 3.14. (1) Let m be a positive measure on $(E, \mathscr{E})$. The following two statements are equivalent:

(i) If $\Gamma \in \mathscr{I}$, then either $P_v[\Gamma] = 1$ for every $v \ll m$ or $P_v[\Gamma] = 0$ for every $v \ll m$;

(ii) If $A \in \mathscr{E}$, then either $P.[R(A)] = 1$ m-a.e. or $P.[R(A)] = 0$ m-a.e.

(2) These conditions imply:

(iii) the bounded harmonic functions are constant m-a.e. Prove by an example that the converse may fail to be true. Prove that the converse is true if m satisfies the following condition: if $m(A^c) = 0$, then $P_v[R(A)] = 1$ for all $v \ll m$.

Exercise 3.15. (1) With the notation of Proposition 3.2, prove that

$$\|h\| = \sup_{x \in E} \|Z\|_{L^\infty(\Omega, P_x)}.$$

(2) Prove that the set of bounded harmonic functions is a C^*-algebra for the above norm and the product defined below by

$$(h \circ h')(x) = E_x \left[\lim_n h(X_n) h'(X_n) \right].$$

Exercise 3.16. If X is Harris and L is a death time (ch. 1, Exercise 3.17 and ch. 2, Exercise 2.21) prove that either $L = \infty$ a.s. or $L = 0$ P_m-a.s.

Exercise 3.17. If $\{V_\alpha\}_{\alpha>0}$ is a resolvent recurrent in the sense of Harris, the supermedian functions are constant m-a.e. If, in addition, the kernels V_α are absolutely continuous with respect to m, the excessive functions are constant.

Exercise 3.18. What can be said in place of Proposition 3.2 if P is not markovian? In particular, prove that, if $\zeta < \infty$ a.s., the only bounded harmonic function is the zero function.

4. Topological recurrence of random walks

In this section we deal with a right random walk X of law μ on a locally compact separable group G. The results will obviously carry over to the case of left random walks.

Definitions 4.1. We shall call T_μ the smallest closed semi-group containing the support of μ and G_μ the smallest closed sub-group containing T_μ.

It is necessary and sufficient for a point g to be in T_μ, that for every neighbourhood V of g, there exists an integer n such that $\mu^n(V) = P_e[X_n \in V] > 0$. The group G being separable, we therefore have

$$P_e\left[\bigcap_1^\infty \{X_n \in T_\mu\}\right] = 1,$$

and by translation in G, for all $g \in G$

$$P_g\left[\bigcap_0^\infty \{X_n \in G_\mu\}\right] = 1.$$

The sub-group G_μ is therefore an absorbing set for X, to which we can restrict ourselves for the probabilistic study of X. In the sequel of this book, unless the contrary is stated, the following hypothesis will always apply when we deal with random walks:

Hypothesis 4.2. *The group G is generated by the support of μ.*

That is, with the above notation, $G_\mu = G$. We now define:

Definition 4.3. The random walk is said to be *recurrent* if for every open set O in G and every $g \in G$,

$$P_g[R(O)] = P_g\left[\varlimsup_{n\to\infty} \{X_n \in O\}\right] = 1.$$

Otherwise it is said to be *transient*.

Theorem 4.4. *A random walk is recurrent if and only if for every neighbourhood V of e,*

$$P_e[R(V)] = P_e\left[\varlimsup_{n\to\infty} \{X_n \in V\}\right] = 1.$$

Proof. Only the sufficiency needs to be shown. Let R_μ be the set of points g in G such that $P_e[R(V)] = 1$ for every neighbourhood V of g. We take $g \in R_\mu$ and $h \in T_\mu$ and we claim that $h^{-1}g \in R_\mu$.

Let U be a neighbourhood of $h^{-1}g$; hUg^{-1} is then a neighbourhood of e and one can find a neighbourhood V of e such that $V^{-1}V \subset hUg^{-1}$. Since Vh is a neighbourhood of h, there exists an integer $k > 0$ such that the event $A = \{X_k \in Vh\}$ is of positive P_e-probability. For $\omega \in A$, the fact that $X_{n+k}(\omega) \in Vg$ implies

$$X_k^{-1}(\omega)\, X_{n+k}(\omega) \in h^{-1}V^{-1}Vg \subset U;$$

and g being in R_μ, for P_e-almost all ω in A, there exist infinitely many integers n such that $X_{n+k}(\omega) \in Vg$, so that

$$P_e\left[\, \overline{\lim_{n\to\infty}} \{X_k^{-1} X_{n+k} \in U\} \cap A \right] = P_e[A].$$

According to ch. 1 §4, the sequence of random variables $\{X_k^{-1} X_{n+k}\}$ has the same law as the sequence $\{X_n\}$ and is independent of $A \in \mathscr{F}_k$, hence

$$P_e\left[\, \overline{\lim_{n\to\infty}} \{X_n \in U\} \right] = 1.$$

We have thus shown that $T_\mu^{-1}R_\mu \subset R_\mu$, and the hypothesis implies that R_μ contains at least the point e. On the other hand it is easily seen that R_μ is closed. The set R_μ is therefore a closed sub-group containing T_μ, and consequently $R_\mu = G$, which completes the proof.

We shall prove below that if X is transient, then for every compact subset K in G and every $g \in G$,

$$P_g[R(K)] = P_g\left[\, \overline{\lim_{n\to\infty}} \{X_n \in K\} \right] = 0.$$

We begin by generalizing some of the results obtained for discrete chains.

Proposition 4.5. *The random walk is recurrent if and only if for every neighbourhood V of e, $P_e[S_V < \infty] = 1$.*

Proof. Only the sufficiency needs to be shown. Let d be a left-invariant metric on G and V_r the corresponding open ball of centre e and radius r. Let $0 < r' < r$ be two reals; from the relation

$$\{X_{m+n} \notin V_r\} \cap \{X_m \in V_{r'}\} \subset \{X_m^{-1} X_{m+n} \notin V_{r-r'}\},$$

we deduce, since the sequence $\{X_m^{-1} X_{m+n}\}_{n \geqslant 0}$ has the same law as the sequence $\{X_n\}_{n \geqslant 0}$, that

$$P_e \left[\{X_m \in V_r\} \cap \bigcap_{n \geqslant 1} \{X_{m+n} \notin V_r\} \right] \leqslant P_e \left[\bigcap_{n \geqslant 1} \{X_m^{-1} X_{m+n} \notin V_{r-r'}\} \right]$$

$$= P_e[S_{V_{r-r'}} = \infty] = 0.$$

Let $\{r_k\}$ increase to r; as

$$\{X_m \in V_r\} = \lim_k \{X_m \in V_{r_k}\},$$

passing to the limit in the above inequality yields

$$P_e \left[\{X_m \in V_r\} \cap \bigcap_{n \geqslant 1} \{X_{m+n} \notin V_r\} \right] = 0.$$

If $L(\omega) = \max\{m : X_m(\omega) \in V_r\}$, we then have

$$P_e[L < \infty] = \sum_m P_e[L = m] = \sum_m P_e \left[\{X_m \in V_r\} \cap \bigcap_{n \geqslant 1} \{X_{m+n} \notin V_r\} \right] = 0,$$

and the random walk is recurrent.

The potential kernel $G(g, \cdot)$ of X is a convolution kernel. We shall call $\bar{G}$ the measure, possibly non-σ-finite, such that $G(g, \cdot) = (\varepsilon_g * \bar{G})(\cdot)$, that is $\bar{G} = \sum_0^\infty \mu^n$.

Theorem 4.6. *The random walk X is recurrent if and only if $\bar{G}(O) = +\infty$ for every open neighbourhood O of e.*

Proof. The necessity is obvious. To show the sufficiency let us resume the notation of the preceding proof. We have

$$1 \geqslant P_e[L < \infty] = \sum_m P_e \left[\{X_m \in V_r\} \cap \bigcap_n \{X_{m+n} \notin V_r\} \right]$$

$$\geqslant \sum_m P_e \left[\{X_m \in V_r\} \cap \bigcap_n \{X_m^{-1} X_{m+n} \notin V_{2r}\} \right],$$

because $x \in V_r$, $x^{-1}y \notin V_{2r}$ implies $y \notin V_r$; as X_m and $X_m^{-1} X_{m+n}$ are independent,

$$1 \geqslant \bar{G}(V_r) \, P_e[S_{V_{2r}} = \infty].$$

By hypothesis $\bar{G}(V_r) = \infty$; thus $P_e[S_{V_{2r}} = \infty] = 0$, and since r is arbitrary, the random walk X is recurrent.

Corollary 4.7. *If the random walk X is transient, then the potential kernel is a proper kernel, the measures $G(g, \cdot)$ are Radon measures, and the set $\{G(g, \cdot), g \in \mathbf{G}\}$ is vaguely relatively compact.*

Proof. By the preceding result there exists an open neighbourhood O of e such that $\bar{G}(O) < \infty$. Let V be an open neighbourhood of e such that $V^{-1}V \subset O$. If $g \in V$,

$$G(g, V) = \bar{G}(g^{-1}V) \leqslant \bar{G}(V^{-1}V) \leqslant \bar{G}(O),$$

and by the maximum principle $G(\cdot, V) \leqslant \bar{G}(O)$ everywhere. For every compact K of $\mathbf{G}$, there exists a finite sequence $g_1, \ldots, g_n$ of points in K such that the sets $g_i^{-1}V$ form an open covering of K. For all $g \in \mathbf{G}$ we then have

$$G(g, K) \leqslant \sum_{i=1}^{n} G(g, g_i^{-1}V) = \sum_{i=1}^{n} G(g_i g, V) \leqslant n\bar{G}(O),$$

which completes the proof.

Remark. If a random walk is recurrent, the dual random walk is also recurrent. On a non-abelian random walk, the right random walk is recurrent if and only if the left random walk is recurrent.

We end this section by studying the relationship between the topological recurrence of random walks and the recurrence in the sense of Harris. This leads us to consider the important class of laws defined below.

Lemma 4.8. *For a probability measure μ on a group $\mathbf{G}$, the following two properties are equivalent:*

    (i) there exists an integer p such that μ^p is not singular with respect to a right Haar measure m on $\mathbf{G}$.

    (ii) there exists an integer q such that μ^q dominates a multiple of m on a non-empty open subset of $\mathbf{G}$.

Proof. That (ii) implies (i) is clear. Conversely if (i) holds, there exists a non-zero function g in $L^\infty(m) \cap L^1(m)$ such that $\mu^p \geqslant gm$. Then $\mu^{2p} \geqslant (g * g) \, m$ and, as $g * g$ is continuous and non-zero (ii) holds for $q = 2p$.

Definition 4.9. A probability measure μ will be called *spread out* if it satisfies the equivalent conditions of Lemma 4.8. A random walk whose law μ is spread out will also be called *spread out*.

This class is much larger than the class of absolutely continuous probability measures. A probability measure can be singular with respect to Haar measure and yet be spread out (see Exercise 4.19). On a discrete group, all probability measures are spread out.

We call S_μ the set of points $g \in G$ such that a power μ^p of μ dominates a multiple of m on a neighbourhood of g. The set S_μ is clearly open, and $S_\mu \subset T_\mu$. Of course S_μ is non-empty if and only if μ is spread out.

Lemma 4.10. $S_\mu T_\mu \subset S_\mu$.

Proof. Let $g_1 \in S_\mu$, $g_2 \in T_\mu$ and V be a neighbourhood of g_1 on which μ^p dominates a multiple αm of m. Since the point g_2 belongs to the open set $W = \{g : g_1 g_2 g^{-1} \in V\}$, there exists an integer q such that $\mu^q(W) > 0$. Set

$$\varphi(h) = \int_G 1_V(hg^{-1})\, d\mu^q(g) = (1_V * \mu^q)(h);$$

the function φ is lower semi-continuous and

$$\varphi(g_1 g_2) = \int_G 1_V(g_1 g_2 g^{-1})\, d\mu^q(g) = \mu^q(W) > 0.$$

On the other hand,

$$\mu^p * \mu^q \geqslant 1_V\, \mu^p * \mu^q \geqslant \alpha 1_V\, m * \mu^q = \alpha \varphi m,$$

and this shows that μ^{p+q} dominates a multiple of m on a neighbourhood of $g_1 g_2$.

Remark. S_μ is an open sub-semi-group of G.

Theorem 4.11. *A recurrent random walk is recurrent in the sense of Harris if and only if its law μ is spread out.*

Proof. Since the right Haar measure m is σ-finite, positive and invariant, if X is Harris, its invariant measure must be m. Then $m(A) > 0$ implies

$$\sum_{n=0}^{\infty} 2^{-n} \mu^n(A) = \sum_{n=0}^{\infty} 2^{-n} P_e[X_n \in A] > 0;$$

the measures m and $\sum_0^\infty 2^{-n}\mu^n$ cannot be mutually singular, and μ is therefore spread out.

Conversely, if X is recurrent, $T_\mu = G$, and if μ is spread out, $S_\mu T_\mu = S_\mu G \subset S_\mu$, which implies that S_μ is a sub-group and then that $S_\mu = G$. Every point in G thus belongs to an open set on which a power μ^p of μ dominates a multiple of m.

Let A be a Borel set such that $m(A) > 0$; it contains a compact set K such that $m(K) > 0$. The compact K can be covered by a finite number of open sets U_i on which m is dominated by a multiple of a power of μ. For at least one of the sets U_i, we have $m(K \cap U_i) > 0$, and therefore there exists an integer p such that $\mu^p(K \cap U_i) > 0$ and consequently $\mu^p(A) > 0$. We have thus shown that $m \ll \sum_1^\infty 2^{-p}\mu^p$, and $\varepsilon_g * m$ being equivalent to m, we get $m \ll \sum_1^\infty 2^{-p}\varepsilon_g * \mu^p$ for all $g \in G$. The random walk X is therefore irreducible.

Let us assume that there exists a bounded and strictly positive function h such that Gh is bounded. Let K be a compact set such that $m(K) > 0$. The function $1_K * h$ is continuous, bounded, and strictly positive, and it is easily checked that $1_K * Gh = G(1_K * h)$. The potential of the continuous function $1_K * h$ is bounded, which is impossible since X is recurrent in open sets.

As a result, X enjoys property (ii) of Theorem 2.6. There exists an absorbing set F such that $m(F^c) = 0$, and for all $g \in F$ and $A \in \mathscr{E}$ with $m(A) > 0$, $P_g[R(A)] = 1$. The random walk X being translation invariant, all the sets obtained from F by translations have the same property and every point in G belongs to one of these sets; so for $m(A) > 0$, $P.[R(A)] = 1$ everywhere on G.

Corollary 4.12. *If X is recurrent and spread out, a set is transient if and only if it is of Haar measure zero; otherwise it is recurrent.*

Proof. This corollary follows immediately from Proposition 3.8.

Exercise 4.13. Every random walk on a compact group is recurrent.

Exercise 4.14. Let G be $\mathbf{R}$ or $\mathbf{Z}$ and assume that

$$\int |x| \, d\mu(x) < \infty, \qquad \lambda = \int x \, d\mu(x) \neq 0.$$

Show that the random walk X is transient. If $\lambda > 0$, show that X_n converges a.s. towards $+\infty$.

[*Hint*: Use the strong law of large numbers.]

Exercise 4.15 (Right continuous random walks on **Z**). (1) Assume that $G = \mathbf{Z}$ and $\mu(x) = 0$ for $x > 1$. Show that, if, with the notation of the preceding exercise, $\lambda > 0$, then $G(0, x) = \lambda^{-1}$ for $x \geqslant 0$.

[*Hint*: Show first that $G(0, x) = G(0, 0)$ for all $x \geqslant 0$. Then write

$$\lambda = P(0, 1) - \sum_{x=1}^{\infty} \sum_{y=-\infty}^{0} P(x, y)$$

and use the identity

$$\sum_{x=-\infty}^{0} G(0, x) - 1 = \sum_{y} G(0, y) \sum_{n=-\infty}^{0} P(y, n).]$$

(2) Particularize to the Bernoulli case: $\mu(1) = p$, $\mu(-1) = 1 - p = q$ with $p > \frac{1}{2}$, and show that for $x < 0$, $G(0, x) = (p - q)(p/q)^x$.

Exercise 4.16. (1) Let X be a transient random walk on **R** or **Z**. Show that $t^{-1} \bar{G}([-t, t])$ is bounded by $\bar{G}([-1, +1])$.

(2) Assume that $\int |x| \, d\mu(x) < \infty$ and $\lambda = \int x \, d\mu(x) = 0$ and show that the random walk is recurrent. Apply this and Exercise 4.14 to give a new proof of Exercise 1.14(3).

[*Hint*: From the law of large numbers, there exists an integer n_ε such that $n > n_\varepsilon$ implies $P_e[|X_n| < \varepsilon n] > \frac{1}{2}$; then show that

$$t^{-1} \bar{G}([-t, t]) > \tfrac{1}{2}(\varepsilon^{-1} - n_\varepsilon t^{-1})$$

and finish by using the fact that ε is arbitrary.]

Exercise 4.17. Let H be the smallest closed normal sub-group containing the support of $\mu * \hat{\mu}$ (where as usual $\hat{\mu}$ is the law of the reversed random walk). Show that H is the smallest closed normal sub-group such that the support of μ is contained in a coset of H in G. Give an example in which H is a proper sub-group of G.

The following exercises are designed to give a collection of easy results about spread-out probability measures.

Exercise 4.18. For a closed semi-group T the three following conditions are equivalent:

(i) There exists a spread-out probability measure μ such that $T_\mu = T$;

(ii) the interior of T is non-empty;

(iii) the Haar measure of T is strictly positive.

Exercise 4.19. Give examples of recurrent random walks non-recurrent in the sense of Harris. Give examples of transient spread-out random walks which are not irreducible. Give examples of singular and spread-out probability measures.

[*Hint*: For the last one, it is possible to use the nilpotent group of upper triangular matrices, that is $\mathbf{R}^3$ with the multiplication law

$$(x, y, z)\,(x', y', z') = (x + x', y + y', z + z' + xy').$$

Check that Lebesgue measure is still the Haar measure and that a probability measure carried by the plane xOy and thus singular, can be spread out.]

Exercise 4.20. If G is a connected group, any spread-out probability measure satisfies Hypothesis 4.2.

Exercise 4.21. Let μ be spread out and D_n a set carrying the absolutely continuous component of μ^n and such that D_n^c carries the singular component of μ^n. Show that $\mu^n(D_n)$ tends to one as n tends to infinity and derive the existence of an a.s. finite stopping time T such that $P_T(x, \cdot)$ is absolutely continuous with respect to Haar measure, for all $x \in G$.

[*Hint*: Take T to be the first time for X_n to be in D_n.]

Exercise 4.22. This exercise is designed to give a proof of Theorem 4.11 which does not rely on the theory of irreducible chains.

(1) Using a countable basis for the topology of G, show that there exists a P_e-negligible set N such that, for $\omega \notin N$ and for every open set O,

$$\sum_{n=1}^{\infty} 1_O(X_n(\omega)) = \infty.$$

(2) Let A be a set such that $m(A) > 0$. Set

$$B(\omega) = \left\{ g \in G : \sum_{n=1}^{\infty} 1_A(g^{-1} X_n(\omega)) < \infty \right\},$$

and show that $m(B(\omega)) = 0$. Then, using Fubini's theorem, derive that for almost all g, the set

$$\left\{ \omega : \sum_{n=1}^{\infty} 1_A(g^{-1} X_n(\omega)) < \infty \right\}$$

is P_e-negligible.

(3) Prove the difficult part of Theorem 4.11. For that purpose one may use the stopping time of Exercise 4.21.

Exercise 4.23. Show that if μ is spread out, bounded harmonic functions are continuous (solution in ch. 5 §1). The result can be extended to random walks on homogeneous spaces.

Exercise 4.24. If X is irreducible with respect to Haar measure, the random walk induced on a homogeneous space is irreducible with respect to quasi-invariant measures.

Exercise 4.25. Derive from Exercise 3.14 that a random walk for which $\mathscr{I}$ is trivial is spread out.

Exercise 4.26. Show that the resolvent of brownian motion (ch. 2, Exercise 4.8) is recurrent in the sense of Harris.

5. Recurrence criteria for random walks and applications

The computation of the potential kernels of the preceding section is not, as a rule, an easy matter. We need therefore a more tractable criterion to decide whether a particular random walk is recurrent or not. A related problem is to find the groups for which there exist recurrent random walks. For abelian groups, the harmonic analysis of transition functions provides satisfactory answers to both questions.

In this section, G will be a locally compact *abelian* and metrizable group. We denote by Γ the dual group of G and 0 the identity in Γ. If $\gamma \in \Gamma$, we denote by $\gamma(g)$ the value of the character on the point $g \in G$. The Haar measure of Γ will be denoted by m_Γ or $d\gamma$, and will be adjusted so that the inversion formula holds. We proceed to study a random walk of law μ on G, whose Fourier transform will be written

$$\varphi(\gamma) = \int_G \gamma(g) \, d\mu(g).$$

The assumption 4.2 still holds, and we transpose it to the dual group.

Proposition 5.1. *The support of μ generates G if and only if 0 is the only point $\gamma \in \Gamma$ such that $\varphi(\gamma) = 1$.*

Proof. As 1 is an extremal point in the unit disc, if $\varphi(\gamma) = 1$ then $\gamma(g)$ must be equal to one μ-a.s., and therefore if $G_\mu = G$, $\varphi(g)$ equals 1 identically. The converse is clear.

In the following, t will stand for a positive real number less than one. It is convenient to remark once for all that if N is a symmetric compact neighbourhood of 0 in Γ, then

$$\int_N \mathrm{Im}\left(\frac{1}{1 - t\,\varphi(\gamma)}\right) \mathrm{d}\gamma = 0.$$

Theorem 5.2. *The random walk X is transient if and only if there exists a neighbourhood N of 0 in Γ such that*

$$\overline{\lim_{t\uparrow 1}} \int_N \mathrm{Re}\left(\frac{1}{1 - t\,\varphi(\gamma)}\right) \mathrm{d}\gamma < +\infty.$$

Proof. Let N_1 be a symmetric compact neighbourhood of 0 in Γ. Making use of the convolution in Γ, we get

$$\left(\int_{N_1} \gamma(g)\,\mathrm{d}\gamma\right)^2 = \int_\Gamma \gamma(g)\left(\int_\Gamma 1_{N_1}(\gamma')\,1_{N_1}(\gamma - \gamma')\,\mathrm{d}\gamma'\right)\mathrm{d}\gamma$$

$$= \int_\Gamma \gamma(g)\, m_\Gamma\,(N_1 \cap \gamma N_1)\,\mathrm{d}\gamma;$$

taking the integrals of both members with respect to μ yields

$$\int_\Gamma \varphi(\gamma)\, m_\Gamma\,(N_1 \cap \gamma N_1)\,\mathrm{d}\gamma = \int_G \mathrm{d}\mu(g)\left(\int_{N_1} \gamma(g)\,\mathrm{d}\gamma\right)^2.$$

The analogous formula being true for all powers of μ, we get, by summing up,

$$\int_\Gamma \frac{m_\Gamma(N_1 \cap \gamma N_1)}{1 - t\,\varphi(\gamma)}\,\mathrm{d}\gamma = \sum_{n=0}^\infty t^n \int_G \mu^n(\mathrm{d}g)\left(\int_{N_1} \gamma(g)\,\mathrm{d}\gamma\right)^2.$$

Let N be a symmetric compact neighbourhood of 0 in Γ and choose N_1 such that $N_1^2 \subset N$. The function $\gamma \to m_\Gamma(N_1 \cap \gamma N_1)$ is zero outside N, so the left-hand side of the preceding equality is a real number less than

$$m_\Gamma(N_1) \int_N \mathrm{Re}\left(\frac{1}{1 - t\,\varphi(\gamma)}\right) d\gamma.$$

In the right-hand side, the function $g \to (\int_{N_1} \gamma(g)\, d\gamma)^2$ is continuous and takes the value $(m_\Gamma(N_1))^2$ at e; it is therefore greater than $2^{-1}(m_\Gamma(N_1))^2$ on a neighbourhood V of e in G. We thus get

$$2 \int_N \mathrm{Re}\left(\frac{1}{1 - t\,\varphi(\gamma)}\right) d\gamma \geqslant m_\Gamma(N_1) \left(\sum_{n=0}^\infty t^n\, P_e[X_n \in V]\right),$$

and if X is recurrent, then

$$\lim_{t\uparrow 1} \int_N \mathrm{Re}\left(\frac{1}{1 - t\,\varphi(\gamma)}\right) d\gamma = +\infty.$$

Conversely, assume X to be transient, and let V_1 be a symmetric compact neighbourhood of e in G. The function

$$(1_{V_1} * 1_{V_1} * \mu)\,(h) = \int_G m_G(hV_1 \cap gV_1)\, \mu(dg)$$

is continuous, positive definite, and in $L^1(G)$, so that it is the inverse Fourier transform of $\varphi(\gamma)\, (\int_{V_1} \gamma(g)\, dg)^2$. We thus get

$$\int_\Gamma \varphi(\gamma) \left(\int_{V_1} \gamma(g)\, dg\right)^2 d\gamma = (1_{V_1} * 1_{V_1} * \mu)\,(e)$$

$$= \int_G m_G(V_1 \cap gV_1)\, \mu(dg) \leqslant m_G(V_1)\, \mu(V_1^2).$$

The similar inequality is also true for μ^n, and we get, by summing up,

$$\int_\Gamma \left(\int_{V_1} \gamma(g)\, dg\right)^2 \frac{1}{1 - t\,\varphi(\gamma)}\, d\gamma \leqslant m_G(V_1) \left(\sum_{n=0}^\infty t^n\, P_e[X_n \in V_1^2]\right).$$

Let us choose a symmetric compact neighbourhood N of 0 in Γ and the neighbourhood V_1 such that $G(e, V_1^2) < \infty$ and $\mathrm{Re}\,\gamma(g) \geqslant \frac{1}{2}$ for all $(g \times \gamma) \in V_1 \times N$. We then have

$$m_G(V_1) \int_N \mathrm{Re}\left(\frac{1}{1 - t\,\varphi(\gamma)}\right) d\gamma \leqslant 4 \sum_{n=0}^\infty t^n\, P_e[X_n \in V_1^2],$$

and letting t converge to one, we get

$$\varliminf_{t\uparrow 1} \int_N \mathrm{Re}\left(\frac{1}{1 - t\,\varphi(\gamma)}\right) \mathrm{d}\gamma < +\infty.$$

Corollary 5.3. *If X is transient, for every compact neighbourhood N of 0 in Γ, $\mathrm{Re}(1 - \varphi(\gamma))^{-1}$ is integrable on N.*

Proof. For all t and γ, $\mathrm{Re}(1 - t\,\varphi(\gamma))^{-1}$ is $\geqslant 0$ and converges to $\mathrm{Re}(1 - \varphi(\gamma))^{-1}$. One can therefore apply Fatou's lemma to the effect that, with the same N as in the above proof,

$$\int_N \mathrm{Re}\left(\frac{1}{1 - \varphi(\gamma)}\right)\mathrm{d}\gamma \leqslant \varliminf_{t\uparrow 1}\int_N \mathrm{Re}\left(\frac{1}{1 - t\,\varphi(\gamma)}\right)\mathrm{d}\gamma < \infty.$$

Since $\mathrm{Re}((1 - \varphi(\gamma))^{-1})$ is continuous and non-zero outside 0, the result is true for all N.

Remarks 5.4. (1) This criterion is in fact necessary and sufficient for X to be transient, but the proof of the sufficiency relies on a profound study of potential theory for recurrent random walks, which will be dealt with in ch. 9.

(2) If G is compact, Γ is discrete, so that $m_\Gamma(\{0\}) > 0$, and it follows from Corollary 5.3 that all random walks on G are recurrent. This is actually straightforward even if G is non-abelian. (See Exercise 4.13.)

The remaining of the section is devoted to applications of the preceding criterion. We first consider the groups $\mathbf{R}^{d_1} \oplus \mathbf{Z}^{d_2}$. We recall that their dual group is isomorphic to $\mathbf{R}^{d_1} \oplus \mathbf{T}^{d_2}$. We shall denote by y the generic element of this group, $y(x)$ its scalar product with $x \in G$, and $\varphi(y) = \int e^{iy(x)}\,\mathrm{d}\mu(x)$, the Fourier transform of μ.

Proposition 5.5. *The random walk of law μ is recurrent in the following two cases:*

(i) $G = \mathbf{R}$ *or* $\mathbf{Z}$, $\int |x|\,\mathrm{d}\mu(x) < \infty$ *and* $\int x\,\mathrm{d}\mu(x) = 0$.

(ii) $G = \mathbf{R}^{d_1} \oplus \mathbf{Z}^{d_2}$ *with*

$$d_1 + d_2 = 2, \qquad \int |x|^2\,\mathrm{d}\mu(x) < \infty, \qquad \int x\,\mathrm{d}\mu(x) = 0.$$

Proof. (i) It is true that

$$\mathrm{Re}\left(\frac{1}{1 - t\varphi}\right) \geqslant \frac{1 - t}{(\mathrm{Re}(1 - t\varphi))^2 + t^2(\mathrm{Im}\,\varphi)^2},$$

and

$$(\mathrm{Re}(1 - t\varphi))^2 = [(1 - t) + \mathrm{Re}\, t(1 - \varphi)]^2 \leqslant 2(1 - t)^2 + 2t^2(\mathrm{Re}(1 - \varphi))^2.$$

The hypothesis implies that φ is continuously differentiable and that its derivative is zero in 0. Take $\varepsilon > 0$; by Taylor's formula there exists $\alpha > 0$ such that for $|y| < \alpha$ we have

$$|\mathrm{Im}\, \varphi(y)| \leqslant \varepsilon|y|, \qquad \mathrm{Re}(1 - \varphi(y)) \leqslant \varepsilon|y|.$$

It follows that

$$\int_{-\alpha}^{+\alpha} \mathrm{Re}\left(\frac{1}{1 - t(y)}\right) dy \geqslant (1 - t) \int_{-\alpha}^{+\alpha} \frac{dy}{2(1 - t)^2 + 3t^2\varepsilon^2 y^2}$$

$$\geqslant \frac{1}{3} \int_{-\alpha(1-t)^{-1}}^{\alpha(1-t)^{-1}} \frac{dy}{1 + \varepsilon^2 y^2},$$

and thus

$$\lim_{t\uparrow 1} \int_{-\alpha}^{+\alpha} \mathrm{Re}\left(\frac{1}{1 - t\,\varphi(y)}\right) dy \geqslant \frac{\pi}{3\varepsilon}.$$

If X were transient, there would exist $\alpha_0 > 0$ such that $\mathrm{Re}((1 - t\,\varphi(y))^{-1})$ was positive on $[-\alpha_0, \alpha_0]$ and

$$\lim_{t\uparrow 1} \int_{-\alpha_0}^{\alpha_0} \mathrm{Re}\left(\frac{1}{1 - t\varphi(y)}\right) dy = M < \infty.$$

For $\alpha < \alpha_0$, we still would have

$$\lim_{t\uparrow 1} \int_{-\alpha}^{+\alpha} \mathrm{Re}\left(\frac{1}{1 - t\varphi(y)}\right) dy \leqslant M < \infty,$$

but this contradicts the fact that ε is arbitrary.

The proof of (ii) is almost identical and is left to the reader as Exercise 5.15.

We now show that, conversely, if $d_1 + d_2 > 2$, all the random walks are transient. For that purpose we need the following

Proposition 5.6. *If* $G = \mathbf{R}^{d_1} \oplus \mathbf{Z}^{d_2}$, *there exists a constant* c *such that*

$$\mathrm{Re}[1 - \varphi(y)] \geqslant c|y|^2$$

on a neighbourhood of 0 *in* Γ.

Proof. Since G is generated by the support of μ, one can find $d = d_1 + d_2$ elements $x_1, \ldots, x_d$ linearly independent and belonging to the support of μ. We set $L = \max|x_i|$; then the quadratic form

$$Q(y) = \int_{\{|x| \leqslant L\}} y(x)^2 \, d\mu(x)$$

is positive-definite. Indeed, if $y \neq 0$, we have $y(x_i) \neq 0$ for at least one x_i and therefore $y(x_i)^2 > 0$ on a neighbourhood of x_i; as a result $Q(y)$ is strictly positive. The smallest, proper value λ of Q is then strictly positive and $Q(y) \geqslant \lambda|y|^2$.

On the other hand,

$$\mathrm{Re}[1 - \varphi(y)] = \int_G (1 - \cos y(x)) \, d\mu(x)$$

$$\geqslant 2 \int_{\{|x| \leqslant L\}} \sin^2 \tfrac{1}{2} y(x) \, d\mu(x).$$

But $|\sin(\tfrac{1}{2} y(x))| \geqslant \pi^{-1}|y(x)|$ if $|y(x)| \leqslant \pi$ and therefore

$$\mathrm{Re}[1 - \varphi(y)] \geqslant 2\pi^{-2} \int_S |y(x)|^2 \, d\mu(x),$$

where $S = \{x : |x| \leqslant L, |y(x)| \leqslant \pi\}$. If $|y| \leqslant \pi L^{-1}$ and $|x| \leqslant L$, then $|y(x)| \leqslant \pi$; thus on the neighbourhood $\{y : |y| \leqslant \pi L^{-1}\}$ of 0 in Γ, we have

$$\mathrm{Re}[1 - \varphi(y)] \geqslant 2\pi^{-2} \int_{\{|x| \leqslant L\}} |y(x)|^2 \, d\mu(x) \geqslant 2\lambda\pi^{-2}|y|^2,$$

which yields the result with $c = 2\lambda\pi^{-2}$.

Theorem 5.7. *If $d_1 + d_2 > 2$, all random walks on $\mathbf{R}^{d_1} \oplus \mathbf{Z}^{d_2}$ are transient.*

Proof. Let P be a neighbourhood of 0 in Γ on which $\mathrm{Re}\,\varphi$ is $\geqslant 0$ and the inequality of Proposition 5.6 holds. Then, for $t < 1$,

$$\mathrm{Re}[(1 - t\,\varphi(y))^{-1}] \leqslant (\mathrm{Re}[1 - \varphi(y)])^{-1},$$

and therefore if $d_1 + d_2 > 2$,

$$\int_P \mathrm{Re}\left[\frac{1}{1 - t\,\varphi(y)}\right] dy \leqslant c^{-1} \int_P \frac{dy}{|y|^2} = M < \infty,$$

which implies that all random walks are transient.

We now deal with the characterization of the groups for which there exist recurrent random walks.

Definition 5.8. A group G (not necessarily abelian) will be called *recurrent* if there exists a probability measure μ on the Borel sets of G such that the random walk of law μ is recurrent.

Compact groups, groups isomorphic to $\mathbf{R}^{d_1} \oplus \mathbf{Z}^{d_2}$ with $d_1 + d_2 \leqslant 2$ are recurrent, but the most general recurrent group is not yet known. We deal below with abelian groups, but the first lemma is true for all groups.

Lemma 5.9. *An open sub-group of a recurrent group is recurrent. In particular every sub-group of a discrete recurrent group is recurrent.*

Proof. Left to the reader as Exercise 5.20.

Lemma 5.10. *Let H be a compact sub-group of an abelian group G and σ the canonical continuous and open mapping from G to G/H. Let μ be a probability on G, and $\bar{\mu}$ its image by σ; then, if the random walk of law $\bar{\mu}$ is recurrent, the random walk of law μ is recurrent.*

Proof. Let V be a compact neighbourhood of the identity in G. The sets VH and $\sigma(VH)$ are then also compact neighbourhoods of the identity in G and G/H. Since, as is easily seen,

$$\sum_0^\infty \mu^n(VH) = \sum_0^\infty \bar{\mu}^n(\sigma(VH)),$$

it follows that the random walk of law μ is recurrent if the random walk of law $\bar{\mu}$ is recurrent.

Theorem 5.11. *A denumerable abelian group is recurrent if and only if its rank (maximal number of linearly independent elements) is at most 2.*

Proof. If the rank of G is greater than 2, there exists a sub-group isomorphic to $\mathbf{Z}^3$ which is not a recurrent group; by Lemma 5.9 the group G cannot be recurrent.

Conversely, let us assume that the rank of G is less than or equal to 2. If G is of rank 1, let a_1 be any element of infinite order; if G is of rank 2, let a_1, a_2 be two linearly independent elements and in all cases (rank 0, 1 or 2) let $\{a_n\}_{n\in\mathbf{N}}$ be a sequence generating G and such that a_{m+1} is not in the sub-group G_m generated by $a_1, \ldots, a_m$. The fundamental theorem on finitely generated abelian groups asserts that, for every m, G_m is of the form $\mathbf{Z}^2 \oplus K$ or $\mathbf{Z} \oplus K$ or K, where K is a finite group. It then follows from Proposition 5.5 and Lemma 5.10 that all the random walks we are about to define on G_m are recurrent.

We define inductively a sequence $\mu^{(m)}$ of probability measures carried by G_m by setting $\mu^{(1)}(a_1) = \mu^{(1)}(-a_1) = \frac{1}{2}$, and for $m \geqslant 2$,

$$\mu^{(m)}(g) = (1 - q_m)\, \mu^{(m-1)}(g)$$

if $g \in G_{m-1}$, and

$$\mu^{(m)}(a_m) = \mu^{(m)}(-a_m) = \tfrac{1}{2} q_m.$$

Every point $g \in G$ belongs to at least one G_m; we can thus define

$$\mu(g) = \prod_{i=m+1}^{\infty} (1 - q_i)\, \mu^{(m)}(g),$$

and it is easily checked that this number does not depend on m. Now if the infinite product $\prod_{i=2}^{\infty} (1 - q_i)$ is convergent, we have

$$\sum_{g \in G} \mu(g) = \lim_m \sum_{g \in G_m} \mu(g) = \lim_m \prod_{i=m+1}^{\infty} (1 - q_i) = 1,$$

and μ defines a probability measure on G.

Plainly G is generated by the support of μ and we shall show that the q_i may be choosen in such a way that μ will be recurrent. Call X^m and X the random walks of law $\mu^{(m)}$ and μ, P_ν^m and P_ν the corresponding probability measures. We choose once for all a sequence of numbers $r_n \in \,]0, 1[$ such that $\prod_1^{\infty} (1 - r_n)$ converges. We choose a number N_1 and a sequence of numbers $A_j^1 \in \,]0, 1[$ such that

$$\prod_{j=1}^{\infty} (1 - A_j^1)^{N_1} \sum_{k=1}^{N_1} P_e^1[X_k^1 = e] > 1,$$

and we set $q_2 = \min(r_1, A_1^1)$. The random walk X^2 is then known and we choose N_2 and A_j^2 such that

$$\prod_{j=1}^{\infty} (1 - A_j^2)^{N_2} \sum_{k=N_1+1}^{N_2} P_e^2[X_k^2 = e] > 1,$$

and we set $q_3 = \min(r_2, A_2^1, A_2^2)$, which allows us to define X^3. We follow this process inductively. Given N_{n-1} and q_{n-1}, we choose N_n and A_j^n such that

$$\prod_{j=1}^{\infty} (1 - A_j^n)^{N_n} \sum_{k=N_{n-1}+1}^{N_n} P_e^{n-1}[X_k^{n-1} = e] > 1,$$

and define

$$q_n = \min(r_{n-1}, A_{n-1}^1, A_{n-1}^2, \ldots, A_{n-1}^{n-1}).$$

Such choices are always possible since the random walks X^n are recurrent.

Plainly, the infinite product $\prod_1^{\infty} (1 - q_i)$ converges, and we have, $\bar{G}$ being the potential measure of X,

$$\bar{G}(e) \geqslant \sum_{k=1}^{\infty} P_e[X_k = e] = \sum_{n=1}^{\infty} \sum_{k=N_{n-1}+1}^{N_n} P_e[X_k = e]$$

$$\geqslant \sum_{n=1}^{\infty} \sum_{k=N_{n-1}+1}^{N_n} \prod_{i=n+1}^{\infty} (1 - q_i)^k P_e^{n-1}[X_k^{n-1} = e]$$

since

$$\prod_{i=n+1}^{\infty} (1 - q_i)^k P_e^{n-1}[X_k^{n-1} = e]$$

is the probability for X to be in e at time k without having gone outside G_{n-1}. We further have

$$\bar{G}(e) \geqslant \sum_{n=1}^{\infty} \sum_{k=N_{n-1}+1}^{N_n} \prod_{i=n+1}^{\infty} (1 - q_i)^{N_n} P_e^{n-1}[X_k^n = e]$$

$$\geqslant \sum_{n=1}^{\infty} \sum_{k=N_{n-1}+1}^{N_n} \prod_{i=1}^{\infty} (1 - A_i^n)^{N_n} P_e^{n-1}[X_k^n = e] = +\infty.$$

Thus X is recurrent and the proof is completed.

5.12. The above result leads to a characterization of abelian locally compact metrizable recurrent groups. By the structure theorems, such a group G is isomorphic to $\mathbf{R}^n \times G_0$, where G_0 is a locally compact abelian group containing a compact open sub-group K. From Lemma 5.10 the group G is recurrent if and only if $G/\{e\} \times K$ is recurrent. But this latter group is isomorphic to $\mathbf{R}^n \times G_1$, where G_1 is countable and of rank r. The group G is recurrent if and only if $n + r \leqslant 2$. Indeed, if $n + r \leqslant 2$, is contains the recurrent and dense sub-group $\mathbf{Q}^n \times G_1$.

For instance, the groups $\mathbf{Q}^2 \times K$, where K is compact, and the groups of p-adic numbers, are recurrent.

Exercise 5.13. Show that $\gamma(X_n)/\varphi(\gamma)^n$ is a complex martingale for P_e.

Exercise 5.14. Continuation of Exercise 4.17. Take G abelian and show that $H = G$ if and only if $|\varphi(\gamma)| < 1$ for all $\gamma \neq 0$.

Exercise 5.15. (1) Prove (ii) of Proposition 5.5.
   [*Hint*: Take the open ball of radius α instead of the interval $[-\alpha, +\alpha]$ and use polar coordinates.]
   (2) Give a proof of Exercise 4.14, using Theorem 5.2.

Exercise 5.16. If G is discrete, Γ is compact. Show that one can then replace N by Γ in Theorems 5.2 and 5.3.
   [*Hint*: Express $\mu^n(e)$ by mean of inverse Fourier transform.]
Show that, if $G = \mathbf{Z}^d$, the inequality 5.6 is true on the whole group Γ.

Exercise 5.17. Show that, if the law μ is *symmetric* ($\mu = \hat{\mu}$), the criterion 5.3 is necessary and sufficient for X to be transient.
   [*Hint*: Notice that φ is real.]

Exercise 5.18. If G is non-discrete, thus Γ non-compact, and if μ is spread out, then
$$\overline{\lim_{\gamma \to \infty}} |\varphi(\gamma)| < 1.$$
This allows one to show that some non-discrete singular laws are not spread out. For example, the probability measure on $\mathbf{R}$ whose characteristic function equals $\prod_{n=1}^{\infty} \cos(t/n!)$ is singular and is not spread out.

The following exercises deal with recurrent, not necessarily abelian groups.

Exercise 5.19. With the notation of Lemma 5.10 but H not necessarily abelian, show that if μ is recurrent, then $\bar{\mu}$ is recurrent.

Exercise 5.20. Prove Lemma 5.9.
   [*Hint*: Use the imbedded random walk of ch. 1 § 4.10.]

Exercise 5.21. Every discrete group such that every finite subset generates a finite sub-group is recurrent.

Exercise 5.22. Let G be the free group with two generators a and b.
   (1) Define a law μ on G by $\mu(a) = \mu(b) = \mu(a^{-1}) = \mu(b^{-1}) = \frac{1}{4}$. Show that the random walk of law μ is transient.

[*Hint*: If $|g|$ is the minimal number of symbols a, b, a^{-1}, b^{-1}, necessary to write $g \in G$, the function $g \rightarrow 3^{-|g|}$ is harmonic.]

(2) More generally show that G is not recurrent.

[*Hint*: Every denumerable group is isomorphic to a sub-group of a quotient group of the free group with two generators.]

Exercise 5.23. A group G is said to have the *fixed point property* if, whenever G acts continuously on a compact convex subset Q of a locally convex linear topological space by affine transformations, then G has a fixed point in Q.

(1) Show that a group G has the fixed point property if and only if for every compact G-space M there exists a probability measure on M invariant by G.

(2) Show that a recurrent group has the fixed point property and is therefore amenable.

[*Hint*: See ch. 2, Exercise 3.20 and ch. 5, Exercise 1.10.]

Deduce from this fact that free groups with more than one generator and semi-simple Lie groups are not recurrent.

CHAPTER 4

POINTWISE ERGODIC THEORY

In this chapter we prove the famous theorem of Chacon and Ornstein, and give some of its applications.

1. Preliminaries

We have already noticed that with a transition probability P we may associate two positive contractions on the Banach spaces $b\mathscr{E}$ and $b\mathscr{M}(\mathscr{E})$; these two contractions are dual in the duality between bounded functions and bounded measures, as is clear from the formula

$$\langle mP, f \rangle = \langle m, Pf \rangle.$$

In this chapter we shall deal mainly with the contraction on $b\mathscr{M}(\mathscr{E})$. Among the closed subspaces of $b\mathscr{M}(\mathscr{E})$, we find the space of bounded measures absolutely continuous with respect to a σ-finite positive measure μ; this space is isomorphic to $L^1(E, \mathscr{E}, \mu)$. We shall be interested in the subspaces of this kind which are invariant by P.

Proposition 1.1. *The space of bounded measures absolutely continuous with respect to the σ-finite positive measure μ is invariant by P if and only if $\mu P \ll \mu$.*

Proof. If $\mu P \ll \mu$ and if $\mu(A) = 0$, then $P(\cdot, A) = 0$ μ-a.e., and consequently for every f in $L^1(\mu)$ we have $\langle f \mu, P(\cdot, A) \rangle = 0$.

Conversely, since μ is σ-finite, there is a sequence $\{f_n\}$ of elements of $L^1(\mu)$ increasing to 1; if $\mu(A) = 0$, the hypothesis implies that, for every n, we have $\langle f_n \mu, P(\cdot, A) \rangle = 0$, and passing to the limit yields $\mu P(A) = 0$.

Remark. The condition $\mu P \ll \mu$ is satisfied if μ is excessive. It is also satisfied if $\mu = \sum_0^\infty 2^{-n} \nu P_n$, where ν is any bounded measure.

Definition 1.2. If $\mu P \ll \mu$ the linear operator which maps $f \in L^1(\mu)$ onto the Radon–Nykodim derivative of $(f \mu) P$ with respect to μ is called *the operator induced* by P on $L^1(\mu)$.

Proposition 1.3. *If $\mu P \ll \mu$, the operator induced by P is a positive contraction.*

Proof. This follows at once from the fact that the map $f \to (f \mu)$ from $L^1(\mu)$ into $b\mathscr{M}(\mathscr{E})$ is an isometry, and that P is a contraction on the latter space. The positivity is obvious.

The adjoint operator of an operator induced by a T.P. on $L^1(\mu)$ is an operator on $L^\infty(\mu)$ which is described in the following result.

Proposition 1.4. *If $\mu P \ll \mu$, then P maps functions equal μ-a.e. to functions in $b\mathscr{E}$ into functions of the same kind, and thus defines on $L^\infty(\mu)$ a positive contraction which is the adjoint operator of the operator induced by P on $L^1(\mu)$.*

Proof. If $f \in \mathscr{E}$ is bounded above μ-a.e. by a number M, the set $A = \{f > M\}$ has μP-measure zero; in other words, $P(\cdot, A) = 0$ μ-a.e. and consequently $Pf \leqslant M$ μ-a.e. In the same way it is seen that if $f = g$ μ-a.e. then $Pf = Pg$ μ-a.e. The proof is now easily completed.

Rather than study the operators just described, we shall study an arbitrary positive contraction T on a space $L^1(E, \mathscr{E}, \mu)$. Its adjoint operator which is a positive contraction on $L^\infty(E, \mathscr{E}, \mu)$ will be denoted T^*. We shall need the following lemma, which is obvious when T is induced by a T.P. For f in $L^1(\mu)$ and g in $L^\infty(\mu)$, we shall set

$$\langle f, g \rangle_\mu = \int_E fg \, d\mu,$$

and often drop μ when there is no risk of ambiguity.

Lemma 1.5. *Let $\{h_n\}$ be a sequence of elements of $L^\infty(\mu)$ increasing μ-a.e. to an element h of $L^\infty(\mu)$; then $\{T^*h_n\}$ increases μ-a.e. to T^*h.*

Proof. The sequence $\{T^*h_n\}$ increases to a function $g \leqslant T^*h$. If $\mu\{g < T^*h\} > 0$, there is a non-zero element f in L^1_+ such that $\langle f, g \rangle < \langle f, T^*h \rangle$; but for every f in L^1_+ we have

$$\langle f, g \rangle = \lim_n \langle f, T^*h_n \rangle = \lim_n \langle Tf, h_n \rangle$$

$$= \langle Tf, h \rangle = \langle f, T^*h \rangle,$$

so that we get a contradiction.

The following proposition is, to some extent, a converse to the preceding discussion. It shows that positive contractions of a space L^1 are not much more general than those induced by transition probabilities. We recall that a compact class $\mathcal{K}$ is a family of subsets of E such that, for every sequence $\{C_n, n \geqslant 1\}$ of sets in $\mathcal{K}$ with intersection $\bigcap C_n$ empty, there exists an integer N such that $\bigcap_{n \leqslant N} C_n$ is empty. It is always possible to assume that such a class is closed under finite unions. The family of compact subsets of a topological space provides an example of compact class.

Proposition 1.6. *Suppose $(E, \mathcal{E})$ is separable, and there is a compact class $\mathcal{K}$ such that μ has the approximation property with respect to $\mathcal{K}$, that is, for every F in $\mathcal{E}$,*

$$\mu(F) = \sup\{\mu(K), K \in \mathcal{K}, K \subset F\}.$$

Then every positive contraction T of $L^1(E, \mathcal{E}, \mu)$ is induced by at least one transition probability.

Proof. Let us call B_n, $n \geqslant 1$, the elements of a countable boolean algebra $\mathcal{B}$ generating $\mathcal{E}$. Since $\mathcal{K}$ may be taken closed under finite unions, there exists for every n an increasing sequence $\{C_n^k\}_{k \geqslant 1}$ of sets in $\mathcal{K}$ such that $\mu(B_n) = \lim_k \mu(C_n^k)$. The boolean algebra $\mathcal{D}$ generated by $\mathcal{B}$ and by the sets C_n^k is countable and generates $\mathcal{E}$.

For $F \in \mathcal{E}$, we pick a function $\bar{P}(\,\cdot\,, F)$ within the equivalence class of T^*1_F. These functions possess the following properties:

(i) for every $D \in \mathcal{D}$, $0 \leqslant \bar{P}(\,\cdot\,, D) \leqslant 1$ μ-a.e.;

(ii) for every pair D, D' of disjoint sets in $\mathcal{D}$

$$\bar{P}(\,\cdot\,, D + D') = \bar{P}(\,\cdot\,, D) + \bar{P}(\,\cdot\,, D') \quad \mu\text{-a.e.};$$

(iii) for every n, the sequence $\{\bar{P}(\,\cdot\,, C_n^k)\}_{k \geqslant 1}$ increases μ-a.e. to $\bar{P}(\,\cdot\,, B_n)$; this follows by applying Lemma 1.5 to the sequence $1_{C_n^k}$ which increases μ-a.e. to 1_{B_n}.

Since $\mathcal{D}$ is countable, there is a negligible set N such that, for $x \in N^c$, the set function $\bar{P}(x, \cdot)$ satisfies the above properties, hence is a positive and additive set function on $\mathscr{B}$. We claim that it is a countably additive set function.

Let $\{B_j\}$ be a subsequence of $\{B_n\}$, decreasing to $\emptyset$. For every j, every $\varepsilon > 0$ and $x \in N^c$, we may find a set $C_j \in \mathscr{K} \cap \mathscr{D}$ such that $C_j \subset B_j$ and

$$\bar{P}(x, B_j) \leqslant \bar{P}(x, C_j) + 2^{-j}\varepsilon.$$

Since $\bigcap C_j \subset \bigcap B_j = \emptyset$, there is an integer J such that $\bigcap_{j \leqslant J} C_j = \emptyset$. From the formula

$$B_J = \bigcap_{j \leqslant J} B_j \subset \bigcup_{j \leqslant J} (B_j - C_j)$$

we get

$$\bar{P}(x, B_J) \leqslant \sum_{j \leqslant J} \bar{P}(B_j - C_j) \leqslant \varepsilon.$$

Since ε is arbitrary it follows that $\bar{P}(x, \bigcap B_j) = 0$ and therefore $\bar{P}(x, \cdot)$ has a unique extension to a countably additive set function $P(x, \cdot)$ on $\mathscr{E}$. For x in N, we set $P(x, \cdot) = \nu(\cdot)$, where ν is any probability measure equivalent to μ.

By construction, the function $P(\cdot, B)$ is measurable for $B \in \mathscr{B}$, and by the monotone class theorem it is measurable for $B \in \mathscr{E}$. It is now plain that P is a transition probability on $(E, \mathscr{E})$ such that $\mu P \ll \mu$ and that T is induced by P.

Remarks. (1) If E is an LCCB space, or more generally a Polish space, and $\mathscr{E}$ is the σ-algebra of Borel sets, and if μ has the approximation property with respect to compact sets, the conditions of the preceding proposition are satisfied.

(2) If μ is bounded and $\mathscr{G}$ is a sub-σ-algebra of $\mathscr{E}$, the map $f \to E[f \mid \mathscr{G}]$ is a positive contraction of $L^1(E, \mathscr{E}, \mu)$. The corresponding T.P. constructed in the above theorem is then called a regular conditional probability.

Exercise 1.7. Prove that T may be uniquely extended to an operator, still denoted T, on $\mathscr{E}_+$, in such a way that for every increasing sequence $\{f_n\}$ of functions in $\mathscr{E}_+$, $T(\lim_n f_n) = \lim_n Tf_n$. Prove the same thing for T^*.
[*Hint*: Look at the discussion preceding Theorem 3.4 below.]

Exercise 1.8. If μ is excessive for P and T is the contraction induced by P on $L^1(\mu)$, then $T1 \leqslant 1$. (For μ unbounded, $T1$ is defined in Exercise 1.7.)

Exercise 1.9. If T is induced by P and $h = T^*h$ μ-a.e., prove that there exists a bounded function h' harmonic for P and such that $\|h\|_\infty = \sup_{x \in E} |h'(x)|$.

Exercise 1.10. Let T be a bounded linear operator on the space $L_{\mathbf{C}}^1$ of equivalence classes of complex integrable functions. Prove that there exists a positive (that is, mapping positive real functions into positive real functions) operator τ on $L_{\mathbf{C}}^1$ such that

    (i) $|Tf| \leqslant \tau|f|$ for every $f \in L_{\mathbf{C}}^1$,

    (ii) $\|\tau\| \leqslant \|T\|$.

For $f \in L_+^1$, τ is given by

$$\tau f = \sup_{|g| \leqslant f} |Tg|.$$

The operator τ is called the *linear modulus* of T. Show that $\tau^n|f| \geqslant |T^n f|$ for every f in $L_{\mathbf{C}}^1$.

2. Maximal ergodic lemma. Hopf's decomposition

In what follows, we shall thus study a positive contraction T of the space $L^1(E, \mathscr{E}, \mu)$ with adjoint T^*. The equalities between sets and functions must always be understood to hold up to μ-equivalence, and we shall indulge in the usual confusion between functions and equivalence classes of functions.

The powers of T and T^* will be denoted T^n and T^{*n}. We shall use with respect to T^* the notations and definitions introduced for transition probabilities. For instance we say that $\varphi \in L_+^\infty(\mu)$ is superharmonic if $T^*\varphi \leqslant \varphi$ μ-a.e., and we set

$$P_A^* = \sum_{n=0}^{\infty} (I_{A^c}T^*)^n I_A.$$

In ch. 2, the proof of the properties of P_A used only the linearity and positivity of the relevant operators. We thus have in the same way that $P_A^* 1$ is the limit of the sequence defined inductively by $g_0 = 1_A$, $g_n = 1_A \vee T^*g_{n-1}$, hence that $P_A^* 1 \leqslant 1$ and that $\lim_n (I_{A^c}T^*)^n P_A^* 1 = 0$. Moreover, if $B \supset A$, then $P_B^* P_A^* = P_A^*$.

Theorem 2.1 (Maximal ergodic lemma). *If $f \in L^1(\mu)$ and*

$$E_f = \bigcup_{n \geqslant 0} \left\{ \sum_{k=0}^{n} T^k f > 0 \right\},$$

then

$$\int_{E_f} \varphi f \, \mathrm{d}\mu \geqslant 0$$

for every superharmonic function φ in $L_+^\infty(\mu)$.

Proof. Let

$$h_N = \sup(0, f, f + Tf, \ldots, f + Tf + \cdots + T^N f);$$

the sequence $\{h_N\}$ is increasing and the sets $E_N = \{h_N > 0\}$ increase to E_f. Since T is a positive operator, we have

$$Th_N \geqslant \sup(0, Tf, Tf + T^2 f, \ldots, Tf + T^2 f + \cdots + T^{N+1} f)$$

and consequently

$$f + Th_N \geqslant \sup(f, f + Tf, \ldots, f + Tf + \cdots + T^{N+1} f).$$

The right term of this inequality being equal to h_{N+1} on E_{N+1}, we have

$$\int_{E_{N+1}} \varphi f \, \mathrm{d}\mu \geqslant \int \varphi \, h_{N+1} \, \mathrm{d}\mu - \int_{E_{N+1}} \varphi \, Th_N \, \mathrm{d}\mu$$

$$\geqslant \int \varphi \, h_{N+1} \, \mathrm{d}\mu - \int \varphi \, Th_N \, \mathrm{d}\mu$$

$$\geqslant \int \varphi \, h_{N+1} \, \mathrm{d}\mu - \int T^* \varphi \, h_N \, \mathrm{d}\mu$$

$$\geqslant \int \varphi \, h_{N+1} \, \mathrm{d}\mu - \int \varphi \, h_N \, \mathrm{d}\mu \geqslant 0.$$

By letting N tend to infinity we thus get the desired result.

In the sequel, for every pair (f, g) of elements of $L^1(\mu)$ we set

$$D_n(f, g) = \sum_{m=0}^{n} T^m f \Big/ \sum_{m=0}^{n} T^m g$$

on the set where the denominator does not vanish. Our goal is to describe the asymptotic behaviour of these ratios when n tends to infinity.

Lemma 2.2. *If f and g are in L^1_+, the function g vanishes almost everywhere on the set $\{\sup_n D_n(f, g) = \infty\}$.*

Proof. By applying the maximal ergodic lemma with $\varphi = 1$ to the function $f - cg$, where c is a strictly positive real, we find

$$\int_{E_{f-cg}} g \, \mathrm{d}\mu \leqslant c^{-1} \|f\|_1.$$

The result follows by letting c tend to infinity.

Theorem 2.3 (Hopf's decomposition theorem). *There exists a set C in $\mathcal{E}$, unique up to equivalence, such that for every f in L^1_+,*

$$\sum_{n=0}^{\infty} T^n f = 0 \quad or + \infty \quad on\ C,$$

$$\sum_{n=0}^{\infty} T^n f < +\infty \qquad on\ D = C^c.$$

Proof. Let g be a strictly positive element in L^1. For every $f \in L^1_+$, Lemma 2.2 implies that $\sum_{n=0}^{\infty} T^n f$ is finite on $\{\sum_{n=0}^{\infty} T^n g < \infty\}$. If f is also strictly positive, it follows that

$$\left\{ \sum_{n=0}^{\infty} T^n g < \infty \right\} = \left\{ \sum_{n=0}^{\infty} T^n f < \infty \right\} \quad \mu\text{-a.e.}$$

The set $C = \{\sum_{n=0}^{\infty} T^n g = \infty\}$ thus does not depend on the choice of g, provided that g is chosen strictly positive.

Let now $h \in L^1_+$ be such that $\sum_{n=0}^{\infty} T^n h < +\infty$ on a subset B of C; then for every k, $\sum_{n=0}^{\infty} T^n(T^k h) < +\infty$ on B, hence $\sup_n D_n(g, T^k h) = +\infty$ on B, and by Lemma 2.2, $T^k h = 0$ μ-a.e. on B. It follows that $\sum_{k=0}^{\infty} T^k h = 0$ μ-a.e. on B and the proof is thus complete.

Definitions 2.4. The set C is called the *conservative part* and the set D the *dissipative part* of E with respect to T. The decomposition of E into its conservative and dissipative part is called *Hopf's decomposition* of E. Finally, if D is empty, T is said to be a *conservative* contraction.

We shall, for a while, restrict ourselves to the study of conservative contractions.

Proposition 2.5. *Assume T to be conservative. The class $\mathcal{C}$ of sets*

$$C_f = \left\{ \sum_{n=0}^{\infty} T^n f = \infty \right\},$$

where f runs through L^1_+, is a sub-σ-algebra of $\mathcal{E}$. For a function $h \in L^\infty_+$, the following properties are equivalent:
   (i) $T^*h \leqslant h$ μ-a.e.;
   (ii) $T^*h = h$ μ-a.e.;
   (iii) h is $\mathcal{C}$-measurable.

In particular, a set B is in $\mathscr{C}$ if $T*1_B = 1_B$ on B and only if $T*1_B = 1_B$ every-where.

Proof. Let $h \in L_+^\infty$ be such that $T*h \leqslant h$ and pick a function f in L^1 and strictly positive; for every integer N,

$$\left\langle \sum_{n=0}^{N-1} T^n f, h - T*h \right\rangle = \langle f, h - T^{*N}h \rangle \leqslant \|f\|_1 \|h\|_\infty < \infty.$$

Since T is conservative, this is impossible unless $h = T*h$ μ-a.e., which shows the equivalence between (i) and (ii). In particular $T*1 = 1$.

Let $\mathscr{H}$ be the convex sub-cone of L_+^∞ of functions h such that $T*h = h$ μ-a.e. It contains the function 1, and is closed under increasing limits. More-over, if h and h' are in $\mathscr{H}$, then $\inf(h, h')$ is in $\mathscr{H}$; indeed,

$$T*(\inf(h, h')) \leqslant \inf(T*h, T*h') = \inf(h, h'),$$

which gives the result by the equivalence of (i) and (ii). Consequently, there exists a sub-σ-algebra $\mathscr{C}$ of $\mathscr{E}$ such that $\mathscr{H} = b\mathscr{C}_+$. If $B \in \mathscr{C}$ we have therefore $T*1_B = 1_B$. On the other hand, if $T*1_B = 1_B$ on B, then $T*1_{B^c} = 0$ on B; hence $T*1_{B^c} \leqslant 1_{B^c}$ so that, by definition of $\mathscr{C}$, B^c, and hence B, is in $\mathscr{C}$.

Next, we get from Theorem 2.3 that

$$0 = \left\langle 1_{C_f^c}, \sum_{n=1}^{\infty} T^n f \right\rangle = \left\langle T*1_{C_f^c}, \sum_{n=0}^{\infty} T^n f \right\rangle,$$

which proves that $T*1_{C_f^c} = 0$ on C_f and consequently that C_f is in $\mathscr{C}$.

Finally, let B be any set in $\mathscr{C}$ and choose f in L_+^1 such that $B = \{f > 0\}$; we have $\sum_{n=0}^{\infty} T^n f = +\infty$ on B, since the first summand is strictly positive on B. On the other hand, for every $n \geqslant 0$, we have

$$\langle 1_{B^c}, T^n f \rangle = \langle T^{*n} 1_{B^c}, f \rangle = \langle 1_{B^c}, f \rangle = 0$$

which implies that $\sum_{n=0}^{\infty} T^n f = 0$ on B^c, hence $B = C_f$.

Definition 2.6. The sets of $\mathscr{C}$ are called the *invariant sets*. The $\mathscr{C}$-measurable functions are called *invariant*. If $\mathscr{C}$ is trivial μ-a.e., the conservative contrac-tion T is said to be *ergodic*.

When T is induced by a transition probability P the superharmonic function for P are invariant (see also Exercise 1.9). Finally we observe that all $\mathscr{E}$-measurable μ-negligible sets are in $\mathscr{C}$.

In the sequel we shall need the following property of invariant functions.

Lemma 2.7. *If h is invariant and bounded, $T(hf) = h(Tf)$ for every f in L^1.*

Proof. We shall first show that $T^*(hg) = h(T^*g)$ for every g in L^∞. It suffices to prove this property when $h = 1_B$ for $B \in \mathscr{C}$ and $g = 1_A$. We have

$$T^*(1_A 1_B) \leqslant \inf(T^*1_A, T^*1_B) = \inf(T^*1_A, 1_B) = 1_B(T^*1_A),$$

and in the same way $T^*(1_{A^c} 1_B) \leqslant 1_B(T^*1_{A^c})$; adding these two inequalities yields that $T^*1_B \leqslant 1_B$. Since by hypothesis $T^*1_B = 1_B$, this shows that the above inequalities are in fact equalities; thus $T^*(1_A 1_B) = 1_B(T^*1_A)$.

The lemma is then a consequence of the following equalities, where g runs through L^∞:

$$\langle h(Tf), g \rangle = \langle Tf, hg \rangle = \langle f, T^*(hg) \rangle = \langle f, h(T^*g) \rangle = \langle T(hf), g \rangle.$$

The dissipative part may be viewed as a "transient" part, while the conservative part may be viewed as a "recurrent" part and the invariant sets as "recurrent classes". The reader is invited to solve Exercise 2.10, which supports this somewhat heuristic assertion. If we refer to the case in which T is induced by a transition probability, the following result states that the chain does not pass from C to D.

Proposition 2.8. $T^*1_D = 0$ μ-a.e. on C.

Proof. Choose a sequence $\{D_k\}$ of sets of finite measure increasing to D and a strictly positive function f of L^1; then for $c > 0$ set

$$h_c = \inf\left\{1, c \Big/ \sum_{n=1}^\infty T^n f\right\}.$$

Plainly, h_c increases to 1_D as c tends to infinity. On the other hand

$$\left\langle T^*(1_{D_k} h_c), \sum_{n=0}^\infty T^n f \right\rangle = \int_{D_k} h_c \left(\sum_{n=1}^\infty T^n f \right) \mathrm{d}\mu \leqslant c\, \mu(D_k) < \infty;$$

since on C, the sum $\sum_{n=0}^\infty T^n f$ is infinite, it follows that $T^*(h_c 1_{D_k}) = 0$. By letting c, then k, tend to infinity, we get the desired result.

It follows from the above proposition that if f is a positive function vanishing on D, then Tf vanishes on D; indeed

$$\int_D Tf \, d\mu = \int f \, T^* 1_D \, d\mu = 0.$$

We can therefore study the restriction of T to C, that is, to the functions vanishing on D, and this restriction is clearly a conservative contraction. In the sequel, by invariant functions we shall mean functions vanishing on D and invariant for the restriction of T to C, and the σ algebra $\mathscr{C}$ will be a σ-algebra of subsets of C. In this setting we prove

Lemma 2.9. *For every measurable subset A of C there exists a smallest (up to equivalence) invariant set $\bar{A}$ containing A, and*

$$\bar{A} = \left\{ \sum_{n=0}^{\infty} T^n 1_A = \infty \right\} = \{E[1_A \mid \mathscr{C}] > 0\},$$

where the conditional expectation is taken with respect to any probability measure equivalent to μ. Moreover, $1_{\bar{A}} = 1_C P_A^* 1$.

Proof. It is a classical exercise to show that $\bar{A} = \{E[1_A \mid \mathscr{C}] > 0\}$ is the smallest set in $\mathscr{C}$ containing A. Now, by Proposition 2.5, the set $\{\sum_{n=0}^{\infty} T^n 1_A = \infty\}$ is invariant and contains A, hence $\bar{A}$. On the other hand, for every n,

$$\langle 1_{\bar{A}^c}, T^n 1_A \rangle = \langle T^{*n} 1_{\bar{A}^c}, 1_A \rangle = \langle 1_{\bar{A}^c}, 1_A \rangle = 0,$$

which implies that $\sum_0^{\infty} T^n 1_A = 0$ on $\bar{A}^c$ and therefore that $\{\sum_{n=0}^{\infty} T^n 1_A = \infty\} = \bar{A}$.

In the same way as in ch. 2, it is seen that $P_A^* 1$ is the smallest superharmonic function greater than 1_A; it is therefore equal to $1_{\bar{A}}$ on C.

Exercise 2.10. Use the results of this section to give another proof of some results in ch. 3 §1, namely that there is a partition $D, C_1, C_2, \ldots$ of the countable space E such that:

(i) $\sum_{n=0}^{\infty} P_n(x, y) < \infty$ for any x in E if $y \in D$;

(ii) $\sum_{n=0}^{\infty} P_n(x, y) = \infty$ or 0 if $x \in C_i$, according as y is in C_i or not.

Exercise 2.11. (1) Let P be a T.P. possessing a bounded invariant measure μ. Show that the contraction induced by P on $L^1(\mu)$ is conservative.

(2) If, in addition, E is countable, all the points with positive μ-measure are recurrent.

Exercise 2.12. Let T be a conservative contraction of $L^1(E, \mathscr{E}, \mu)$.

(1) Prove that a function f in L^1 belongs to the closure of the image of $I - T$ if and only if it is orthogonal to $L^\infty(E, \mathscr{C}, \mu)$.

(2) Given that f and g are two functions in $L^1(E, \mathscr{E}, \mu)$, prove that $n^{-1} \sum_{k=0}^{n-1} T^k(f - g)$ converges to zero in the L^1 sense as $n \to \infty$ if and only if, for every $C \in \mathscr{C}$,

$$\int_C f \, d\mu = \int_C g \, d\mu.$$

Exercise 2.13. Continuation of Exercise 1.10. Assume that τ is conservative and let $\mathscr{C}$ be the relevant σ-algebra of invariant sets. Prove that there is a function s in $L_{\mathbb{C}}^\infty$ and a set $\Gamma \in \mathscr{C}$ such that

(i) $|s| = 1$ μ-a.e. on Γ and $Tf = \bar{s}\tau(sf)$ for every $f \in L^1(\Gamma)$ (we denote by $L^1(A)$ the set of functions of L^1 vanishing outside A);

(ii) if $\Delta = E \backslash \Gamma$, $(I - T) L^1(\Delta)$ is dense in $L^1(\Delta)$;

(iii) this partition of E is unique up to equivalence;

(iv) a function r satisfies the properties stated for s if and only if there is a function $l \in L_{\mathbb{C}}^\infty(\mu)$ such that $|l| = 1$ μ-a.e. on Γ, $\tau^* l = l$ μ-a.e. on Γ, and $r = sl$.

Exercise 2.14. Let X be a Harris chain and, with the notations of ch. 3 § 2.19, call S_n the positive contraction of $L^1(m)$ induced by P_n^1. Prove that for every $f \in L^1(m)$,

$$\sum_0^\infty S_n f < + \infty \quad m\text{-a.e.}$$

Exercise 2.15. By using the sets $D_c = \{h_c > \frac{1}{2}\}$, where h_c has been defined in the proof of Proposition 2.8, prove that there exists an increasing sequence of sets D_c with union D such that $\sum_{n=0}^\infty T^{*n} 1_{D_c} < \infty$. Give an interpretation of this result when T is induced by a T.P.

Exercise 2.16. If P satisfies the equivalent conditions of ch. 3, Exercise 3.14 for every x in E, and if the contraction it induces on $L^1(E, \mathscr{E}, \nu)$ is conservative, the σ-algebra $\mathscr{C}$ is atomic.

Exercise 2.17. (1) If P is Harris with invariant measure m, prove that the contraction induced on $L^1(m)$ is conservative and ergodic. More generally the reader should compare the results in ch. 3 § 2 with Theorem 2.3 of the present section.

(2) Conversely, if P induces on the space $L^1(\nu)$ of a probability measure ν a conservative and ergodic contraction, and if the measures $P_n(x, \cdot)$ are not all singular relative to ν for every n, then P is Harris.

Exercise 2.18 (Another proof of Hopf's decomposition theorem). We assume that $\mu(E) < \infty$.
(1) For $c > 1$ and $f \in L_+^\infty$ with $\|f\|_\infty \leqslant 1$, set

$$h_c = \left(cf - \sum_{m=1}^\infty T^{*m}f\right)^+.$$

Show that on $\{h_c > 0\}$, $\sum_{n=0}^N T^*h_c \leqslant c^2$ for every integer N. Prove that the same inequality holds on $\{h_c = 0\}$, hence everywhere.
(2) When c tends to infinity, the sets $B_c = \{h_c \geqslant c^{-1}\}$ increase to

$$\{f > 0\} \cap \left\{\sum_{n \geqslant 1} T^{*n}f < \infty\right\};$$

prove that $\sum_{n \geqslant 0} T^{*n}1_{B_c} \in L^\infty$.
(3) Consider the family

$$\mathscr{B} = \left\{B \in \mathscr{E} : \sum_{n \geqslant 0} T^{*n}1_B \in L^\infty\right\};$$

it is closed under finite unions. Set $\mathbf{D} = \text{ess sup } \mathscr{B}$ and $\mathbf{C} = \mathbf{D}^c$, and prove that for $h \in L_+^\infty$ one has $\sum_{n \geqslant 0} T^{*n}h = 0$ or $+\infty$ on $\mathbf{C}$. Prove that $T^*1_{\mathbf{D}} = 0$ on $\mathbf{C}$.
(4) Prove that the partition of E into $\mathbf{C}$ and $\mathbf{D}$ is a Hopf's decomposition of E.

3. The Chacon-Ornstein theorem for conservative contractions and applications

Lemma 3.1. *Let g be a strictly positive element in $L^1(\mu)$; then for every f in $L^1(\mu)$*

$$\lim_n \left(T^nf \Big/ \sum_{m=0}^n T^mg\right) = 0 \quad \mu\text{-a.e.}$$

Proof. Let ν be the bounded measure $g\mu$, and for $\varepsilon > 0$, set

$$f_0 = f - \varepsilon g, \ldots, f_n = T^nf - \varepsilon\left(\sum_{m=0}^n T^mg\right), \qquad A_n = \{f_n > 0\}.$$

We have $f_n = Tf_{n-1} - \varepsilon g$, and consequently

$$f_n^+ = f_n 1_{A_n} \leqslant T f_{n-1}^+ - \varepsilon 1_{A_n} g,$$

which implies

$$\varepsilon \nu(A_n) \leqslant \langle T f_{n-1}^+, 1 \rangle - \langle f_n^+, 1 \rangle \leqslant \langle f_{n-1}^+, 1 \rangle - \langle f_n^+, 1 \rangle,$$

and summing up on n, we obtain

$$\varepsilon \sum_1^\infty \nu(A_n) \leqslant \int f^+ \, \mathrm{d}\mu < \infty.$$

By the Borel–Cantelli lemma we conclude that $\nu(\overline{\lim} \, A_n) = 0$, which completes the proof.

In the remainder of the section, the positive contraction T is assumed to be conservative.

Theorem 3.2 (Chacon–Ornstein theorem). *If T is conservative and g is a strictly positive element in $L^1(\mu)$, then for every element f in $L^1(\mu)$ the ratios $D_n(f, g)$ converge almost everywhere to $E[f \mid \mathscr{C}]/E[g \mid \mathscr{C}]$ as n tends to infinity.*

The meaning of the ratios of conditional expectations when μ is not bounded will be explained in the proof.

Proof. We first assume that μ is bounded. The principle of the proof is to show the result for larger and larger classes of functions.

(a) If $f = hg$ with h invariant, then by Lemma 2.7 we have $T^n f = h(T^n g)$; hence $D_n(f, g) = h$. The result follows at once since

$$E[hg \mid \mathscr{C}] = h E[g \mid \mathscr{C}].$$

(b) If $f = (I - T) k$ with $k \in L^1$, then $E[f \mid \mathscr{C}] = 0$; indeed

$$\langle h, f \rangle = \langle h, (I - T) k \rangle = 0$$

for every invariant h. Since $\sum_{m=0}^n T^m f = k - T^{n+1}k$, it suffices to show that $T^{n+1}k / \sum_0^n T^m g$ converges to zero as n tends to infinity, but this follows from Lemma 3.1 applied to $f = Tk$.

(c) The subspace L_g of L^1 of functions of the form $hg + (I - T) k$ is dense in L^1. Indeed, let l be an element of L^∞ orthogonal to L_g. Then $\langle l, (I - T) k \rangle = 0$ for every $k \in L^1$, which proves that $T^* l = l$, that is that l is invariant. Thus lg is in L_g, and therefore we have also $\langle l, lg \rangle = \int l^2 g \, \mathrm{d}\mu = 0$, which shows that $l = 0$, since g is strictly positive.

It remains thus to show the result for the functions in the closure L_g of L_g.

Let $\{f_p\}$ be a sequence of elements in L^1 such that $\sum_p \|f_p\|_1 < +\infty$. By a classical application of the Borel–Cantelli lemma the sequence $\{f_p\}$ converges to zero a.s. and we claim that the sequence $\sup_n |D_n(f_p, g)|$ converges also to zero a.s. Pick $\varepsilon > 0$; by the maximal ergodic lemma applied to $|f_p| - \varepsilon g$ it follows that

$$\varepsilon \sum_p \int_{E_{|f_p|-\varepsilon g}} g \, d\mu \leqslant \sum_p \int |f_p| \, d\mu < \infty.$$

By the Borel–Cantelli lemma,

$$(g\mu)\left(\overline{\lim_p} \, E_{|f_p|-\varepsilon g}\right) = 0,$$

which proves that $\sup_n D_n(f_p, g)$ converges to zero μ-a.e. as p tends to infinity.

Let now f be in L_g; we may find a sequence of functions f_p in L_g converging to f in the L^1-sense and such that $\sum_p \|f - f_p\|_1 < \infty$ (this may be achieved by taking a sub-sequence); we have therefore

$$\lim_p \sup_n D_n(f - f_p, g) = 0 \quad \text{a.s.}$$

But

$$|D_n(f, g) - E[f \mid \mathscr{C}]/E[g \mid \mathscr{C}]| \leqslant |D_n(f_p, g) - E[f_p \mid \mathscr{C}]/E[g \mid \mathscr{C}]|$$
$$+ \sup_n |D_n(f - f_p, g)| + |E[f - f_p \mid \mathscr{C}]/E[g \mid \mathscr{C}]|.$$

If we let n and then p tend to infinity, we see that on the right-hand side of the inequality the first term converges to zero because f_p is in L_g, the second one on account of the above remark and the third one because the conditional expectation is a continuous operator for the L^1-norm. The proof is thus complete for the case in which μ is a bounded measure.

When μ is unbounded, the conditional expectations are no longer meaningful. For instance, if $\mathscr{C}$ contains an atom B such that $\mu(B) = \infty$, the conditional expectation of a function $f \in L^1_+$ should be constant on B, which is impossible, since we should then have $\int_B E[f \mid \mathscr{C}] \, d\mu = 0$ or $+\infty$, whereas $0 < \int_B f \, d\mu < \infty$. This is due to the fact that the restriction of μ to $\mathscr{C}$ is not bound to be σ-finite, and therefore that the Radon–Nykodim theorem does not apply. This difficulty will be dealt with in the following way.

Suppose now that μ is σ-finite, and let h be a strictly positive function in $L^1(\mu)$; call μ' the bounded measure $h\mu$ which is equivalent to μ. A function

f is in $L^1(\mu')$ if and only if hf is in $L^1(\mu)$. For $f \in L^1(\mu')$, we define $T'f = h^{-1}T(fh)$; T' is a positive and conservative contraction of $L^1(\mu')$, as is easily seen. Moreover, the spaces $L^\infty(\mu)$ and $L^\infty(\mu')$ are identical, and the adjoint contraction of T' is still T^*, since

$$\langle T'f, g \rangle_{\mu'} = \langle T(fh), g \rangle_\mu = \langle f, T^*g \rangle_{\mu'}.$$

The σ-algebra of invariant sets is thus the same for T and T', and for $f, g \in L^1(\mu')$ such that $\{g > 0\} = E$,

$$\lim_n D'_n(f, g) = E_{\mu'}[f \mid \mathscr{C}]/E_{\mu'}[g \mid \mathscr{C}] \quad \mu\text{-a.e.}$$

Let f, g be now in $L^1(\mu)$ and such that $\{g > 0\} = E$; by applying the preceding result to f/h and g/h, we find that

$$\lim_n D_n(f, g) = E_{\mu'}[f/h \mid \mathscr{C}]/E_{\mu'}[g/h \mid \mathscr{C}] \quad \mu\text{-a.e.}$$

The ratio on the right-hand side thus does not depend on the particular function h – this can be seen directly – and we say that it is equal to $E_\mu[f \mid \mathscr{C}]/E_\mu[g \mid \mathscr{C}]$, thus defining the ratio of two conditional expectations even if conditional expectations themselves are meaningless. The proof of the Chacon–Ornstein theorem is now complete.

The hypothesis of the Chacon–Ornstein theorem may be weakened in several ways that we shall indicate in the sequel and in the exercises. We prove below that it is not necessary to take g strictly positive.

Indeed if we call $A = \{g > 0\}$, the set $\bar{A}$ being in $\mathscr{C}$, then by the same argument as below Proposition 2.8, we may restrict T to $\bar{A}$ and then apply the Chacon–Ornstein theorem to the functions g and $E[g \mid \mathscr{C}]$, since the latter is strictly positive on $\bar{A}$. We thus find that $D_n(g, E[g \mid \mathscr{C}])$ tends to 1 on $\bar{A}$. If f is now any function in L^1, by considering the product

$$D_n(f, E[g \mid \mathscr{C}]) \, D_n(E[g \mid \mathscr{C}], g)$$

we obtain, on account of Lemma 2.9, the following.

Proposition 3.3. *If T is conservative and g positive, for every function f in L^1, the ratio $D_n(f, g)$ converges a.e. to $E[f \mid \mathscr{C}]/E[g \mid \mathscr{C}]$ on the set*

$$\{E[g \mid \mathscr{C}] > 0\} = \left\{ \sum_0^\infty T^n g = \infty \right\}.$$

If we think of the case in which T is induced by a T.P., we see that we have obtained a theorem about T, but that it is T^* which has probabilistic significance. It is therefore advisable to prove an ergodic theorem for T^*. To this end we shall need an additional hypothesis.

Let h be a positive finite function in $\mathscr{E}$, not necessarily in L^1. We can still define Th as the limit of the sequence Th_n, where $\{h_n\}$ is a sequence of L^1-functions increasing to h. The function Th does not depend on the particular sequence $\{h_n\}$; indeed if $\{g_p\}$ is another sequence increasing to h,

$$\lim_n Th_n \geqslant \lim_n T(h_n \wedge g) = Tg_p,$$

since $\{h_n \wedge g_p\}$ converges to g_p in L^1 for every p. The conclusion is now clear. This enables us to state

Theorem 3.4. *If T is conservative, and if there exists a finite and strictly positive function h (not necessarily in L^1), and such that $Th \leqslant h$ μ-a.e., then for every pair f, g of functions in $L^1(h\mu)$, the ratios*

$$\sum_0^n T^{*m}f \bigg/ \sum_0^n T^{*m}g$$

converge μ-a.e. to $E[fh \mid \mathscr{C}]/E[gh \mid \mathscr{C}]$ on the set $\{E[gh \mid \mathscr{C}] > 0\}$.

Proof. We first note that the space $\mathscr{H} = \{f \in L^1 : f/h \in L^\infty\}$ is dense in L^1. Indeed f/h is in L^∞ if and only if there is a constant M such that $|f| < Mh$ a.e.; if g is in L_+^1, the functions $g_n = g \wedge nh$ are in $\mathscr{H}$ and increase to g, hence converge to g in the L^1 sense.

Next, for $f \in \mathscr{H}$, set $Sf = hT^*(g/h)$; for $f \geqslant 0$ we have

$$\|Sf\|_1 = \int h \, T^*(f/h) \, d\mu = \int Th(f/h) \, d\mu \leqslant \int f \, d\mu,$$

and consequently the operator S may be uniquely extended into a positive contraction of $L^1(\mu)$. We shall try to apply the Chacon–Ornstein theorem to S.

For this purpose we first notice that T and S play completely symmetric roles. If $f \in L_+^\infty$ and $g \in \mathscr{H}$, we have

$$\langle S^*f, g \rangle = \langle f, Sg \rangle = \langle f, hT^*(g/h) \rangle$$

$$= \langle fh, T^*(g/h) \rangle = \langle T(fh), g/h \rangle,$$

which proves that for f in $\mathscr{H}$ we have $Tf = hS^*(f/h)$. (Note that $Sh \leqslant h$.)

Let now f be a strictly positive element in L^1, and suppose that the set $A = \{\sum_0^\infty S^n f < \infty\}$ is of positive μ-measure; then there is a function g vanishing outside A, such that

$$\langle \mu, g \rangle > 0 \quad \text{and} \quad \left\langle g, \sum_{n=0}^\infty S^n f \right\rangle < \infty.$$

By duality, this implies that

$$\left\langle g, h \sum_{n=0}^\infty T^{*n}(f/h) \right\rangle = \left\langle h^{-1} \sum_{n=0}^\infty T^n(gh), f \right\rangle < \infty;$$

but this is a contradiction since the series in the right-hand side diverges a.e. As a result, S is a conservative contraction.

In addition the invariant functions are the same for S and T. Indeed, let g be a bounded function invariant for T; on account of Lemma 2.7, it is easily checked that $T(gh) = g\, Th$, hence that $S^*g = g\, Th/h \leqslant g$. The function g is thus invariant for S and we conclude from the symmetric roles played by S and T.

The theorem then follows by applying the Chacon–Ornstein theorem to S.

When T is induced by a T.P., we have already noticed (cf. Exercise 1.8) that if μ is excessive, then the hypotheses of the preceding theorem are satisfied with $h = 1$; in that case $S = T^* = P$. We may thus apply the above theorem to a Harris T.P. In that case it is plain that S, hence T, is conservative, and on the other hand the σ-algebra $\mathscr{C}$ is trivial as a consequence of ch. 3, Proposition 3.6; in this situation, if $g \in L^1_+(m)$, the set $\{E[g \mid \mathscr{C}] > 0\}$ is either equal to E or to θ according to whether $m(g)$ is > 0 or zero. Since

$$T^{*n}f(x) = P_n f(x) = E_x[f(X_n)],$$

the above theorem then yields

Theorem 3.5. *If X is a Harris chain with invariant measure m and if f, g are in $L^1_+(m)$ with $m(g) > 0$, then*

$$\lim_n E. \left[\sum_{k=0}^n f(X_k) \right] \Big/ E. \left[\sum_{k=0}^n g(X_k) \right] = m(f)/m(g) \quad m\text{-a.e.}$$

If X is an irreducible recurrent discrete chain, the empty set is the only set of measure zero, so that the above convergence holds everywhere. If f and g are characteristic functions of sets in $\mathscr{E}$, the preceding theorem expresses that the ratio of the mean times spent by the chain in these two sets tends eventually to the ratio of their measures. This result will be sharpened in ch. 6. We proceed with another application to Harris chains.

Let X be a canonical chain recurrent in the sense of Harris, with invariant measure m. The map $T: Z \rightarrow T \circ \theta$ is a positive contraction of $L^1(\Omega, \mathscr{F}, P_m)$, since by the Markov property, we have

$$\int_\Omega Z \circ \theta \, dP_m = \int_E m(dx) \, E_x[Z \circ \theta] = \int_E m \, P(dx) \, E_x[Z] = \int_\Omega Z \, dP_m.$$

We claim that this contraction is conservative and ergodic. If $m(A) > 0$ and if $Z = 1_A(X_0)$, then by ch. 3 § 3,

$$\sum_{n=0}^{\infty} T^n Z = \sum_{n=0}^{\infty} 1_A(X_n) = \infty \quad P_m\text{-a.e.}$$

On the other hand the sets

$$\left\{ \sum_{n=0}^{\infty} T^n Z = \infty \right\} = \left\{ \sum_{n=0}^{\infty} Z \circ \theta_n = \infty \right\}$$

are invariant by θ, hence equal P_m-a.e. to Ω or to $\emptyset$.

Theorem 3.6. *Let* f, g *be in* $L^1_+(E, \mathscr{E}, m)$ *with* $m(g) > 0$, *then the ratios* $\sum_0^n f(X_k)/\sum_0^n g(X_k)$ *converge* P_v-*a.s. to* $m(f)/m(g)$ *for any probability measure* v.

Proof. Let Λ be the set of ω's for which the above ratios converge to the assigned limit, that is

$$\Lambda = \left\{ \omega \in \Omega : \lim \sum_0^n f(X_k(\omega)) \Big/ \sum_0^n g(X_k(\omega)) = m(f)/m(g) \right\}.$$

By the above discussion and the Chacon–Ornstein theorem we have $P_m[\Lambda^c] = 0$. On the other hand it is easily seen that the equivalence class of the set Λ is invariant by θ, so that, by the results in ch. 3 § 3, the function $P.[\Lambda]$ is identically zero or one. The proof is now easily completed.

In ch. 3, Theorem 1.10, we have shown, for recurrent discrete chains, the existence of a dual chain which is also recurrent. Our final result aims at extending this property.

Theorem 3.7. *If* P *is a Harris T.P., and if the invariant measure* m *has the approximation property with respect to a compact class, there exists at least one transition probability* $\hat{P}$ *which is Harris and in duality with* P *with respect to* m.

Proof. We have already seen that the operator $S: f \to Pf$ is a positive contraction of $L^1(m)$. By Proposition 1.6, there exists a T.P. denoted by $\hat{P}$ such that $m\hat{P} \ll m$ and $Sf = \mathrm{d}(fm)\,\hat{P}/\mathrm{d}m$. If f and g are in $b\mathscr{E} \cap L^1_+(m)$ we have, confusing functions and equivalence classes of functions,

$$\langle Pf, g \rangle = \langle Sf, g \rangle = \int_E g \frac{\mathrm{d}(fm)\,\hat{P}}{\mathrm{d}m}\,\mathrm{d}m = \langle f, \hat{P}g \rangle,$$

and therefore $\hat{P}$ is in duality with P with respect to m. Now by ch. 3, Theorem 2.16, there exists a modification of $\hat{P}$ which satisfies the required conditions.

Remarks. (1) A similar statement may be obtained without the hypothesis that P is Harris.

(2) Every Harris chain on a Polish space such that m has the approximation property with respect to compact sets has a dual chain which is also Harris. It may have several Harris dual chains, but in some cases, for instance random walks, one of them has a canonical character.

Exercise 3.8. (1) Using Exercise 1.7, prove that in Lemma 2.7 one may drop the assumption that h is bounded, and take h merely $\mathscr{C}$-measurable.

(2) Prove that the Chacon–Ornstein theorem is still true if f, g are not supposed integrable but merely such that $E[f \mid \mathscr{C}] < \infty$ and $E[g \mid \mathscr{C}] < \infty$. [*Hint*: $f/E[f \mid \mathscr{C}]$ is integrable.]

Exercise 3.9 (Doeblin's ratio limit theorem). Let X be discrete and irreducible recurrent; then for any four states x, y, z, t show that

$$\lim_n \left(\sum_0^n P_k(x, y) \middle/ \sum_0^n P_k(z, t) \right) = m(y)/m(t);$$

[*Hint*: Use the dual chain.]

Exercise 3.10. (1) (Birkhoff's theorem). Let θ be a point transformation on the space $(E, \mathscr{E}, m)$, where m is a probability measure invariant by θ. Let $\mathscr{I}$ be the σ-algebra of sets A such that $A = \theta^{-1}(A)$ m-a.s. Show that for every function f in $L^1(m)$,

$$\lim_n (n+1)^{-1} \sum_0^n f \circ \theta^m = E[f \mid \mathscr{I}]$$

m-a.s. and in the L^1 sense.

[*Hint*: To show the convergence in the L^1 sense start with bounded functions.]

(2) If θ is the shift operator of a canonical Markov chain, under what condition on ν does the space $(\Omega, \mathscr{F}, P_\nu)$ satisfy the conditions of (1)? Give an interpretation of the result in (1) for $f = 1_A(X_0)$, where $A \in \mathscr{E}$.

(3) Use (1) and the space $(W, \mathscr{A}, P)$ of ch. 1, Exercise 4.12 to give a proof of the law of large numbers.

Exercise 3.11. (1) Let f, g be in L_+^1 and set $h = \sup_n D_n(f, g)$. Show that, for $p > 1$, one gets

$$\|h\|_p \leqslant (p/(p-1)) \|f/g\|_p$$

where the norm is that of $L^p(E, \mathscr{E}, g\mu)$.

[*Hint*: Prove that

$$\int_{\{h>a\}} f \, d\mu \geqslant a \int_{\{h>a\}} g \, d\mu$$

and integrate this inequality with respect to the measure $p a^{p-2} \, da$ on $[0, \infty[$.]

(2) Given that T is conservative and g strictly positive, prove that

$$\lim_n D_n(f, g) = E[f \mid \mathscr{C}]/E[g \mid \mathscr{C}]$$

in the sense of $L^p(E, \mathscr{E}, g\mu)$, provided that $f/g \in L^p(E, \mathscr{E}, g\mu)$.

(3) By using the restriction of the Lebesgue measure to $[1, \infty[$ and the inequality $a \log b \leqslant a \log^+ a + b e^{-1}$, solve the same problem for $p = 1$ and prove that the convergence holds in the sense of $L^1(g\mu)$ provided that

$$\int f g^{-1} \log^+(f g^{-1}) g \, d\mu < \infty.$$

Exercise 3.12 (Continuation of Exercise 2.13). Let g be a real, strictly positive function in L^1 and f any element in L_C^∞. Prove that the ratio $\sum_1^n T^k f / \sum_1^n \tau^k g$ converges μ-a.s. to a $\mathscr{C}$-measurable limit $l(f, g)$. Moreover, for every $C \in \mathscr{C}$, show that

$$\lim_n \int_C s \, T^n f \, d\mu = \int_C s \, l(f, g) g \, d\mu.$$

Exercise 3.13. Prove that if $Th \leqslant h$ and if T is conservative, then $Th = h$.

Exercise 3.14. Use the notation and situation of Theorem 3.4, but assume that T is no longer conservative; prove that the dissipative parts of E for T and S are equal.

Exercise 3.15. Prove Theorem 3.5 by a direct use of the Chacon–Ornstein theorem and ch. 2, Exercise 3.17.

[*Hint*: To prove that $\mathscr{C}$ is trivial, use the results in ch. 3 § 3.]

Exercise 3.16. Let μ be a probability measure on a group G; the random walk of law μ ($\hat\mu$) is supposed to be recurrent but not necessarily Harris. Recall that the convolution by μ ($\hat\mu$) is a positive contraction of $L^1(m_G)$.

(1) Prove that these contractions are conservative. Derive that $G(\cdot, A) = \infty$ m_G-a.e. if and only if $m_G(A) > 0$; otherwise it is zero m_G-a.e.

(2) The corresponding σ-algebras $\mathscr{C}$ are trivial, in other words, if $f \in b\mathscr{E}$ and $f = f * \mu$ m_G-a.e., then f is constant m_G-a.e.

(3) Prove in this setting a result similar to Theorem 3.5.

(4) Derive from (1) and (2) that if $\nu \ll m_G$ and $A \in \mathscr{E}$, then $P_\nu[R(A)] = 0$ or 1 according as $m_G(A)$ is positive or zero. (See ch. 3, Exercise 3.14.)

Exercise 3.17. Let P be a T.P. and m a σ-finite measure such that $mP \ll m$. If the contraction induced by P on $L^1(m)$ is conservative and ergodic, and if there is a set O in $\mathscr{E}$ such that $m(O) > 0$ and for $x \in O$, $U_c(x, \cdot)$ is not singular relative to m, then there is an absorbing set F such that $m(F^c) = 0$ and the restriction of P to F is Harris.

4. Brunel's lemma and the general Chacon-Ornstein theorem

In this section, we give another method of proof, which will enable us to state the Chacon–Ornstein theorem in a slightly more general fashion. This method also sheds more light on the relationship with the potential theory of ch. 2. Finally, it is easily extended to resolvents, as will be seen in the exercises at the end of the section.

We could write this section independently of the results in §§ 2 and 3, but this would involve repeating some definitions and proofs already given, and therefore we shall not do so. As before, T is a positive contraction of $L^1(E, \mathscr{E}, \mu)$.

Theorem 4.1 (Brunel's maximal ergodic lemma). *For $f \in L^1(\mu)$ and any set*

$$A \subset E_f' = \left\{ \varlimsup_n \sum_{k=0}^{k=n} T^k f \geqslant 0 \right\},$$

we have

$$\int f P_A^* 1 \, d\mu \geqslant 0.$$

Proof. Let h be a strictly positive element of L^1, and assume that for $\varepsilon > 0$, we have

$$\sum_0^n T^k f \geqslant \varepsilon \sum_0^n T^k h$$

on A for infinitely many n. If $g_m = \sum_0^m (TI_{A^c})^k f$, we have

$$f = 1_A g_m + (TI_{A^c})^{m+1} f + 1_{A^c} g_m - (TI_{A^c}) g_m,$$

and consequently

$$\sum_0^n T^k f = \sum_0^n T^k (1_A g_m + (TI_{A^c})^{m+1} f) + 1_{A^c} g_m - T^{n+1}(1_{A^c} g_m).$$

Dividing by $\sum_{k=0}^n T^k h$, we see easily that, on the set A,

$$\frac{\sum_{k=0}^n T^k (1_A g_m + (TI_{A^c})^{m+1} f)}{\sum_{k=0}^n T^k h} \geqslant \varepsilon + \frac{T^{n+1}(1_{A^c} g_m)}{\sum_{k=0}^n T^k h}$$

for infinitely many n. Since $1_A g_m + (TI_{A^c})^{m+1} f$ is in $L^1(\mu)$, we derive from Lemma 3.1 that

$$A \subset E_{1_A g_m + (TI_{A^c})^{m+1} f} = E_m;$$

since $P_A^* 1$ is superharmonic, the maximal ergodic Lemma 2.1 yields

$$\int_{E_m} (1_A g_m + (TI_{A^c})^{m+1} f) \, P_A^* 1 \, d\mu \geqslant 0.$$

It follows that

$$\int_E f \left(\sum_0^m (I_{A^c} T^*)^k 1_A \right) d\mu = \int_E 1_A g_m \, d\mu$$

$$= \int_{E_m} 1_A g_m P_A^* 1 \, d\mu \geqslant - \int_{E_m} P_A^* 1 (TI_{A^c})^{m+1} |f| \, d\mu$$

$$\geqslant - \int_E |f| (I_{A^c} T^*)^{m+1} P_A^* 1 \, d\mu.$$

When m tends to infinity, the last term tends to zero, and the first one to $\int_E f P_A^* 1 \, d\mu$, which gives, in that case, the desired conclusion. Now the function $f + \varepsilon h$ always satisfies the requirements of the beginning of the proof; thus

$$\int (f + \varepsilon h) P_A^* 1 \, d\mu \geqslant 0,$$

and since ε is arbitrary the proof is complete.

Our next step is to use the above result to show the existence of a limit for the ratios D_n.

Proposition 4.2. *If* $f \in L^1(\mu)$ *and* $g \in L^1_+(\mu)$, *the sequence* $\{D_n(f, g)\}$ *has* μ-*a.e. a finite limit on the set* $\{\sum_0^\infty T^n g > 0\}$.

Proof. Set

$$A = \{T^n g > 0\} \cap \{\overline{\lim} \, D_n(f, g) = +\infty\}.$$

For every real number $c > 0$, one has $A \subset E'_{f-cg}$; hence by Theorem 4.1,

$$\int f \, P_A^* 1 \, d\mu \geqslant c \int g \, P_A^* 1 \, d\mu.$$

Since $T^* P_A^* 1 \leqslant P_A^* 1$, one has furthermore

$$\int f \, P_A^* 1 \, d\mu \geqslant c \int g \, T^{*n} P_A^* 1 \, d\mu = c \int T^n g \, P_A^* 1 \, d\mu.$$

Since $T^n g$ is strictly positive on A and $P_A^* 1 \geqslant 1_A$, by taking c arbitrarily large we see that $\mu(A) = 0$. As a result, $\overline{\lim} \, D_n(f, g)$ is finite μ-a.e. on

$$\bigcup_0^\infty \{T^n g > 0\} = \left\{ \sum_0^\infty T^n g > 0 \right\}.$$

Let a, b be two rational numbers such that $a < b$. The set

$$A = \{T^n g > 0\} \cap \{\underline{\lim} \, D_n(f, g) < a, \, \overline{\lim} \, D_n(f, g) > b\}$$

is contained in $E'_{ag-f} \cap E'_{f-bg}$ so that, by Theorem 4.1,

$$\int (ag - f) \, P_A^* 1 \, d\mu \geqslant 0 \quad \text{and} \quad \int (f - bg) \, P_A^* 1 \, d\mu \geqslant 0;$$

summing up these two inequalities gives

$$(a - b) \int g \, P_A^* 1 \, d\mu \geqslant 0,$$

which is impossible unless the integral is zero. But

$$\int g\, P_A^* 1\, \mathrm{d}\mu \geqslant \int g\, T^{*n} P_A^* 1\, \mathrm{d}\mu = \int T^n g\, P_A^* 1\, \mathrm{d}\mu$$

which is > 0 unless A is negligible. The proof is thus complete.

We then derive Hopf's decomposition theorem.

Theorem 4.3. *There exists a set C, unique up to equivalence, such that for every f in L_+^1,*

$$\sum_0^\infty T^n f = 0 \quad or + \infty \quad on\ C,$$

$$\sum_0^\infty T^n f < + \infty \qquad on\ D = C^c.$$

Proof. Let h be a strictly positive element of L^1, and set $C = \{\sum_0^\infty T^n h = \infty\}$. If $f \in L_+^1$, the preceding proposition applied to $D_n(f, h)$ implies that $\sum_0^\infty T^n f = + \infty$ on $C \cap \{\sum_0^\infty T^n f > 0\}$; applied to $D_n(h, f)$, it implies that $\sum_0^\infty T^n f < + \infty$ on D. The proof is complete, since it is now plain that C is independent of the choice of h.

As in §§ 2 and 3, one may restrict T to C and define the σ-algebra $\mathscr{C}$ of invariant sets. We are now going to identify the limit, the existence of which was shown in Proposition 4.2.

Proposition 4.4. *If T is conservative, the limit in Proposition 4.2 is equal to $E[f \mid \mathscr{C}]/E[g \mid \mathscr{C}]$.*

Proof. We assume that μ is bounded; the extension to σ-finite μ, as well as the definition for that case of the ratios of conditional expectations, is dealt with as in Theorem 3.2.

We may also assume f positive. Given two real numbers a, b such that $0 \leqslant a < b < \infty$, we will prove that

$$a \leqslant E[f \mid \mathscr{C}]/E[g \mid \mathscr{C}] \leqslant b \quad \mu\text{-a.e.}$$

on the set $A = \{a \leqslant \lim D_n(f, g) \leqslant b\}$; this will imply the desired conclusion, because simple functions which approximate $\lim D_n(f, g)$ will also approximate μ-a.s. the ratio of conditional expectations.

Since this ratio is $\mathscr{C}$-measurable we must prove that it lies between a and b on the set $\bar{A}$, hence that for $B \in \mathscr{C}$, $B \subset \bar{A}$ we have

$$\int_B (E[f \mid \mathscr{C}] - a\, E[g \mid \mathscr{C}])\, \mathrm{d}\mu \geqslant 0 \quad \text{and} \quad \int_B (b\, E[g \mid \mathscr{C}] - E[f \mid \mathscr{C}])\, \mathrm{d}\mu \geqslant 0,$$

which is equivalent to

$$\int_B (f - ag)\, \mathrm{d}\mu \geqslant 0 \quad \text{and} \quad \int_B (bg - f)\, \mathrm{d}\mu \geqslant 0.$$

But $B = \overline{B \cap A}$, otherwise $B \backslash \overline{B \cap A}$ would be an invariant set contained in $\bar{A}$ and in A^c, which is impossible by definition of $\bar{A}$; therefore $1_B = P^*_{A \cap B}1$. The above integrals may thus be written

$$\int P^*_{A \cap B}1\,(f - ag)\, \mathrm{d}\mu \quad \text{and} \quad \int P^*_{A \cap B}1\,(bg - f)\, \mathrm{d}\mu;$$

it follows from Theorem 4.1 and the definition of A that they are positive, thus completing the proof.

Now let T be such that the conservative and dissipative parts are non-empty. For $f, g \in L^1_+$, it is plain that $D_n(f, g)$ converges on $\boldsymbol{D} \cap \{\sum_0^\infty T^n g > 0\}$ to $\sum_0^\infty T^n f / \sum_0^\infty T^n g$. If f, g vanish on $\boldsymbol{D}$, then the preceding result gives the limit on $\boldsymbol{C}$. In order to find this limit when these functions do not vanish on $\boldsymbol{D}$, we introduce the operator $H_C = I_C \sum_0^\infty (TI_D)^n$, which is adjoint to P^*_C and similar to the operator $\hat{H}_C$ of ch. 2. For $g \in L^1_+$, the functions $H_C g$ vanish on $\boldsymbol{D}$, and if g vanishes on $\boldsymbol{D}$, then $H_C g = g$. Furthermore

Proposition 4.5. *The ratio $D_n(H_C g, g)$ converges to 1 on $\boldsymbol{C} \cap \{\sum_0^\infty T^n g > 0\}$ whenever n tends to infinity.*

Proof. On $\boldsymbol{C}$, the ratios $D_n(H_C g, g)$ and $D_n(T^k H_C g, T^k g)$ have the same limit. For $a > 1$, the set $\{\lim D_n(H_C g, g) \geqslant a\}$ is contained in $E'_{H_C g - ag}$. If

$$A \subset \{T^k g > 0\} \cap \{\lim D_n(H_C g, g) \geqslant a\},$$

Theorem 4.1 implies that

$$\int P^*_A 1\,(T^k H_C g - aT^k g)\, \mathrm{d}\mu \geqslant 0.$$

But on the one hand P_A^*1 is harmonic for T^*, since $P_A^*1 = 1_{\bar{A}}$ on C and $T^*P_A^*1 = P_A^*1$ on D, as is easily checked; on the other hand, since $C \supset A$, we have $P_C^* P_A^*1 = P_A^*1$. Thus we may write

$$\langle P_A^*1, T^k H_C g \rangle = \langle T^{*k} P_A^*1, H_C g \rangle = \langle P_A^*1, H_C g \rangle$$

$$= \langle P_C^* P_A^*1, g \rangle = \langle P_A^*1, g \rangle,$$

$$= \langle T^{*k} P_A^*1, g \rangle = \langle P_A^*1, T^k g \rangle,$$

and consequently the above inequality involving integrals reduces to

$$(1 - a) \int P_A^*1 \, T^k g \, \mathrm{d}\mu \geqslant 0,$$

which is impossible unless P_A^*1, and hence A, is negligible. That the limit cannot be less than one is shown in the same way.

We are now ready to summarize all these results and state the general form of the Chacon–Ornstein theorem.

Theorem 4.6. *If f, g are in $L_+^1(\mu)$, the sequence of ratios $D_n(f, g)$ converges μ-a.e. as n tends to infinity to*

$$\sum_0^\infty T^n f \bigg/ \sum_0^\infty T^n g \quad \text{on } D \cap \left\{ \sum_0^\infty T^n g > 0 \right\},$$

$$E[H_C f \mid \mathscr{C}]/E[H_C g \mid \mathscr{C}] \quad \text{on } C \cap \left\{ \sum_0^\infty T^n g > 0 \right\}.$$

Proof. By the preceding proposition,

$$\lim D_n(f, g) = \lim D_n(H_C f, H_C g),$$

and since $H_C f$ and $H_C g$ vanish outside C, the result follows from Proposition 4.4.

Exercise 4.7 (Ergodic theory for Abel sums). (1) Let T be a positive contraction of L^1 and set, for $\lambda \in [0, 1]$,

$$G_\lambda = \sum_0^\infty \lambda^n T^n.$$

For $f \in L^1$, set $E_f'' = \{\lim_{\lambda \to 1} G_\lambda f > 0\}$. Prove that E_f'' is measurable, that $E_f'' \subset E_f'$, and derive that if $A \subset E_f''$, then

$$\int_A P_A^* 1 \, f \, \mathrm{d}\mu \geqslant 0.$$

(2) If T is conservative, then for $f, g \in L_+^1$ the ratio $D_\lambda(f, g) = G_\lambda f / G_\lambda g$ converges μ-a.e., when λ tends to 1, to $E[f \mid \mathscr{C}]/E[g \mid \mathscr{C}]$ on $\{G_1 g > 0\}$. For the case in which T is not conservative, prove a result similar to Theorem 4.6.

(3) Let $\{V_\alpha\}_{\alpha > 0}$ be a Harris resolvent with invariant measure m; prove that if f, g are in $L_+^1(m)$, with $m(g) > 0$, then

$$\lim_{\alpha \to 0} (V_\alpha f / V_\alpha g) = m(f)/m(g) \quad m\text{-a.e.}$$

CHAPTER 5

TRANSIENT RANDOM WALKS. RENEWAL THEORY

This chapter is devoted to the study of transient random walks on abelian groups, that is, mainly to renewal theory and its applications. For non-abelian groups the results which are presently available are far from being as complete as in the abelian case. In the first section we show the fundamental theorem of Choquet and Deny. The renewal theorem will be shown in §§3 and 4, and will be applied to the study of hitting probabilities and recurrent sets in the last section.

1. The theorem of Choquet and Deny

For a random walk on an abelian group, the theorem of Choquet and Deny asserts that all bounded continuous harmonic functions are constant. We shall need the following

Lemma 1.1. *Let T_1 and T_2 be two commuting contractions of a Banach space B. If α_1 and α_2 are two positive real numbers such that $\alpha_1 + \alpha_2 = 1$ and $(\alpha_1 T_1 + \alpha_2 T_2) x = x$ for some $x \in B$, then $T_1 x = T_2 x = x$.*

Proof. If T is a contraction of B, then

$$\lim_n \| (I - T) \exp[- n(I - T)] \| = 0.$$

Indeed,

$$\exp[- n(I - T)] = \sum_{j \geqslant 0} \alpha_{j,n} T^j,$$

where $\alpha_{j,n} = n^j / e^n j!$. For fixed n, the sequence $\alpha_{j,n}$ increases up to $j = n$ and then decreases. Therefore

$$\| (I - T) \exp[- n(I - T)] \| \leqslant \sum_j |\alpha_{j,n} - \alpha_{j-1,n}| \leqslant 2\alpha_{n,n},$$

and the Stirling formula shows that $\alpha_{n,n}$ tends to zero as n tends to infinity.

133

Let us now set $S = \alpha_1 T_1 + \alpha_2 T_2$; as T_1 and T_2 commute, we have

$$\exp[-\alpha_1^{-1}]\exp[\alpha_1^{-1}S] = \exp[-(I - T_1)]\exp[1 - \alpha_1^{-1}]\exp[(\alpha_1^{-1} - 1)T_2],$$

and taking the nth power,

$$\exp[-n\alpha_1^{-1}]\exp[n\alpha_1^{-1}S] = \exp[-n(I - T_1)]U^n,$$

where U is a contraction. From $Sx = x$ we get

$$x = \exp[-n(I - T_1)]U^n x,$$

$$(I - T_1)x = (I - T_1)\exp[-n(I - T_1)]U^n x,$$

and letting n tend to infinity yields $(I - T_1)x = 0$.

We shall now prove the theorem of Choquet and Deny in a slightly more general setting. Let S be a locally compact separable semi-group, and μ a probability measure on S. As usual, a Borel function h on S is called μ-harmonic if

$$h(x) = \int_S h(xy)\,\mu(dy).$$

Theorem 1.2. *If S is abelian and if g belongs to the support of μ, then $h(xg) = h(x)$ for all $x \in S$ and all bounded continuous μ-harmonic functions.*

Proof. Let g be a point in the support of μ and V_n, $n \in N$, a basis of neighbourhoods of g. For each n, the restriction μ_n of μ to V_n is non-zero; hence if h is a bounded, continuous harmonic function, we can write

$$h(x) = \|\mu_n\| \int_S h(xy)\,\|\mu_n\|^{-1}\,\mu_n(dy)$$

$$+ \|\mu - \mu_n\| \int_S h(xy)\,\|\mu - \mu_n\|^{-1}\,(\mu - \mu_n)\,(dy).$$

For every probability measure ν on S, the mapping $h \to Th$, where

$$Th(x) = \int h(xy)\,\nu(dy)$$

is a positive contraction on the Banach space of bounded continuous functions. The semi-group S being abelian, we may apply the preceding lemma and find that

$$h(x) = \int_S h(xy) \, \|\mu_n\|^{-1} \, \mu_n(\mathrm{d}y).$$

But as n tends to infinity, the sequence $\|\mu_n\|^{-1} \mu_n$ converges weakly to ε_g, so that $h(x) = h(xg)$ for all $x \in S$, and the proof is complete.

From now on we study a random walk of law μ on an abelian separable locally compact group G. We shall denote by e or 0 the identity of G, and by m a Haar measure of G. We suppose that, as usual, μ satisfies ch. 3, Hypothesis 4.2. In this context, the preceding result reads as follows.

Theorem 1.3 (Choquet–Deny theorem). *The bounded continuous harmonic functions are constant.*

Proof. It is easily checked that the set of points y in G such that $h(x + y) = h(x)$ for all x in G and every bounded continuous harmonic function h is a closed sub-group of G. The result thus follows immediately from Theorem 1.2 and ch. 3, Hypothesis 4.2.

This theorem implies the following corollaries.

Corollary 1.4. *If v is an invariant measure for X (i.e. $\mu * v = v$), and if the set $\{\varepsilon_x * v; x \in G\}$ is vaguely relatively compact, then v is a Haar measure.*

Proof. For any $\varphi \in C_K^+$, the function f defined by

$$f(x) = \int \varphi(x + y) \, v(\mathrm{d}y) = \langle \varepsilon_x * v, \varphi \rangle$$

is bounded and continuous. Furthermore, f is μ-harmonic, since

$$\int f(x + y) \, \mu(\mathrm{d}y) = \iint \varphi(x + y + z) \, \mu(\mathrm{d}y) \, v(\mathrm{d}z) = \int \varphi(x + y) \, v(\mathrm{d}y) = f(x).$$

The function f is therefore constant and it follows that v is a Haar measure.

Corollary 1.5. *The bounded harmonic functions are constant m-a.e.*

Proof. If h is bounded harmonic, the measure $v = hm$ satisfies the conditions of Corollary 1.4 for the dual random walk. Indeed

$$\hat{\mu} * (hm) = (\hat{\mu} * h) \, m = hm,$$

and it is easily checked that $\{\varepsilon_x * \nu, x \in \boldsymbol{G}\}$ is vaguely relatively compact. Therefore ν is a Haar measure and h is constant m-a.e.

Remark. These results may be carried over to some classes of non-abelian groups but are not true for every group, as is shown in Exercises 1.10 and ch. 3, Exercise 5.22.

When the law μ is spread out, matters become even nicer: all harmonic bounded functions are constant, so that the σ-algebra of invariant events is trivial (ch. 3 § 3). This follows from the following important proposition, which does not require $\boldsymbol{G}$ to be abelian.

Proposition 1.6. *If μ is spread out, every bounded harmonic function is continuous.*

Proof. Choose n such that $\mu^n = \alpha + \beta$, where α is absolutely continuous with respect to m and β singular with $\|\beta\| < 1$. Call α_p and β_p the absolutely continuous and singular parts of μ^{np}; it is easily seen that $\|\beta_p\| < \|\beta\|^p$.

If h is bounded and harmonic, for every p we have

$$\|h - h * \hat{\alpha}_p\| = \|h * \hat{\mu}^{np} - h * \hat{\alpha}_p\| \leqslant \|h\|_\infty \|\beta\|^p.$$

The function $h * \hat{\alpha}_p$ is continuous, since it is the convolution of a bounded function and an integrable one. The function h is thus the uniform limit of continuous functions, and is therefore continuous.

In the subsequent section the Choquet–Deny theorem will be used as a tool in renewal theory. Exercise 1.11 and ch. 6, Exercise 2.22 give an insight into the relationship between the Choquet–Deny theorem and the limit theorems for powers of transition functions. This relationship is necessary to enlarge the scope of validity of the Choquet–Deny theorem to certain classes of non-abelian groups, but it will not be used in the remainder of the book.

Exercise 1.7 (another proof of the Choquet–Deny theorem).

(1) Let φ be a μ-harmonic bounded function. Prove that for every $x \in \boldsymbol{G}$ the sequence of random variables $\varphi(x + Z_1 + \cdots + Z_n)$ defined on the probability space $(W, \mathscr{A}, P)$ of ch. 1, Exercise 4.12 is a martingale which converges a.s. and in the mean to a random variable H_x which is symmetric and thus constant a.s. The reader will notice that the fact that $\boldsymbol{G}$ is abelian is necessary.

(2) Derive from (1) that $\varphi(x + Z_1) = \varphi(x)$ a.s.; hence $\varphi(x + x') = \varphi(x)$ for φ-almost every x'.

(3) Prove the Choquet–Deny theorem.

Exercise 1.8. (1) Let X be a random walk on an abelian group G. Prove that $\mathcal{T}$ is P_ν-trivial whenever ν is absolutely continuous with respect to m.

(2) Derive that for a recurrent random walk (not necessarily Harris) the function $P.[R(A)] = 1$ m-a.e. or 0 m-a.e. according as $m(A) > 0$ or $m(A) = 0$.

(3) If $\mathcal{T}$ is a.s. trivial, then μ is spread out. (See also ch. 7, Theorem 1.13.)

Exercise 1.9. A continuous homomorphism of an abelian group G into the multiplicative group of positive real numbers is called an *exponential*. Show that extremal (cf. ch. 7 § 3) harmonic functions are exponentials.

Exercise 1.10. The theorem of Choquet–Deny is not true for all groups (see also ch. 3 § 5.22). Every element in the group $G = \mathrm{SL}(2, \mathbf{R})$ of real, unimodular matrices of order 2 can be written uniquely as the product of an element of the group K of rotations by an element of the group S of upper-triangular unimodular matrices (a special case of the Iwasawa decomposition of semi-simple Lie groups with finite centre). The circle S^1 may be identified with G/S, and is thus a compact homogeneous space of G.

(1) Prove that there does not exist any measure on S^1 invariant by G.

(2) Let μ be a spread-out probability measure on G. Prove that there exists at least one probability measure ν on S^1 such that $\mu * \nu = \nu$, and derive the existence of non-constant μ-harmonic functions.

[*Hint*: See ch. 2, Exercise 3.20.]

Exercise 1.11. If μ is a probability measure on a group G such that $\lim_n \|\mu^n * \nu\| = 0$ for all $\nu \ll m$ and such that $\nu(E) = 0$, then the Choquet–Deny theorem is true for the left random walk of law μ on G. What can be said if the assumption $\nu \ll m$ is dropped?

2. General lemmas

From now on, the random walk X is supposed to be transient. According to ch. 3 § 4, the potential measure $\bar{G}$ is then a Radon measure, the asymptotic behaviour of which we are going to study. Throughout the sequel, f stands for an arbitrary function in C_K^+.

Proposition 2.1. (i) *The set of measures* $\{G(x, \cdot\,), x \in G\}$ *is vaguely relatively compact.*

(ii) *The function Gf is uniformly continuous.*

Proof. The statement (i) was proved in ch. 3, Corollary 4.7. For every compact K, there exists therefore a constant M_K such that $G(x, K) \leqslant M_K$ for all $x \in G$.

Let H be the compact support of f, and let J be a compact neighbourhood of the identity e. Since f is uniformly continuous, for every $\varepsilon > 0$, we can pick a compact neighbourhood $J' \subset J$ of e, such that $|f(x + y) - f(x)| < \varepsilon$ for $y \in J'$ and all $x \in G$. For $y \in J'$, the function $g(\cdot) = f(\cdot + y) - f(\cdot)$ vanishes outside the compact $K = H + J$, and it is easily checked that $Gg(x) = Gf(x + y) - Gf(x)$. We thus get, from (i),

$$|Gf(x + y) - Gf(x)| \leqslant \varepsilon M_K$$

for all $x \in G$ and $y \in J'$, which yields (ii).

We now aim at finding the closure of the set $\{G(x, \cdot\,), x \in G\}$ in the vague topology. Since the mapping $x \to G(x, \cdot\,)$ is continuous, as follows from Proposition 2.1, this is equivalent to the problem of finding the limit points of the set $\{G(x, \cdot\,), x \in G\}$ when x tends to $\varDelta$, the point at infinity in the Alexandroff compactification of G.

Theorem 2.2. *The limit points of the set* $\{G(x, \cdot\,), x \in G\}$ *when x tends to $\varDelta$ are Haar measures.*

Proof. Let $\{x_n\}$ be a sequence of points in G, converging to $\varDelta$ and such that the measures $G(x_n, \cdot\,)$ converge to the measure ν in the vague topology. As $\{\varepsilon_{x_n}\}$ converges to zero when x_n tends to $\varDelta$, passing to the limit in the equality

$$\varepsilon_{x_n} * \bar{G} = \varepsilon_{x_n} + \varepsilon_{x_n} * \bar{G} * \mu$$

yields $\nu = \nu * \mu$. It is now clear from Proposition 2.1 that ν satisfies the hypothesis of Corollary 1.4 and is therefore a Haar measure.

Corollary 2.3. *For every compact K,*

$$\lim_{x \to \varDelta}(Gf(x + y) - Gf(x)) = 0$$

uniformly in $y \in K$.

Proof. After Propositions 2.1–2.2 every sequence converging to Δ contains a subsequence $\{x_n\}$ such that the measures $G(x_n, \cdot)$ converge in the vague sense towards a Haar measure αm. Then

$$\lim_{x_n \to \Delta}(Gf(x_n + y) - Gf(x_n)) = \alpha(\langle \varepsilon_y * m, f \rangle - \langle m, f \rangle) = 0,$$

which shows that the limit in the statement exists. For every $\varepsilon > 0$, there exists a compact K_y such that $|Gf(x + y) - Gf(x)| < \frac{1}{2}\varepsilon$ for $x \notin K_y$.

Moreover, Gf being uniformly continuous, for every $\varepsilon > 0$, every $y \in G$ possesses a neighbourhood V_y such that $z \in V_y$ implies

$$|Gf(x + z) - Gf(y + z)| < \frac{1}{2}\varepsilon$$

uniformly in $x \in G$. Then, for $z \in V_y$ and $x \notin K_y$,

$$|Gf(x + z) - Gf(x)| < \varepsilon,$$

and the corollary follows by applying the Heine–Borel property.

Lemma 2.4. *Moreover*, $\varliminf_{x \to \Delta} Gf(x) = 0$.

Proof. Set $a = \inf_{x \in G} Gf(x)$; for every n, we have $a \leqslant P_n Gf(x)$. Letting n tend to infinity we get $a = 0$. If Gf is strictly positive we thus have $\varliminf_{x \to \Delta} Gf(x) = 0$. If not, there exists a point $x_0 \in G$ such that $Gf(x_0) = 0$, and therefore $P_n Gf(x_0) = 0$ for every n. But for every compact set K, there exists an integer n such that $P_n(x_0, K^c) > 0$, and therefore there exists a point $x \in K^c$ such that $Gf(x) = 0$. We still get that $\varliminf_{x \to \Delta} Gf(x) = 0$.

The following proposition is a key for further results. It can be extended to large classes of non-abelian groups. (See Exercises 2.9–2.10.)

Proposition 2.5. *For every* $f \in C_K^+$,

$$\lim_{x \to \Delta} Gf(x) \, Gf(-x) = 0.$$

Proof. Take $\varepsilon > 0$; by Corollary 2.3, there is a compact set K_ε such that for $x \notin K_\varepsilon$ and every y in the compact support K of f we have

$$Gf(x) \leqslant Gf(x + y) + \varepsilon,$$

and a fortiori,

$$Gf(x) \, Gf(y)/\|Gf\| \leqslant Gf(x + y) + \varepsilon. \tag{2.1}$$

Applying the complete maximum principle to $Gf(y)$ yields that the inequality (2.1) holds for every $x \notin K_\varepsilon$ and every $y \in G$.

Now by Lemma 2.4, we may choose a point y_ε such that $Gf(y_\varepsilon) \leqslant \varepsilon$, and putting $- x + y_\varepsilon$ in place of y in eq. (2.1) yields

$$Gf(x) \, Gf(- x + y_\varepsilon) \leqslant 2\|Gf\| \, \varepsilon.$$

The proposition then follows from the fact that $Gf(- x) - Gf(- x + y_\varepsilon)$ tends to zero when x tends to Δ.

Theorem 2.6. *The set of measures* $\{G(x, \cdot\,), x \in G\}$ *has always the measure zero as limit point when x tends to Δ. It has at most one other limit point, which must take the form cm for some positive constant c.*

Proof. We already know by Theorem 2.2 that the only possible limit points are the measures cm with $c \geqslant 0$. Now if the sequence $\{G(x_n, \cdot\,)\}$ converges to a non-zero measure, by Proposition 2.5 the sequence $\{G(- x_n, \cdot\,)\}$ converges to the measure zero, which proves the first statement.

In order to prove the second one we suppose that there exists two non-zero limit points. Then there is a function $f \in C_K^+$, of support K, such that the set $\{Gf(x), x \in G\}$ has two strictly positive limit points when x tends to Δ. Let us call l the smaller one.

We take $\varepsilon > 0$ and define inductively a sequence $\{x_n\}$ of points in G in the following way: we set $x_0 = e$; then by Corollary 2.3 and Proposition 2.5, we may choose a point $x_1 \in G$ such that

$$Gf(x_1) < l + 2^{-2}\varepsilon, \qquad Gf(- x_1) < 2^{-2}\varepsilon,$$

$$|Gf(x_1) - Gf(x_1 + x)| < 2^{-2}\varepsilon \quad \text{for } x \in K,$$

$$|Gf(- x_1) - Gf(- x_1 + x)| < 2^{-2}\varepsilon \quad \text{for } x \in K;$$

the sets $K \cup \{x_1 + K\}$ and $K \cup \{- x_1 + K\}$ being also compact, we may choose x_2 such that

$$Gf(x_2) < l + 2^{-3}\varepsilon, \qquad Gf(- x_2) < 2^{-3}\varepsilon,$$

$$|Gf(x_2) - Gf(x_2 + x)| < 2^{-3}\varepsilon \quad \text{for } x \in K \cup \{- x_1 + K\},$$

$$|Gf(- x_2) - Gf(- x_2 + x)| < 2^{-3}\varepsilon \quad \text{for } x \in K \cup \{x_1 + K\};$$

in the same way, for every n, we choose x_n such that

$$Gf(x_n) < l + 2^{-n-1}\varepsilon, \qquad Gf(- x_n) < 2^{-n-1}\varepsilon,$$

$$|Gf(x_n) - Gf(x_n + x)| < 2^{-n-1}\varepsilon \quad \text{for } x \in \bigcup_{i=0}^{n-1} \{-x_i + K\},$$

$$|Gf(-x_n) - Gf(-x_n + x)| < 2^{-n-1}\varepsilon \quad \text{for } x \in \bigcup_{i=0}^{n-1} \{x_i + K\}.$$

The support of the function

$$f(\cdot) + f(\cdot + x_1) + \cdots + f(\cdot + x_n)$$

is contained in $\bigcup_{i=0}^{n} \{-x_i + K\}$. Let $x \in \{-x_p + K\}$, $1 \leqslant p \leqslant n$; we have

(i) $Gf(x + x_p) \leqslant \|Gf\|$;

(ii) for $i = 1, 2, \ldots, n - p$, since $x \in \{-x_p + K\}$,

$$Gf(x + x_{p+i}) = Gf(x_{p+i}) + Gf(x + x_{p+i}) - Gf(x_{p+i})$$

$$\leqslant l + 2^{-(p+i)-1}\varepsilon + 2^{-(p+i)-1}\varepsilon;$$

(iii) for $i = 1, 2, \ldots, p$,

$$Gf(x + x_{p-i}) = Gf(z - x_p),$$

where $z = x_p + x + x_{p-i} \in \{x_{p-i} + K\}$, and this can be written

$$Gf(-x_p) + Gf(z - x_p) - Gf(-x_p) \leqslant 2^{-p-1}\varepsilon + 2^{-p-1}\varepsilon.$$

Summing up all these inequalities yields

$$G[f(\cdot) + f(\cdot + x_1) + \cdots + f(\cdot + x_n)](x) \leqslant \|Gf\| + nl + \varepsilon,$$

for every $x \in \bigcup_{i=0}^{n} \{-x_i + K\}$. The complete maximum principle implies that this inequality holds everywhere. By Corollary 2.3, we have

$$\overline{\lim_{x \to \Delta}} G[f(\cdot) + f(\cdot + x_1) + \cdots + f(\cdot + x_n)](x) = (n + 1) \overline{\lim_{x \to \Delta}} Gf(x);$$

hence, for every n,

$$\overline{\lim_{x \to \Delta}} Gf(x) \leqslant (nl/(n + 1)) + (\|Gf\| + \varepsilon)/n.$$

Since l is the smallest of the positive limits, we have a contradiction. This leads us to lay down the following

Definition 2.7. A transient random walk X will be said to be of *type I* if the measures $G(x, \cdot)$ converge vaguely to zero as x tends to Δ. It will be said to be of *type II* if there exist a non-zero limit point.

The preceding theorem states that for type II random walks there exists only one non-zero limit point and that every random walk is either of type I or of type II. In the following sections, we shall classify all random walks according to these two types.

Exercise 2.8. All symmetric walks ($\mu = \hat{\mu}$) are of type I.

Exercise 2.9. Let X be a spread out transient random walk on a non-abelian unimodular group $\boldsymbol{G}$. (1) Prove that the set of measures $\{\varepsilon_x * \bar{G} * \varepsilon_{x'}; x, x' \in \boldsymbol{G}\}$ is vaguely relatively compact.

[*Hint*: use Theorem 5.1.]

(2) Assume that the Choquet–Deny theorem is true for X, and show that Theorem 2.2 and Corollary 2.3 still hold. Show that Proposition 2.5 is true if x tends to $\varDelta$ in the centre of $\boldsymbol{G}$.

Exercise 2.10. Show that Proposition 2.5 is true for all random walks on a (not necessarily abelian) discrete group; more precisely

$$\lim_{x \to 0} G(x, e) \, G(xy^{-1}, e) = 0$$

for y arbitrary but fixed in $\boldsymbol{G}$.

[*Hint*: Setting $N(x, e) = P_{S_{\{e\}}}(x, e)$, show that

$$G(x, e) = I(x, e) + N(x, e) \, G(e, e);$$

then for $x \neq e$ and $x \neq y^{-1}$

$$E_x \left[\sum_{n > S_{\{e\}}} 1_{xy}(X_n) \right] = G(x, e) \, G(e, xy)/G(e, e).$$

For every p, the first member of this equality is less than

$$\sum_{n=0}^{p} P_x[S_{\{e\}} < n] + \sum_{n=p+1}^{\infty} P_x[X_n = xy],$$

and therefore tends to zero as x tends to $\varDelta$.]

3. The renewal theorem for the groups R and Z

In this section we study the cases of the group $\boldsymbol{R}$ of real numbers and of the group $\boldsymbol{Z}$ of integers. In the latter case the proofs will be written down only if they are really different from those in the former case. The letter m

will stand for the Lebesgue measure (counting measure for **Z**) and we shall often abbreviate $m(dx)$ to dx. The notations $\lim_{x \to +\infty}$ and $\lim_{x \to -\infty}$ have their usual meaning.

Theorem 3.1. *When x tends to $+\infty$ (resp. $-\infty$), the measures $G(x, \cdot)$ converge vaguely towards a multiple $c_+ m$ (resp. $c_- m$) of the Lebesgue measure. At least one of the two constants c_+ and c_- is zero, the other one being positive or zero.*

Proof. First consider the case of **Z**. Suppose that when x tends to $+\infty$ there exist two limit points, which by Theorem 2.6 are 0 and cm with $c > 0$. Then, for any function $f \in C_K^+$ and any $\varepsilon > 0$, and for x sufficiently large, $Gf(x)$ is either greater than $cm(f) - \varepsilon$ or less than ε. One can therefore find a sequence $\{x_n\}$ converging to $+\infty$ and such that for every n

$$Gf(x_n) < \varepsilon, \qquad Gf(x_n + 1) > cm(f) - \varepsilon.$$

By Corollary 2.3, this is impossible, and we have a contradiction. Let us now consider the group **R**. As the function Gf is continuous, if there exist two limit points 0 and $cm(f)$, every point in the interval $[0, cm(f)]$ would also be a limit point, and by Theorem 2.6 this is impossible.

In the following, we want to identify the constants c_+ and c_-. For this purpose we need some prerequisites.

Let f be a measurable function on **R**. For $h > 0$ we call $\underline{U}_n$ and $\bar{U}_n$ the minimum and maximum of f in the interval $[(n-1)h, nh]$, $n \in \mathbf{Z}$, and we set

$$\underline{\sigma} = h \sum_{-\infty}^{+\infty} \underline{U}_n, \qquad \bar{\sigma} = h \sum_{-\infty}^{+\infty} \bar{U}_n.$$

Definition 3.2. The function f will be said to be directly Riemann integrable (abbreviated R-integrable) if the series $\underline{\sigma}$ and $\bar{\sigma}$ converge, and if for every $\varepsilon > 0$, $\bar{\sigma} - \underline{\sigma} < \varepsilon$, for h sufficiently small.

The functions in C_K are R-integrable. Let f be a function vanishing on $]-\infty, 0[$, decreasing on $[0, \infty[$ and such that $f(\infty) = 0$; we have $\sum_0^\infty (\bar{U}_n - \underline{U}_n) \leqslant f(0)$, so that the two series $\underline{\sigma}$ and $\bar{\sigma}$ either both diverge or both converge. The function f is then R-integrable if and only if f is integrable in the ordinary Lebesgue sense. This example will be useful below in connection with the following.

Proposition 3.3. *If f is R-integrable, the function Gf is bounded and converges to $c_+m(f)$ (resp. $c_-m(f)$) as x tends to $+$ (resp. $-\infty$).*

Proof. From the vague convergence it is easy to derive the convergence of functions Gf, where f is the characteristic function of an interval.

Fix now $h > 0$ and set $f_n = 1_{[(n-1)h, nh]}$. By the maximum principle, there is a constant M such that $Gf_n \leqslant M$ for every n. Let $\{a_n\}_{n\in\mathbf{Z}}$ be a sequence of positive real numbers such that $\sum_{-\infty}^{+\infty} a_n < +\infty$, and set $f = \sum_{-\infty}^{+\infty} a_n f_n$. For every n

$$\sum_{-n}^{+n} a_k Gf_k(x) \leqslant Gf(x) \leqslant \sum_{-n}^{+n} a_k Gf_k(x) + M \sum_{|k|>n} a_k,$$

which shows that Gf is bounded. Then letting x tend to $\pm \infty$ shows that the proposition is true for a function f of this kind.

Let now f be a positive R-integrable function; with the previous notation, we set

$$\underline{f} = \sum_{-\infty}^{+\infty} \underline{U}_n f_n, \qquad \bar{f} = \sum_{-\infty}^{+\infty} \bar{U}_n f_n.$$

Obviously $G\underline{f} \leqslant Gf \leqslant G\bar{f}$, and as $\underline{f}$ and $\bar{f}$ are of the kind just studied, letting x tend to infinity yields

$$\lim_{x\to\pm\infty} G\underline{f}(x) \leqslant \varliminf_{x\to\pm\infty} Gf(x) \leqslant \varlimsup_{x\to\pm\infty} Gf(x) \leqslant \lim_{x\to\pm\infty} G\bar{f}(x).$$

Thus

$$c_{\pm}\underline{\sigma} \leqslant \varliminf_{x\to\pm\infty} Gf(x) \leqslant \varlimsup_{x\to\pm\infty} Gf(x) \leqslant c_{\pm}\bar{\sigma},$$

which completes the proof.

We now proceed to compute c_+ and c_-. The features are different according to whether there exists or does not exist a first moment for μ, that is whether $\int |x| \, d\mu(x) < \infty$ or not; if it exists we shall call the *mean* of X the number

$$\lambda = \int x \, d\mu(x).$$

We recall that λ cannot be zero, since the random walk is transient (ch. 3 § 5).

Proposition 3.4. *If the first moment exists, the random walk is of type II. If $\lambda > 0$, then $c_- = \lambda^{-1}$ and $c_+ = 0$. For $\lambda < 0$, the symmetric conclusion holds.*

Proof. Set $g(x) = \mu([-x, \infty[)$ for $x \leqslant 0$, and $g(x) = -\mu(]-\infty, -x[)$ for $x > 0$. Let k be the function defined on $\mathbf{R}^2$ by $k(x, y) = 1$ for $x < 0$, $y \geqslant -x$, $k(x, y) = -1$ for $x \geqslant 0$, $y < -x$ and $k(x, y) = 0$ elsewhere.

Since

$$\int_{\mathbf{R}^2} |k(x, y)| \, \mathrm{d}m(x) \, \mathrm{d}\mu(y) = \int_{-\infty}^{+\infty} |y| \, \mathrm{d}\mu(y) < +\infty,$$

we may apply the Fubini theorem to $\int k(x, y) \, \mathrm{d}m(x) \, \mathrm{d}\mu(y)$, and get $\int_{-\infty}^{+\infty} g(x) \, \mathrm{d}m(x)$ $= \lambda$. The function g is thus R-integrable, hence the potential Gg is bounded. Set $h = 1_{]-\infty, 0[}$; we have $Ph(x) = \mu(]-\infty, -x[)$ and thus $(I - P) h = g$. The function $l = h - Gg$ is therefore a bounded harmonic function which is ·almost surely equal to a constant a. We may find two sequences x_n and y_n of points in **R** converging respectively to $-\infty$ and $+\infty$ and such that for every n, $l(x_n) = l(y_n) = a$. Passing to the limit in the equalities

$$h(x_n) = Gg(x_n) + l(x_n), \qquad h(y_n) = Gg(y_n) + l(x_n)$$

yields, by Proposition 3.3, that

$$1 = c_-\lambda + a, \qquad 0 = c_+\lambda + a.$$

We cannot have $c_+ > 0$, since it would imply $c_- = 0$, $a = 1$ and therefore $\lambda < 0$. We thus have $c_+ = 0$; hence $a = 0$ and $c_- = \lambda^{-1}$, which completes the proof.

Remark. The reader will find, in ch. 3, Exercise 4.15, examples of random walks for which the above result is obvious. The reader will also find in Exercise 3.10 why it is natural to consider the function g in the above proof.

The same argument works when μ is carried by $[0, \infty]$. The expression $\lambda = \int_{\mathbf{R}} x \, \mathrm{d}\mu(x)$ is then always meaningful, but λ may be $+\infty$ and we will then put $\lambda^{-1} = 0$.

Corollary 3.5. *If μ is carried by $[0, \infty]$, then $c_- = \lambda^{-1}$* (of course we have $c_+ = 0$).

Proof. If $\lambda < \infty$, this is Proposition 3.4. To deal with $\lambda = +\infty$, we use the notation of Proposition 3.4. The function g vanishes on $]0, \infty[$, the potential Gg is positive, and as h is also zero on $]0, \infty[$, we have $Gg = h$.

The function $g_n = g \, 1_{[-n,0]}$ is R-integrable and $Gg_n \leqslant Gg = h$. Letting x tend to $- \infty$ in this inequality yields

$$c_- \int_{-\infty}^{+\infty} g_n(x) \, \mathrm{d}x \leqslant 1 ;$$

this cannot be true for every n unless $c_- = 0$.

The foregoing results are now applied to prepare the final proof of this section. However, the following lemmas are of intrinsic interest. We call T_+ the hitting time of $[0, \infty]$.

Lemma 3.6. If $\lambda^+ = \int_0^{+\infty} x \, \mathrm{d}\mu(x) = + \infty$, the measures $P_{T_+}(x, \cdot)$ converge vaguely to zero as x tends to $- \infty$.

Proof. Let f be a positive continuous function with compact support contained in $[0, + \infty]$. By the strong Markov property,

$$Gf(x) = \int_0^\infty P_{T_+} (x, \mathrm{d}y) \, Gf(y).$$

If μ is carried by $[0, \infty]$, by Corollary 3.5 the function $Gf(x)$ tends to zero as x tends to $- \infty$, and as $Gf \geqslant f$ this implies the desired conclusion.

If μ is not carried by $[0, \infty]$, we define inductively a sequence $\{S_k\}$ of stopping times by

$$S_1 = T_+, \ldots, S_k = \inf\{n : X_n > X_{S_{k-1}}\}, \ldots,$$

where the infimum of the empty set is understood to be $+ \infty$. By ch. 1, Exercise 3.12 and ch. 1, Exercise 4.9 the random variables $X_{S_k} - X_{S_{k-1}}$ are independent and equidistributed with law $\mu'(\cdot) = P_{T_+}(0, \cdot)$. The sequence $\{X_{S_k}\}$ is thus a random walk whose law is carried by $[0, \infty]$ and since μ' is clearly greater than the restriction of μ to $[0, \infty]$, we have $\int_0^\infty x \, \mathrm{d}\mu'(x) = + \infty$. Now the hitting distributions of $[0, \infty]$ are the same for μ and μ'; applying the first part of the proof to μ' thus completes the proof.

Lemma 3.7. If $\lambda^- = \int_{-\infty}^0 (- x) \, \mathrm{d}\mu(x) < \infty$ and if $\lambda > 0$, then $P_x[T_+ < \infty] = 1$ for all $x \in \mathbf{R}$.

Proof. Let us first assume that $\lambda^+ < \infty$; the strong law of large numbers then implies that X_n/n converges P_0-a.s. towards λ. Thus X_n converges a.s. to $+ \infty$ and $P_x[T_+ < \infty] = 1$ for every $x \in \mathbf{R}$.

Now if $\lambda^+ = \infty$, we choose a number c such that $\int_0^c x \, d\mu(x) > \lambda^-$, and set $Z_n^c = Z_n$ if $Z_n \leqslant c$ and $Z_n^c = c$ if $Z_n > c$. We may apply the above reasoning to $X_n^c = \sum_1^n Z_k^c$, and as $X_n \geqslant X_n^c$ a.s., this completes the proof.

We are now ready to prove the renewal theorem for the case in which the first moment does not exist.

Theorem 3.8. *If the first moment does not exist, the random walk is of type I.*

Proof. Assume $c_- > 0$, so that also $c_+ = 0$, and let us suppose that $\lambda^+ = +\infty$. By the strong Markov property, if $f \in C_K^+$ vanishes on $]-\infty, 0[$,

$$Gf(x) = \int_0^\infty P_{T_+}(x, dy) \, Gf(y).$$

Since $c_+ = 0$ for every $\varepsilon > 0$, there is a number $a > 0$ such that $y > a$ implies $Gf(y) < \varepsilon$, and hence

$$Gf(x) \leqslant \int_0^a P_{T_+}(x, dy) \, Gf(y) + \varepsilon;$$

if we let x tend to $-\infty$, $P_{T_+}(x, \cdot)$ converges vaguely to zero, and therefore for x sufficiently small we get $Gf(x) \leqslant 2\varepsilon$, which is impossible since c_- is strictly positive. We thus have $\lambda^+ < \infty$ and therefore $\lambda^- = +\infty$.

If we consider $\hat{\mu}$ in place of μ, this is equivalent to supposing that $c_- = 0$, $c_+ > 0$, $\lambda^- < \infty$, $\lambda^+ = \infty$. We then have $P_x[T_+ < \infty] = 1$ for every $x \in \mathbf{R}$; on the other hand $P_{T_+}(x, \cdot)$ converges vaguely to zero as x tends to $-\infty$. We thus get

$$0 = c_- m(f) = \lim_{x \to -\infty} Gf(x)$$

$$= \lim_{x \to -\infty} \int_{\mathbf{R}} P_{T_+}(x, dy) \, Gf(y) = \lim_{y \to \infty} Gf(y) = c_+ m(f);$$

we have a contradiction and the proof is completed.

These results extend to the groups which are isomorphic to $\mathbf{R} \oplus K$ and $\mathbf{Z} \oplus K$, where K is a compact group. As before, we write the proof only in the former case.

Let $G = \mathbf{R} \oplus K$; every point $x \in G$ can be written uniquely as a pair (y, k), with $y \in \mathbf{R}$ and $k \in K$. We call ψ the canonical mapping from G to

R: $(y, k) \to y$ and we shall say that x tends to $+ \infty$ (resp. $- \infty$) in G if $\psi(x)$ tends to $+ \infty$ (resp. $- \infty$) in **R**. Finally, the Haar measure m_G on G will be taken equal to the product of the Lebesgue measure m on **R** and of the normalized Haar measure on K.

Theorem 3.9. *If G is isomorphic to $\mathbf{R} \oplus K$ or $\mathbf{Z} \oplus K$, and if the random walk of law μ is of type II, then*

$$\int_G |\psi(x)| \, d\mu(x) < \infty.$$

In that case, if $\lambda = \int_G \psi(x) \, d\mu(x) > 0$, then in the vague topology,

$$\lim_{x \to +\infty} G(x, \cdot) = 0 \quad \text{and} \lim_{x \to -\infty} G(x, \cdot) = \lambda^{-1} m.$$

For $\lambda < 0$ the symmetric conclusion holds.

Proof. By § 2, from every sequence converging to $+ \infty$ we can extract a sequence $\{x_n\} = \{(y_n, k_n)\}$ such that $\{G(x_n, \cdot)\}$ converges vaguely to a multiple αm_G of the Haar measure of G. Let $f \in C_K^+$ be constant on the co-sets of K. By Corollary 2.3, we have

$$\lim_{x_n \to +\infty} Gf(x_n) = \lim_{y_n \to +\infty} Gf(y_n, 0).$$

Put $\tilde{f}(y) = f(x)$ and $\tilde{\mu} = \psi(\mu)$, and call $\tilde{G}$ the potential of the random walk of law $\tilde{\mu}$ on **R**. Then $Gf(y_n, 0) = \tilde{G}\tilde{f}(y_n)$, and moreover, applying Propositions 3.4–3.8 to this random walk, we get

$$\lim_{y_n \to +\infty} \tilde{G}\tilde{f}(y_n) = c_+ m(\tilde{f}),$$

where c_+ is non-zero if and only if

$$\int_{-\infty}^{+\infty} |y| \, d\tilde{\mu}(y) = \int_G |\psi(x)| \, d\mu(x) < + \infty$$

and

$$\int_{-\infty}^{+\infty} |y| \, d\tilde{\mu}(y) = \int_G |\psi(x)| \, d\mu(x) < 0.$$

Since furthermore $m(\tilde{f}) = m_G(f)$, the proof is complete.

In the following section we shall show that, up to an isomorphism, these groups are the only abelian ones for which there exist type II random walks.

Exercise 3.10. (1) Under the hypothesis of Corollary 3.5, show that $]-\infty, 0[$ is a transient set and that g is the probability of never returning to $]-\infty, 0[$.

(2) Similarly, show that if $a > 0$, $1_{]-\infty, a[} = Gg(x - a)$. Show that $P_{T_+}(x, [0, a[)$ is the potential of a function vanishing outside $[0, a[$. Compute this function and derive that if A is a relatively compact subset of $]0, +\infty[$ whose boundary is of Haar measure zero, then

$$\lim_{x \to -\infty} P_{T_+}(x, A) = \lambda^{-1} \int_A g(-x) \, dx.$$

[*Hint*: Use the duality between the kernels H_B and P_B described in ch. 2 § 3. This result will be generalized in § 5.]

Exercise 3.11. (1) Set $\mathbf{R}_+ = [0, \infty[$, and show that for a transient random walk the set of measures $\{H_{\mathbf{R}_+}(x, \cdot), x \in \mathbf{R}\}$ is vaguely relatively compact.

(2) Under the hypothesis of Corollary 3.5, prove that $\lim_{x \to -\infty} H_{\mathbf{R}_+}(x, \cdot)$ exists for the vague topology, and compute this limit.

[*Hint*: Consider sequences for which the limit exists and then apply the duality between P_A and H_A.]

Exercise 3.12. Assume the hypothesis of Corollary 3.5, with $\lambda < \infty$, and set

$$N_t(\omega) = \sum_{n=1}^{\infty} 1_{\{X_n(\omega) \leqslant t\}}.$$

(1) Show that N_t is an a.s. finite random variable.

(2) Find the starting measure ν such that the function $t \to E_\nu[N_t]$ is linear.

[*Hint*: Show that this amounts to finding ν such that $\nu * \bar{G} = \alpha m^+$, where $\alpha \in \mathbf{R}_+$ and m^+ is the restriction of the Lebesgue measure to $[0, \infty[$. It turns out that ν has density $\lambda^{-1} \mu([t, \infty[)$.] If $\lambda = +\infty$ there is no such measure.

Exercise 3.13. Under the hypothesis of Corollary 3.5, with $\lambda < \infty$ and $\sigma^2 = \int x^2 \, d\mu(x) < \infty$, show that

$$\lim_{x \to \infty} G([0, x]) - \lambda^{-1}x = \sigma^2/2\lambda^2.$$

[*Hint*: Use the Poisson equation with second member

$$\lambda^{-1} 1_{[0, \infty[}(x) \int_x^{\infty} \mu([t, \infty[) \, dt.]$$

Exercise 3.14. Let X be a recurrent irreducible discrete chain.

(1) Using the notation of ch. 3 § 1, set

$$Y_0 = S_x, \ldots, \; Y_n = S^{n+1} - S^n, \ldots .$$

Prove that for every probability measure P_v, the random variables $\{Y_n\}_{n \geq 1}$ are independent and equidistributed, of law $\mu(\cdot) = P_x[S_x = \cdot]$.

(2) Show that for every pair (x, y) of points in E

$$\lim_{n \to \infty} P_n(y, x) = (E_x[S_x])^{-1}.$$

(3) Show that the measure $m(\cdot) = (E.[S.])^{-1}$ is invariant for X, and derive that either $E_x[S_x] < \infty$ for all $x \in E$, or $E_x[S_x] = \infty$ for all $x \in E$. The reader will compare with ch. 3, Corollary 1.11 and ch. 6 § 2.

4. The renewal theorem

We now return to the case of a general abelian LCCB group G. As before, f is an arbitrary non-zero function in C_K^+.

Proposition 4.1. *If G has a compactly generated, open, non-compact sub-group G_1 such that G/G_1 is infinite, all transient random walks on G are type I.*

Proof. Suppose that a random walk X on G is of type II and let $\{x_n\}$ be a sequence such that the measures $G(x_n, \cdot)$ converge vaguely to cm ($c > 0$). We shall work towards a contradiction.

We may assume that the cosets $x_n + G_1$ are pairwise disjoint. Indeed if no sub-sequence of $\{x_n\}$ has this property, then there is a coset of G_1 which contains infinitely many x_n. This amounts to assuming that $\{x_n\}$ is contained in one and the same co-set. Pick now a sequence $\{z_k\}$, such that the cosets $z_k + G_1$ are pairwise disjoint. By Corollary 2.3, for every k we have

$$\lim_n Gf(x_n + z_k) = cm(f).$$

For every k, pick an integer n_k such that

$$|Gf(x_{n_k} + z_k) - cm(f)| < 2^{-k},$$

and set $y_k = x_{n_k} + z_k$; then the sequence $\{y_k\}$ has the desired property.

Now, since G_1 is compactly generated but non-compact, there exists a point $x \in G_1$ such that $nx \to \Delta$ as $n \to \infty$. Using Proposition 2.5 and Corollary

2.3 in the same way as in the proof of Theorem 3.1, it is easily seen that $\lim_n Gf(nx) = 0$ or $\lim_n Gf(-nx) = 0$. Without loss of generality we assume the former contingency. Then, for every n, there is a smallest integer h_n such that for $n' \geqslant h_n$

$$Gf(x_n + n'x) \leqslant \tfrac{1}{2}c\, m(f).$$

For otherwise there would be an integer n_0 and a subsequence $\{n'\}$ such that

$$Gf(x_{n_0} + n'x) > \tfrac{1}{2}c\, m(f),$$

and this is impossible since, by Corollary 2.3, $Gf(x_{n_0} + n'x)$ and $Gf(n'x)$ have the same limit, which is zero.

For fixed l, $Gf(x_n + lx)$ tends to $c\, m(f)$; hence $h_n > 1$ for n sufficiently large. Thus, for n sufficiently large,

$$Gf(x_n + h_n x - x) > \tfrac{1}{2}c\, m(f),$$

$$Gf(x_n + h_n x) \leqslant \tfrac{1}{2}c\, m(f).$$

The first of these two sequences converges therefore to $c\, m(f)$, and the second to zero.

But on the other hand, since G_1 is open, G/G_1 is discrete and every compact subset of G is contained in the union of a finite number of co-sets of G_1. Thus $x_n + nx$ tends to $\varDelta$ uniformly in n, and by Corollary 2.3,

$$\lim_{n \to \infty} |Gf(x_n + h_n x - x) - Gf(x_n + h_n x)| = 0$$

and we have a contradiction.

Corollary 4.2. *If G is isomorphic to $\mathbf{R}^{d_1} \oplus \mathbf{Z}^{d_2} \oplus K$ (K a compact group) and if $d_1 + d_2 > 1$, every transient random walk on G is of type I.*

Proof. By the argument of Theorem 3.9, it suffices to consider the case $G = \mathbf{R}^{d_1} \oplus \mathbf{Z}^{d_2}$. If $d_2 \geqslant 1$, we are done, recalling Proposition 4.1. If $G = \mathbf{R}^{d_1}$, with $d_1 > 1$, then G is the union of an increasing sequence of compact sets whose complements are connected. If the continuous function Gf has a non-zero limit a, every point in $[0, a]$ is also a limit point, which by Theorem 2.6 is a contradiction.

Before we proceed let us recall that a compact sub-semigroup of a group is a compact subgroup.

Proposition 4.3. *If every element of the group* **G** *is compact, then every transient random walk on* **G** *is of type I.*

Proof. Let X be a type II random walk, and let $\{z_n\}$ be a sequence such that $\{G(z_n, \cdot)\}$ converges to cm $(c > 0)$. For every n, the closure of the set $\{kz_n, k > 0\}$ is a compact sub-semigroup of **G**, hence a subgroup of **G**, and there is a sequence k_p of positive integers such that $\{k_p z_n\}$ converges to $- z_n$ as p tends to infinity.

Thus for every $\varepsilon > 0$, one can find an integer k_n such that

$$Gf(k_n z_n) \leqslant Gf(- z_n) + \varepsilon n^{-1}$$

and since, by Proposition 2.5, $Gf(- z_n)$ tends to zero as n tends to infinity, the sequence $Gf(k_n z_n)$ tends to zero.

Choose $M > \max(\|Gf\|, \tfrac{1}{4}c\, m(f))$. For all sufficiently large values of $n \geqslant 1$, we may pick the largest integer $h_n < k_n$ such that

$$Gf(h_n z_n) \geqslant \frac{c^2\, m(f)^2}{4M}, \qquad Gf((h_n + 1)\, z_n) < \frac{c^2\, m(f)^2}{4M},$$

since $c^2\, m(f)^2/4M < cm(f)$. By the proof of (2.5), for n sufficiently large,

$$Gf(h_n z_n)\, Gf(z_n) \leqslant M[\varepsilon + Gf((h_n + 1)\, z_n)].$$

Moreover, for n sufficiently large, $Gf(z_n) \geqslant \tfrac{1}{2}c\, m(f)$, which implies

$$Gf(h_n z_n) \leqslant \frac{2M}{cm(f)}\, [Gf((h_n + 1)\, z_n) + \varepsilon]$$

$$\leqslant \tfrac{1}{2}c\, m(f) + \frac{2M\varepsilon}{cm(f)} \leqslant \tfrac{1}{2}c\, m(f) + \tfrac{1}{2}\varepsilon,$$

and

$$\frac{c^3\, m(f)^3}{8M^2} - \varepsilon \leqslant Gf((h_n + 1)\, z_n).$$

Choosing ε in an appropriate way, we see that there exist four constants $\alpha, \beta, \gamma, \delta$ such that for n sufficiently large,

$$0 < \alpha \leqslant Gf(h_n z_n) \leqslant \beta < cm(f),$$

$$0 < \gamma \leqslant Gf((h_n + 1)\, z_n) \leqslant \delta < cm(f).$$

Since $\{z_n\}$ tends to Δ when n tends to infinity, at least one of the sequences $\{h_n z_n\}$ and $\{(h_n + 1) z_n\}$ contains a subsequence $\{y_n\}$ converging to Δ. The sequence $Gf(y_n)$ has at most 0 and $cm(f)$ as limit points; we thus have a contradiction.

Theorem 4.4 (renewal theorem). *If there exists on G a random walk of type II, the group G is isomorphic to $\mathbf{R} \oplus K$ or $\mathbf{Z} \oplus K$, where K is a compact group. The asymptotic behaviour of the measures $G(x, \cdot)$ is then described by Theorem 3.9.*

Proof. By Proposition 4.3, there exists a non-compact element y. As every group G has a compactly generated open sub-group G', the subgroup G_1 generated by G' and y is non-compact, compactly generated and open. Thus by Proposition 4.1, the group G/G_1 is finite; hence G also is compactly generated. The theorems on the structure of abelian groups then assert that G is isomorphic to $\mathbf{R}^{d_1} \oplus \mathbf{Z}^{d_2} \oplus K$, where K is a compact group. By Corollary 4.2, the proof is complete.

5. Refinements and applications

Throughout this section, μ will be taken spread out, and we shall give applications of the renewal theorem to hitting probabilities and to recurrent sets.

The first result is true even if G is non-abelian.

Theorem 5.1. *The measure $\bar{G}$ can be written $\bar{G} = \bar{G}' + \bar{G}''$, where $\bar{G}'$ is an absolutely continuous measure having a bounded continuous density p and $\bar{G}''$ a finite measure.*

Proof. By hypothesis, there is an integer k and a bounded integrable function f such that $\mu^k = \psi m + \alpha$, where α is a finite measure of norm less than 1. Setting $n_0 = 2k$ it is easily seen that one can write $\mu^{n_0} = \varphi m + \nu$, where $\varphi \in C_K^+$ and $\|\nu\| < 1$. The measure $\bar{G}$ can be written

$$\bar{G} = \left(\sum_{n=0}^{n_0-1} \mu^n\right) * \left(\sum_{n=0}^{\infty} \mu^{n n_0}\right).$$

Setting $\tilde{G} = \sum_{n=0}^{\infty} \mu^{n n_0}$, we have

$$\tilde{G} = \varepsilon_e + (\varphi m + \nu) * \tilde{G}$$

$$= \varepsilon_e + \varphi m * \tilde{G} + \nu * (\varepsilon_e + (\varphi m + \nu) * \tilde{G})$$

and inductively, for every $n \geqslant 1$,

$$\tilde{G} = \varepsilon_e + \nu + \cdots + \nu^n + (\varepsilon_e + \cdots + \nu^n) * \varphi m * \tilde{G} + \nu^{n+1} * \tilde{G}. \qquad (5.1)$$

If $f \in C_K$, the function $x \to \int f(xx')\, \tilde{G}(dx')$ is bounded and continuous, since $\tilde{G}$ is the potential measure corresponding to μ^{n_0}. From this remark, we derive easily that $\lim_{n \to \infty} \nu^{n+1} * \tilde{G} = 0$ in the vague topology. On the other hand, $\nu' = \sum_0^\infty \nu^n$ is a finite measure, and letting n tend to infinity in eq. (5.1) yields

$$\tilde{G} = \nu' + \nu' * \varphi m * \tilde{G},$$

which shows that Theorem 5.1 is true for $\tilde{G}$. It is then verified for $\bar{G}$ with $\bar{G}'' = (\sum_0^{n_0-1} \mu^n) * \nu'$ and $p = \bar{G}'' * \varphi * \tilde{G}$.

As is apparent from the proof, this decomposition is not unique, but the renewal theorem settles the asymptotic behaviour of p.

Theorem 5.2. *If the random walk is of type I, then*

$$\lim_{x \to \Delta} p(x) = 0.$$

If the random walk is of type II with $\lambda > 0$, then

$$\lim_{x \to +\infty} p(x) = \lambda^{-1}, \qquad \lim_{x \to -\infty} p(x) = 0.$$

For $\lambda < 0$, the symmetric conclusion holds.

Proof. If X is of type I, the random walk of law μ^{n_0} is also type I and therefore $\lim(\tilde{G} * \varphi)(x) = 0$, that is $\tilde{G} * \varphi \in C_0$; since $\bar{G}''$ is finite, $p = \bar{G}'' * \varphi * \tilde{G}$ is also in C_0, and the proof is completed in that case.

If X is of type II with $\lambda > 0$, then using the notation of Theorem 3.9,

$$\int_G \psi(x)\, d\mu^{n_0}(x) = n_0 \lambda,$$

and therefore, by the renewal theorem for $\tilde{G}$,

$$\lim_{x \to -\infty} (\tilde{G} * \varphi)(x) = 0, \qquad \lim_{x \to +\infty} (\tilde{G} * \varphi)(x) = m(\varphi)/n_0 \lambda.$$

Since $\bar{G}''(G) = n_0/m(\varphi)$, it follows that

$$\lim_{x \to -\infty} p(x) = 0 \quad \text{and} \lim_{x \to +\infty} p(x) = \lambda^{-1}.$$

Corollary 5.3. *For every bounded Borel function f with compact support,*

$$\lim_{x \to \Delta} Gf(x) = 0$$

if the random walk is of type I, and

$$\lim_{x \to -\infty} Gf(x) = \lambda^{-1} m(f), \qquad \lim_{x \to +\infty} Gf(x) = 0$$

if the random walk is of type II with $\lambda > 0$.

Proof. We have

$$Gf(x) = \langle \varepsilon_x * \bar{G}'', f \rangle + \int_G f(y)\, p(y - x)\, m(dy).$$

The first term tends to zero as x tends to Δ since $\bar{G}''$ is finite, and the result follows by a simple application of the Lebesgue theorem.

We now turn to the study of the asymptotic behaviour of hitting probabilities. As usual, the symbol ˆ refers to the dual random walk.

Theorem 5.4. *Let B be any relatively compact Borel set, and f any bounded Borel function with compact support. Then if X is type I*

$$\lim_{x \to \Delta} U_B f(x) = 0$$

and if X is type II with $\lambda > 0$,

$$\lim_{x \to +\infty} U_B f(x) = 0, \qquad \lim_{x \to -\infty} U_B f(x) = \lambda^{-1} \int f(y)\, \hat{g}_B(y)\, dy,$$

where $\hat{g}_B = \hat{P}.[S_B = \infty]$.

Proof. Consider first the type II case. Clearly the kernels $U_0(x, \cdot)$ and $G(x, \cdot)$ have the same limits on functions with compact supports as n tends to infinity. Passing to the limit in the identity

$$U_0 f(x) = U_B f(x) + U_0 1_B U_B f(x)$$

yields

$$\lim_{x \to -\infty} U_B f(x) = \lambda^{-1} m(f) - \lambda^{-1} m(1_B U_B f).$$

Using the duality between the kernels U_B and $\hat{U}_B$ (ch. 2, Proposition 3.10) then yields

$$\lim_{x \to -\infty} U_B f(x) = \lambda^{-1} \langle 1 - \hat{U}_B 1_B, f \rangle_m = \lambda^{-1} \int f(y) \, \hat{P}_y[S_B = \infty] \, dy.$$

The proof is then easily completed.

Corollary 5.5. *With the same hypothesis, the hitting distributions* $P_B(x, \cdot)$ *converge vaguely to zero or to* $\lambda^{-1} \hat{g}_B m$.

Proof. Straightforward.

By ch. 3 § 3 and the Choquet–Deny theorem, when μ is spread out every set is either recurrent or transient. This raises the problem of characterizing the recurrent sets. The following result gives a partial but useful answer.

If the group G is isomorphic to $\mathbf{R} \oplus \mathbf{K}$ or $\mathbf{Z} \oplus \mathbf{K}$, with $\mathbf{K}$ a compact group, we denote by G_+ the set of points (x, k) such that $x \geqslant 0$.

Proposition 5.6. *If the random walk is of type II with* $\lambda > 0$, *a set* A *is recurrent if and only if* $m(A \cap G_+) = +\infty$.

Proof. We take $G = \mathbf{R}$, the other groups requiring only obvious changes. The set $G_- = G \backslash G_+$ is transient as is easily seen by applying the law of large numbers (ch. 3, Exercise 4.14). We therefore take $A \subset G_+$. If $m(A) < +\infty$, Theorem 5.2 implies that $G(x, A) < \infty$ for every $x \in G$, and thus A is transient.

Suppose conversely that $m(A) = +\infty$. We can write $A = \sum_1^\infty A_k$, where the sets A_k can be chosen disjoint, of finite measure and such that the sequence $\{m(A_k)\}$ increases to $+\infty$. Each of the A_k being transient by the preceding argument, to hit A infinitely many times, the random walk must hit infinitely many sets A_k and therefore

$$P_e\left[\varlimsup_n \{X_n \in A\}\right] = P_e\left[\varlimsup_k \{T_{A_k} < \infty\}\right] \geqslant \varlimsup_k P_e[T_{A_k} < \infty].$$

By the strong Markov property, we get easily (see ch. 2, Theorem 1.12)

$$P_e[T_{A_k} < \infty] \geqslant \bar{G}(A_k) / \sup_{y \in A_k} G(y, A_k).$$

Next, by Theorem 5.1,

$$\sup_{y \in A_k} G(y, A_k) \leqslant \|\bar{G}''\| + \|p\| \, m(A_k),$$

which implies

$$P_e[T_{A_k} < \infty] \geqslant \bar{G}(A_k)/(\|\bar{G}''\| + \|p\|\, m(A_k)).$$

As k tends to infinity, $\bar{G}(A_k)$ is equivalent to $\lambda^{-1} m(A_k)$, by Theorem 5.1, hence

$$\varlimsup_{k \to \infty} P_e[T_{A_k} < \infty] \geqslant (\lambda\|p\|)^{-1} > 0.$$

The set A is recurrent and the proof is complete.

Corollary 5.7. *A set $A \subset G_+$ is recurrent if and only if $\bar{G}(A) = +\infty$.*

Proof. Obvious.

Remark. For the case in which the first moment does not exist, but $\int_{-\infty}^{0} |x|\, d\mu(x) < \infty$, one could hope for similar results, but in fact they are not true (cf. Exercise 5.12).

Exercise 5.8. Investigate the asymptotic behaviour as x tends to Δ of $P_x[T_A < T_B]$ and of $G^A(x, B)$, where A and B are relatively compact Borel sets.

Exercise 5.9. Try to carry over Theorem 5.4 to non-spread-out laws.
[*Hint*: Use relatively compact Borel sets whose boundaries have zero Haar measure.]

Exercise 5.10. Prove Theorem 5.4 without relying on Theorem 5.1.

Exercise 5.11. Let A be a transient set of infinite Haar measure. Prove that its capacity (ch. 2, Exercise 3.15) is equal to $+\infty$ if the random walk is of type I and to $|\lambda|$ if the random walk is of type II with mean λ.

Exercise 5.12. Every transient spread out random walk has transient sets of infinite Haar measure. If $G = \mathbf{R}$ or $\mathbf{Z}$, if the first moment does not exist and if $\int_{-\infty}^{0} |x|\, d\mu(x) < \infty$, there exist transient subsets of G_+ of infinite Haar measure.

Exercise 5.13. Let X be a transient random walk on a discrete group. Prove that $P_e[T_{\{x\}} < \infty] < 1$ for all $x \neq e$ with one and only one exception: the group is isomorphic to $\mathbf{Z}$ and either X is right continuous (ch. 3, Exercise 4.15) and the mean λ exists and is > 0, or X is left continuous with the symmetric conditions.

Exercise 5.14. Let H be a Borel sub-group of G. Show that H is a recurrent set if and only if $G(e, H) = + \infty$.

CHAPTER 6

ERGODIC THEORY OF HARRIS CHAINS

In this chapter, we aim at proving limit theorems for Harris chains. For this purpose we shall need a certain amount of potential theory, which will be introduced in §§ 4 and 5, but potential theory for Harris chains will really be dealt with in ch. 8. Throughout the chapter, the state space $(E, \mathcal{E})$ is separable.

1. Cyclic classes

In the next section, we shall study the asymptotic behaviour of the powers P_n of the T.P. Simple examples (see Exercise 1.5) show that no limit theorem can hold if the chain has a periodic behaviour of some kind. We therefore begin by the study of such phenomena.

Let λ be a probability measure equivalent to m. According to ch. 1, Lemma 5.3, there exists for every k an $\mathcal{E} \otimes \mathcal{E}$-measurable function q_k such that

$$P_k(x, \mathrm{d}y) = q_k(x, y)\, \lambda(\mathrm{d}y) + P_k^1(x, \mathrm{d}y),$$

where the measure $P_k^1(x, \cdot)$ is singular with respect to λ.

Let k, j be two integers; it is easily seen that for every $x \in E$,

$$q_{k+j}(x, \cdot) \geqslant \int_E P_k(x, \mathrm{d}z)\, q_j(z, \cdot) \geqslant \int_E q_k(x, z)\, \lambda(\mathrm{d}z)\, q_j(z, \cdot)$$

λ-a.s. The function

$$p_k(x, y) = q_k(x, y) \vee \left(\sup_{j<k} \int P_{k-j}(x, \mathrm{d}z)\, q_j(z, y) \right)$$

is an $\mathcal{E} \otimes \mathcal{E}$-measurable density for $P_k(x, \cdot)$, and for every pair of integers m and n,

$$p_{m+n}(x, y) \geqslant \int_E P_m(x, \mathrm{d}z)\, p_n(z, y) \geqslant \int_E p_m(x, z)\, \lambda(\mathrm{d}z)\, p_n(z, y). \qquad (1.1)$$

It is this function that we shall use below as a density for $P_n(x, \cdot)$.

Let $C \in \mathscr{E}$ be such that $\lambda(C) > 0$, or equivalently $m(C) > 0$. We put

$$I(C) = \left\{ n > 0 \colon \inf_{(x,y) \in C \times C} p_n(x, y) > 0 \right\}.$$

The set $I(C)$ is a sub-semigroup of $\mathbf{N}$, and we have

Lemma 1.1. *There exists a set C such that $I(C)$ is non-empty.*

Proof. If U is a set in the σ-algebra $\mathscr{E} \otimes \mathscr{E}$, its sections will be written

$$U_1(x) = \{y \colon (x, y) \in U\}, \qquad U_2(y) = \{x \colon (x, y) \in U\}.$$

Let

$$H^{(m,n)} = \{(x, y) \in E \times E \colon p_m(x, y) \geqslant 1/n\},$$

and $H = \bigcup_{m=1}^{\infty} \bigcup_{n=1}^{\infty} H^{(m,n)}$. For every $x \in E$, we have $\lambda(H_1(x)) > 0$; indeed $\lambda(H_1(x_0)) = 0$ would imply that $G(x_0, \cdot)$ is singular with respect to λ, which is impossible by virtue of the irreducibility of X.

By Fubini's theorem,

$$(\lambda \otimes \lambda)(H) = \int_E \lambda(H_1(x))\, \lambda(\mathrm{d}x) = \int_E \lambda(H_2(y))\, \lambda(\mathrm{d}y);$$

hence

$$\lambda\{y \colon \lambda(H_2(y)) > 0, \ \lambda(H_1(y)) > 0\} = \lambda\{y \colon \lambda(H_2(y)) > 0\} > 0.$$

Consequently, there exist two sets $F = H^{(m_1, n_1)}$ and $G = H^{(m_2, n_2)}$ such that

$$\lambda\{y \colon \lambda(F_2(y)) > 0 \quad \text{and} \quad \lambda(G_1(y)) > 0\} > 0. \tag{1.2}$$

Using the product partitions, we may apply the differentiation lemma of ch. 1, Lemma 5.3 to the probability measure $\lambda \otimes \lambda$ and to its restriction to sets F and G; we may therefore assert that there exists a $\lambda \otimes \lambda$-null set N such that

$$\frac{(\lambda \otimes \lambda)(F \cap (E_x^n \times E_y^n))}{(\lambda \otimes \lambda)(E_x^n \times E_y^n)} \to 1_F(x, y) \qquad \text{for } (x, y) \in E \times E \setminus N,$$

$$\frac{(\lambda \otimes \lambda)(G \cap (E_x^n \times E_y^n))}{(\lambda \otimes \lambda)(E_x^n \times E_y^n)} \to 1_G(x, y) \qquad \text{for } (x, y) \in E \times E \setminus N.$$

As $(\lambda \otimes \lambda)(N) = 0$, it follows from eq. (1.2) that

$$\lambda\{y \colon \lambda(F_2(y) - N_2(y)) > 0 \quad \text{and} \quad \lambda(G_1(y) - N_1(y)) > 0\} > 0.$$

So, there exist points x_0, y_0, z_0 and an integer n such that $x_0 \in F_2(y_0) - N_2(y_0)$, $z_0 \in G_1(y_0) - N_1(y_0)$ and

$$(\lambda \otimes \lambda)\,(F \cap (E_{x_0}^n \times E_{y_0}^n)) \geqslant \tfrac{3}{4}\lambda(E_{x_0}^n)\,\lambda(E_{y_0}^n),$$

$$(\lambda \otimes \lambda)\,(G \cap (E_{y_0}^n \times E_{z_0}^n)) \geqslant \tfrac{3}{4}\lambda(E_{y_0}^n)\,\lambda(E_{z_0}^n). \qquad (1.3)$$

Let us put

$$A = \{x \in E_{x_0}^n : \lambda(E_{y_0}^n \cap F_1(x)) \geqslant \tfrac{3}{4}\lambda(E_{y_0}^n)\},$$

$$B = \{z \in E_{z_0}^n : \lambda(E_{y_0}^n \cap G_2(z)) \geqslant \tfrac{3}{4}\lambda(E_{y_0}^n)\}.$$

Since, in eq. (1.3), the left members are equal to

$$\int_{E_{x_0}^n} \lambda(F_1(x) \cap E_{y_0}^n)\,\lambda(dx) \quad \text{and} \quad \int_{E_{z_0}^n} \lambda(G_2(z) \cap E_{y_0}^n)\,\lambda(dz),$$

we see that $\lambda(A) > 0$ and $\lambda(B) > 0$. For $x \in A$, $z \in B$, we have

$$\lambda\{(F_1)\,(x) \cap G_2(z)\} \geqslant \tfrac{1}{2}\lambda(E_{y_0}^n).$$

If, moreover, $y \in F_1(x) \cap G_2(z)$, then $(x, y) \in F$, $(y, z) \in G$, and by virtue of the definition of F and G,

$$p_{m_1+m_2}(x, z) \geqslant \int p_{m_1}(x, y)\, p_{m_2}(y, z)\, \lambda(dy)$$

$$\geqslant \int_{F_1(x) \cap G_2(z)} p_{m_1}(x, y)\, p_{m_2}(y, z)\, \lambda(dy) \geqslant \frac{\lambda(E_{y_0}^n)}{2n_1 n_2} = \alpha > 0.$$

By the irreducibility of X, there exist an integer m and a number $\eta > 0$ such that the set

$$C = \{x \in B : P_m(x, A) \geqslant \eta\}$$

has positive λ-measure; for $x \in C$, $y \in B$ it follows that

$$p_{m_1+m_2+m}(x, y) \geqslant \int_A P_m(x, dz)\, p_{m_1+m_2}(z, y) \geqslant \alpha\eta > 0.$$

The set C is the desired set.

In the same way we could have shown that every set of positive λ-measure contains a set C such that $I(C)$ is non-empty. We call $d(C)$ the greatest common divisor of $I(C)$.

Proposition 1.2. (i) *If C' is another set with the property that $I(C')$ is non-empty, then $d(C) = d(C')$.*

(ii) *The set $I(C)$ contains all sufficiently large multiples of $d(C)$.*

Proof. By the irreducibility of X, there exist sets $\Gamma \subset C$ and $\Gamma'' \subset C'$ of positive λ-measure, and integers k and k', such that $P_k(\cdot, C') \geqslant \alpha > 0$ on Γ and $P_{k'}(\cdot, C) \geqslant \alpha' > 0$ on Γ''. For $n \in I(C)$ and $n' \in I(C')$, the inequalities (1.1) yield

$$n + k + n' + k' + n \in I(C).$$

Since $2n'$ is also in $I(C')$, we get

$$(n + k + 2n' + k' + n) - (n + k + n' + k' + n) = n' \in I(C) - I(C);$$

thus n' is a multiple of $d(C)$, and so is $d(C')$. In the same way $d(C)$ is a multiple of $d(C')$, so $d(C) = d(C')$, and the proof of (i) is completed. Since $d(C)$ does not depend on C, we shall write henceforward d instead of $d(C)$.

We now prove (ii). There exists a finite set n_i, $i = 1, 2, \ldots, k$ of members of $I(C)$ with greatest common divisor d; hence, there exist elements a_i, $i = 1, \ldots, k$, in $\mathbf{Z}$, such that

$$n_1 a_1 + \cdots + n_k a_k = d.$$

Shifting to the right all negative terms yields that there are in $I(C)$ two integers of the form p and $p + d$. Then, for every integer m, the numbers

$$mp, mp + d, \ldots, mp + md$$

are in $I(C)$. Let $p_1 = p/d$; then all numbers $mp + md = d(mp_1 + n)$, $0 \leqslant n \leqslant m$, are in $I(C)$, so that all multiples of d greater than dp_1^2 are in $I(C)$.

Theorem 1.3. *There exists a finite sequence $C_1, C_2, \ldots, C_d$ of pairwise disjoint sets such that*

(i) *the set $F = (\bigcup_{i=1}^{d} C_i)^c$ has measure zero;*

(ii) *$P(\cdot, C_{i+1}) = 1$ on C_i for $i = 1, 2, \ldots, d - 1$ and $P(\cdot, C_1) = 1$ on C_d.*

Proof. The set C being the same as above, let us define, for $i \leqslant d$,

$$\bar{C}_i = \{x: P_{nd-i}(x, C) > 0 \quad \text{for an } n \geqslant 1\}.$$

The irreducibility of X implies that every $x \in E$ is in at least one of the sets $\bar{C}_i$.

Let $k, l \leqslant d$ be such that $\lambda(\bar{C}_k \cap \bar{C}_l) > 0$. There exist two integers m, n such that the intersection of the sets

$$B_k = \{x: P_{md-k}(x, C) > 0\} \quad \text{and} \quad B_l = \{x: P_{nd-l}(x, C) > 0\}$$

has positive λ-measure. By the irreducibility of X, there exist an integer r and a set $A \subset C$ such that $\lambda(A) > 0$ and

$$P_r(\cdot, B_k \cap B_l) \geqslant a > 0 \quad \text{on } A.$$

Then if $i \in I(C)$, the composition of T.P.'s yields, by eq. (1.1),

$$i + r + md - k + i \in I(C),$$

$$i + r + nd - l + i \in I(C);$$

hence $(k - l) - (m - n) d$ is a multiple of d, which implies $k = l$. The set $G = \bigcup_{i,j} (\bar{C}_i \cap \bar{C}_j)$ has thus λ-measure zero.

Let F be a transient set containing G^c and such that F^c is an absorbing set (ch. 3, Corollary 3.10), and define $C_i = \bar{C}_i \backslash F$. The sets C_i are disjoint. Let $x \notin F$, and suppose that $P(x, C_i) > 0$; clearly $x \in C_{i-1}$, and since the sets C_i are disjoint, $P(x, C_i) = 1$, which completes the proof.

Definition 1.4. The integer d is called the *period* of X. When $d = 1$ the chain is said to be *aperiodic*; otherwise it is said to be *periodic*. The sets C_i are then called the *cyclic classes*, and the partition of E into $C_1, \ldots, C_d, F$ is called a *cyclic decomposition* of E.

Remarks. (1) For a discrete recurrent irreducible chain, the proofs are evidently simpler, since we may take as set C any point in E; the proofs of the present section then work in the same way; of course the set F is empty.

(2) The proofs of the present section do not need the recurrence of X, but merely its irreducibility.

(3) The cyclic decomposition is unique up to sets of measure zero.

Exercise 1.5 (the Ehrenfest model of diffusion). N particles are distributed in two containers U_1 and U_2. At every time n a particle is chosen at random and is moved from its container into the other. Define X_n to be the random number of particles in U_1 at time n. Show that the sequence X_n is a Markov chain; write down its T.P. and compute its invariant measure. Prove that the chain is periodic of period 2, and that the powers P_n of P cannot converge everywhere to a limit as n tends to infinity.

Exercise 1.6. For a Harris random walk on a group G, show that the set F of Theorem 1.3 is empty. If G is connected, the random walk is aperiodic. If G is not connected, the cyclic class containing the neutral element e is an open sub-group.

Exercise 1.7. Let Σ be the σ-algebra of subsets $\Gamma \in \mathcal{E}$ such that for every $n \in \mathbf{N}$ there exists a set Γ_n such that $P_n 1_\Gamma = 1_{\Gamma_n}$ λ-a.s. Without the use of the results of the present section, show that Σ is generated, up to a λ-equivalence, by a finite partition C_i $(i = 1, \ldots, d)$ such that $P(\cdot, C_i) = 1_{C_{i+1}}$ λ-a.s.

Exercise 1.8. Continuation of ch. 3, Exercise 1.18. If this chain is recurrent, when is it aperiodic? Describe the cyclic classes for the periodic case.

2. Orey's theorem

In this section, we prove a fundamental limit theorem for the powers P_n of the T.P. of a Harris chain.

Definition 2.1. The events of the σ-algebra

$$\mathcal{A} = \bigcap_{n \geqslant 0} \theta_n^{-1}(\mathcal{F}) = \bigcap_{n \geqslant 0} \sigma(X_m, m \geqslant n)$$

are called *asymptotic*. A random variable defined on $(\Omega, \mathcal{F})$ is called *asymptotic* if it is measurable with respect to $\mathcal{A}$.

Clearly, an event A is asymptotic if and only if for every n there exists an event $A_n \in \mathcal{F}$ such that $A = \theta_n^{-1}(A_n)$. The σ-algebra $\mathcal{I}$ of invariant events is thus contained in $\mathcal{A}$. Moreover, the sets A_n may be chosen in a canonical fashion. The shift operator θ is not one-to-one, so that θ^{-1} is not a mapping and $\theta^{-1}(\omega)$ is the set of trajectories ω' such that $\theta(\omega') = \omega$. However, if $Z \in \sigma(X_m, m \geqslant n)$, this random variable does not depend on the first $n - 1$ coordinates and one can define unambiguously $Z \circ \theta^{-1}$ and $Z \circ \theta^{-p}$ for $p < n$. For $\omega = (x_0, x_1, \ldots)$,

$$Z \circ \theta^{-1}(\omega) = Z(y, x_0, x_1, \ldots),$$

where y is arbitrary in E. If Z is asymptotic, one can therefore define unambiguously and for every $n \in \mathbf{N}$ another asymptotic random variable Z_n, by setting $Z_n = Z \circ \theta^{-n}$. We then have $Z = Z_n \circ \theta_n$ and $Z_n = Z_{n+m} \circ \theta_n$ for every pair of integers n and m. We shall write θ_{-n} rather than θ^{-n}, in order to make θ_n $(n \in \mathbf{Z})$ appear as a transformation group of $\mathcal{A}$.

Definition 2.2. Two asymptotic random variables Z and Z' are said to be *equivalent* if, for every $n \in \mathbf{Z}$, the asymptotic random variables $Z \circ \theta_n$ and $Z' \circ \theta_n$ are almost surely equal.

Notice that if suffices to have the equality for $n \leqslant 0$, the equality for $n > 0$ following from the Markov property. This notion of equivalence is stronger than the usual almost sure equality; two invariant random variables equivalent in this sense are equivalent in the sense of ch. 3 § 3. Finally, the operators θ_n operate on the equivalence classes of asymptotic random variables, and the classes of invariant random variables are those which are invariant under θ_n.

We shall state a result similar to ch. 3, Proposition 3.2, for which we need the following notational device: we define a T.P. denoted by Q on $(E \times \mathbf{N}, \mathscr{E} \otimes \mathscr{P}(\mathbf{N}))$ by setting

$$Q((x, n), A \times \{m\}) = \begin{cases} P(x, A) & \text{if } m = n + 1, \\ 0 & \text{if } m \neq n + 1. \end{cases}$$

For every probability measure P_x on $(\Omega, \mathscr{F})$ and every integer m, the sequence $\{Y_n\} = \{(X_n, n + m)\}$ is a homogeneous Markov chain with T.P. Q, called a *space–time* chain (ch. 1, Exercise 2.17(2)).

Proposition 2.3. *The formula*

$$h(x, n) = E_x[Z_n] = E_x[Z \circ \theta_{-n}]$$

sets up a one-to-one correspondence between the equivalence classes of asymptotic and bounded random variables and the bounded Q-harmonic functions. Moreover,

$$\lim_{n \to \infty} h(X_n, n) = Z \quad a.s.$$

Proof. If $Z \in \mathrm{b}\mathscr{A}$, we have

$$Qh(x, n) = E_x[E_{X_1}[Z_{n+1}]] = E_x[Z_{n+1} \circ \theta_1] = E_x[Z_n] = h(x, n),$$

and h is therefore Q-harmonic. Conversely if h is Q-harmonic and bounded, $h(X_n, n)$ is a bounded martingale which converges P_x-a.s. and in $L^1(P_x)$ for every $x \in E$. The limit Z is almost surely asymptotic, since for every $m \in \mathbf{N}$ the sequence $h(X_n, n + m)$ converges also to a limit Z_m, and obviously $Z = Z_m \circ \theta_m$ a.s. The convergence in the L^1 sense implies clearly that $h(x, n) = E_x[Z_n]$.

Before we proceed, let us recall that a sub-σ-algebra $\mathscr{G}$ of $\mathscr{F}$ is said to be a.s. trivial if for every $A \in \mathscr{G}$ the function $P.[A]$ is identically zero or one; this is a more stringent condition than to be P_x-trivial for every $x \in E$.

Proposition 2.4. *The three following statements are equivalent:*
   (i) *the σ-algebra $\mathscr{A}$ is a.s. trivial;*
  (ii) *the bounded Q-harmonic functions are constant;*
 (iii) *for every pair (ν_1, ν_2) of probability measures on $\mathscr{E}$,*

$$\lim_{n \to \infty} \|(\nu_1 - \nu_2)\, P_n\| = 0,$$

where the norm is the usual norm for bounded measures.

Proof. (ii) implies (i), since the notion of equivalence for $\mathscr{A}$ is more stringent than almost sure equality.

We show that (i) implies (iii). Set $\mathscr{A}_n = \theta_n^{-1}(\mathscr{F})$; choose $B \in \mathscr{F}$ and ν a bounded measure on $\mathscr{E}$. We have

$$\lim_{n \to \infty} \sup_{A \in \mathscr{A}_n} |P_\nu(A \cap B) - P_\nu(A)\, P_\nu(B)| = 0. \tag{2.1}$$

Indeed

$$\sup_{A \in \mathscr{A}_n} |P_\nu(A \cap B) - P_\nu(A)\, P_\nu(B)| = \sup_{A \in \mathscr{A}_n} \left| \int_A (1_B - P_\nu(B))\, \mathrm{d}P_\nu \right|$$

$$= \sup_{A \in \mathscr{A}_n} \left| \int_A (P_\nu(B \mid \mathscr{A}_n) - P_\nu(B))\, \mathrm{d}P_\nu \right| \leqslant \int_\Omega |P_\nu(B \mid \mathscr{A}_n) - P_\nu(B)|\, \mathrm{d}P_\nu,$$

and the latter integral tends to zero since $\bigcap \mathscr{A}_n = \mathscr{A}$ is P_ν-a.s. trivial.

Let then ν^+ and ν^- be the positive and negative parts of the measure $\nu_1 - \nu_2$, E^+ and E^- the sets of its Jordan–Hahn decomposition. Put $\nu = \nu^+ + \nu^-$ and choose $\Gamma \in \mathscr{E}$. Applying eq. (2.1) twice with $A = \{X_n \in \Gamma\}$, $B = \{X_0 \in E^+\}$ or $\{X_0 \in E^-\}$ yields

$$\lim_{n \to \infty} \sup_{\Gamma \in \mathscr{E}} |P_{\nu+}(X_n \in \Gamma) - P_{\nu+}(X_0 \in E^+)\, P_\nu(X_n \in \Gamma)| = 0,$$

$$\lim_{n \to \infty} \sup_{\Gamma \in \mathscr{E}} |P_{\nu-}(X_n \in \Gamma) - P_{\nu-}(X_0 \in E^-)\, P_\nu(X_n \in \Gamma)| = 0;$$

as $P_{\nu+}(X_0 \in E^+) = P_{\nu-}(X_0 \in E^-)$, it follows that

$$\lim_{n \to \infty} \sup_{\Gamma \in \mathscr{E}} |P_{\nu+}(X_n \in \Gamma) - P_{\nu-}(X_n \in \Gamma)| = 0,$$

that is,

$$\lim_{n \to \infty} \|(\nu_1 - \nu_2) P_n\| = 0.$$

Finally we show that (iii) implies (ii). Let h be a bounded Q-harmonic function; for every n we have

$$|h(x, n) - h(y, n)| = \left| \int h(z, n + m) (P_m(x, dz) - P_m(y, dz)) \right|$$
$$\leqslant \|h\| \|P_m(x, \cdot) - P_m(y, \cdot)\|,$$

and by (iii) this can be made arbitrarily small. The function h thus depends only on n and is then easily seen to be constant.

In the course of the proof we have shown the following:

Corollary 2.5. *If ν is a bounded measure such that $\nu(E) = 0$ and $\mathscr{A}$ is $P_{|\nu|}$-a.s. trivial, then*

$$\lim_{n \to \infty} \|\nu P_n\| = 0.$$

We are now going to apply these results to Harris chains. Some applications to random walks are given in Exercises 2.19–2.21.

Theorem 2.6. *If X is an aperiodic Harris chain, the σ-algebra $\mathscr{A}$ is almost surely trivial.*

Proof. By Proposition 2.4, it suffices to show that the bounded Q-harmonic functions h are constant. It is enough to prove that they do not depend on n, since the function $h(x) = h(x, n)$ will then be P-harmonic and bounded and therefore constant.

If h is not constant in the second coordinate, there exists x_0 such that $h(x_0, 0) \neq h(x_0, 1)$. Let Z and Z_1 be the asymptotic variables that are the limits of the sequences $h(X_n, n)$ and $h(X_n, n + 1)$.

We have $P_{x_0}[Z \neq Z_1] > 0$ and we may assume $P_{x_0}[Z < Z_1] > 0$. (The other case can be treated in the same way.) There exist two real numbers a, b such that $P_{x_0}[Z < a < b < Z_1] = \delta > 0$ and if we set

$$A = \{(x, n): h(x, n) < a\} \quad \text{and} \quad B = \{(x, n): h(x, n + 1) > b\}$$

then

$$P_{x_0}\left[\varliminf_n \{(X_n, n) \in A \cap B\} \right] \geqslant \delta.$$

Put

$$g(x, m) = P_x \left[\bigcap_{n=0}^{\infty} \{(X_n, n + m) \in A \cap B\} \right];$$

from martingale theory (ch. 0, Proposition 2.2) we deduce that

$$g(X_n, n) = P_x \left[\bigcap_{p=n}^{\infty} \{(X_p, p) \in A \cap B\} \,\middle|\, \mathscr{F}_n \right]$$

converges a.s. to $\underline{\lim}_n \{(X_n, n) \in A \cap B\}$, so that $g(X_n, n)$ converges to one on an event of positive P_{x_0}-probability.

Since X is taken aperiodic, there exists, by § 1, a set C of positive measure, an integer m and a number $\varepsilon > 0$ such that

$$\inf\{p_m(x, y) \colon (x, y) \in C \times C\} \geqslant \varepsilon,$$

$$\inf\{p_{m+1}(x, y) \colon (x, y) \in C \times C\} \geqslant \varepsilon.$$

Since the chain X is in C infinitely often P_{x_0}-a.s., there exists a point (x_1, n_1) such that $x_1 \in C$ and $1 - g(x_1, n_1) < \frac{1}{4}\varepsilon\lambda(C)$. Put

$$C' = C \cap \{x \colon (x, n_1 + m) \notin A \cap B\};$$

we have

$$\varepsilon\lambda(C') \leqslant P_{x_1}[X_m \in C'] \leqslant P_{x_1}[(X_m, n_1 + m) \notin A \cap B] \leqslant 1 - g(x_1, n_1) \leqslant \tfrac{1}{4}\varepsilon\lambda(C).$$

In the same way, if

$$C'' = C \cap \{x \colon (x, n_1 + m + 1) \notin A \cap B\},$$

then $\lambda(C'') \leqslant \frac{1}{4}\lambda(C)$. Thus C contains a point x which does not belong to $C' \cup C''$, so that $(x, n_1 + m) \in A \cap B$ and $(x, n_1 + m + 1) \in A \cap B$. But this is impossible, since $(x, n_1 + m) \in B$ implies $h(x, n_1 + m) > b$ and therefore $(x, n_1 + m + 1) \notin A$. The proof is thus complete.

Corollary 2.7. *If X is a Harris chain of period d and $C_1, \ldots, C_d$ is a cyclic decomposition of E (F is assumed to be $\emptyset$) the σ-algebra $\mathscr{A}$ is a.s. equivalent to the σ-algebra generated by the events $\{X_0 \in C_i\}$.*

Proof. For every $n \in \mathbf{N}$,

$$\{X_0 \in C_i\} = \{X_{n(d-1)} \circ \theta_n \in C_i\} \quad \text{a.s.,}$$

and thus $\{X_0 \in C_i\}$ is an asymptotic event. If $A \in \mathscr{A}$, there exist sets A_{nd} such that $A = \theta_{nd}^{-1}(A_{nd})$, so that $A \cap \{X_0 \in C_i\}$ is asymptotic for the chain having transition probability P_d, which is aperiodic and to which we apply the above result.

Theorem 2.8 (Orey's theorem). *If X is Harris and aperiodic, for every pair (ν_1, ν_2) of probability measures on $\mathscr{E}$,*

$$\lim_{n \to \infty} \|(\nu_1 - \nu_2)\, P_n\| = 0.$$

In particular if $m(E) = 1$, for every probability measure ν on $\mathscr{E}$

$$\lim_{n \to \infty} \|\nu P_n - m\| = 0.$$

If X is periodic with period d, the statement is still true provided that for $i \leqslant d$, $\nu_1(C_i) = \nu_2(C_i)$ and $\nu_1(F) = \nu_2(F) = 0$.

Proof. The theorem follows immediately from Proposition 2.4 and Theorem 2.6.

If X is periodic, the preceding result may be stated in a different way. Each class C_i is an absorbing set for the chain with T.P. P_d; the restriction of this chain to C_i is Harris, aperiodic, and its invariant measure m_i is the restriction of m on C_i. If ν_1 and ν_2 vanish outside C_i, for every integer k

$$\lim_{n \to \infty} \|(\nu_1 - \nu_2)\, P_{nd}\| = \lim_{n \to \infty} \|(\nu_1 - \nu_2)\, P_{nd+k}\| = 0.$$

If $m(E) = 1$ then

$$\lim_{n \to \infty} \|\nu P_{nd+k} - m_{i+k}\| = 0,$$

where $i + k$ is understood modulo d. We can therefore state

Corollary 2.9. *If $m(E) = 1$ and $\nu(F) = 0$, for every integer k*

$$\lim_{n \to \infty} \left\| \nu P_{nd+k} - \sum_{i=1}^{d} \nu(C_i)\, m_{i+k} \right\| = 0.$$

It is customary to lay down the following

Definition 2.10. The chain X is said to be *positive* or *ergodic* if $m(E) < \infty$ (and then we always take $m(E) = 1$) and *null* if $m(E) = \infty$.

Null chains and positive chains have quite different asymptotic behaviours.[/]
We have just seen that, for a positive and aperiodic chain, $\lim_n P_n f(x) = m(f)$
for every $x \in E$ and $f \in b\mathscr{E}$. The following result, which does not require X
to be aperiodic, shows that a null chain is "less recurrent" than a positive
chain. Other evidence to support this statement is given in ch. 3, Corollary
1.11.

Theorem 2.11. *If X is null, for every function $f \in L^1(m) \cap b\mathscr{E}$ and every $x \in E$,*

$$\lim_{n \to \infty} P_n f(x) = 0.$$

Proof. We shall show the more stringent property: for every $x \in E$ and $\varepsilon > 0$,

$$\lim_n \{P_n f(x)/(m(f) + \varepsilon)\} = 0,$$

the convergence being uniform in $f \in \{f \colon \|f\|_\infty \leqslant K\}$.

We first assume that X is aperiodic. If our statement were false, there would
exist a sequence $\{n_k\}$ tending to infinity, a sequence of functions f_k bounded
by a number K, a point x_0, and two numbers $\varepsilon, \delta > 0$ such that

$$P_{n_k} f_k(x_0)/(m(f_k) + \varepsilon) \geqslant \delta$$

for every k. Since $m(E) = \infty$, Egoroff's theorem and Proposition 2.4 allow
us to pick a set B in $\mathscr{E}$ such that $m(B) > 2\delta^{-1}$ and such that

$$\|P_{n_k}(x_0, \cdot\,) - P_{n_k}(y, \cdot\,)\|$$

tends to zero uniformly in y on B. Hence

$$m(f_k) \geqslant \int_B m(\mathrm{d}x)\, P_{n_k} f_k(x) \geqslant \int_B m(\mathrm{d}x)\, (P_{n_k} f_k(x_0) - \tfrac{1}{2}\varepsilon\delta)$$

if k is sufficiently large to have

$$K\|P_{n_k}(x_0, \cdot\,) - P_{n_k}(y, \cdot\,)\| < \tfrac{1}{2}\varepsilon\delta$$

on B. These two relations together imply

$$1 > m(f_k)/(m(f_k) + \varepsilon) \geqslant \int_B m(\mathrm{d}x)\, (\delta - \tfrac{1}{2}\varepsilon\delta)\, (m(f_k) + \varepsilon) \geqslant \tfrac{1}{2}\delta m(B),$$

which is a contradiction.

Suppose that X is periodic and let $C_1, \ldots, C_d, F$ be a cyclic decomposition
of E. If $x \in C_i$, then $P(f 1_F)(x) = 0$. Considering the chain on C_i of T.P.

P_d, we conclude from above that $P_n f(x)/(m(f) + \varepsilon)$ tends to zero uniformly in $\{f \colon \|f\| \leqslant K\}$. If $x \in F$, then for $r < n$

$$\frac{P_n f(x)}{m(f) + \varepsilon} = \sum_{j=1}^{r} \int_F \cdots \int_F \int_{E \setminus F} P(x, dx_1) \cdots P(x_{j-1}, dx_j) \frac{P_{n-j} f(x_j)}{m(f) + \varepsilon}$$

$$+ \int_F \cdots \int_F P(x, dx_1) \cdots P(x_{r-1}, dx_r) \frac{P_{n-r} f(x_r)}{m(f) + \varepsilon}.$$

Since F is transient, $P_n(x, F)$ tends to zero as n tends to infinity, and one can choose r large enough to make the second term on the right as small as we please uniformly in n and f. After r has been chosen, since $P_{n-j} f(x_j)/(m(f) + \varepsilon)$ tends to zero on $E \setminus F$, and is dominated by the integrable function $1/\varepsilon$, we can make the first term as small as we choose by taking n sufficiently large.

Exercise 2.12. A point transformation θ on $(E, \mathscr{E})$ (ch. 1, Examples 1.4) possessing an invariant probability measure ν, is said to be *strongly mixing* if, for every pair (A, B) of sets in $\mathscr{E}$,

$$\lim_n \nu(\theta^{-n}(A) \cap B) = \nu(A)\nu(B).$$

Show that the shift operator of a positive recurrent Harris chain is strongly mixing on $(\Omega, \mathscr{F}, P_m)$.

Exercise 2.13. Show that, if X is Harris and positive, then for every $f \in L^p(m)$, the sequence $P_n f$ converges to $m(f)$ in the L^p sense $(1 \leqslant p < \infty)$.

Exercise 2.14. With the notation of § 1, prove that if X is Harris, for every pair (x, y) of points in E the sequence of functions $p_n(x, \cdot) - p_n(y, \cdot)$ converges to zero in $L^1(m)$. If X is positive $p_n(x, \cdot)$ converges to 1 in $L^1(m)$.

Exercise 2.15. If X is null then $P_n f$ converges to zero for all functions f which belong to the closure of $b\mathscr{E} \cap L^1(m)$ in the topology of uniform convergence. If E is LCCB and P maps C_K into C_0, then $P_n f$ converges to zero for all functions f in C_0.

Exercise 2.16. Consider the following discrete chain. The states are labelled (n, m) with $n \geqslant 1$ and $1 \leqslant m \leqslant 2^n$. The T.P. is given by

$$P((n, m), (n, m + 1)) = 1 \quad \text{if } m < 2^n$$

and

$$P((n, 2^n), (n + 1, 1)) = P((n, 2^n), (n + 2, 1)) = \tfrac{1}{2}.$$

(1) Prove that the σ-algebra $\mathcal{T}$ is a.s. trivial.

(2) Show that the σ-algebra $\mathcal{A}$ is not atomic and thus contains $\mathcal{T}$ strictly.

[*Hint*: The knowledge of $X_n(\omega) = (N_n(\omega), M_n(\omega))$ implies the knowledge of all the differences $N_k(\omega) - N_{k-1}(\omega)$ for $k \leqslant n$; hence the events $\{N_k - N_{k-1} = 1\}$ and $\{N_k - N_{k-1} = 2\}$ are in $\mathcal{A}$ for every k.]

Exercise 2.17. For a periodic chain, show that the powers P_n converge in the sense of Cesaro.

Exercise 2.18. Let $A = \{g_1, \ldots, g_m\}$ be a finite set of generators of a group G. Every element g in G can be written as at least one "word" $g_{i_1} \cdots g_{i_n}$, where $g_{i_n} \in A$. Denote by $r_n(g)$ the number of words of length n representing g.

(1) Show that G is finite if and only if the numbers $r_n(g)/m^n$ converge in the sense of Cesaro to a non-zero limit as n tends to infinity.

[*Hint*: Use the T.P. defined by $P(g, h) = 1/n$ if $gg_i = h$ for a $g_i \in A$, $P(g, h) = 0$ otherwise.]

(2) Prove that one cannot use the ordinary limit instead of the Cesaro limit in (1).

[*Hint*: Use the cyclic group of order k which has only one generator.]

Exercise 2.19. Let μ be a probability measure on a group G, and H the smallest closed normal subgroup containing the support of $\mu * \hat{\mu}$ (cf. ch. 3, Exercise 4.17).

(1) Prove that the set of bounded measures on G such that $\lim_n \|\mu^n * \nu\| = 0$ is an ideal (in the convolution algebra of G) contained in the kernel of the canonical mapping from $b\mathcal{M}(G)$ into $b\mathcal{M}(G/H)$.

(2) If the left random walk of law μ is recurrent in the sense of Harris prove that G/H is finite, that the cosets of H are the cyclic classes (cf. Exercise 1.6) and that the inclusion in (1) is an equality. If X is not Harris but merely recurrent, state and prove a similar result.

[*Hint*: Use ch. 3, Exercise 3.14.]

Exercise 2.20. By using the random variables $Z \circ \theta_n$ for $n < 0$, show that one can extend uniquely Q-harmonic functions on $E \times \mathbf{N}$ to Q-harmonic functions on $E \times \mathbf{Z}$, and restate Proposition 2.3 in that case.

Exercise 2.21. Continuation of Exercises 2.19 and 2.20. Let μ be a spread-out probability measure on an abelian group G.

(1) Prove that the sub-group H' of periods of Q-harmonic functions is such that $G \times \mathbf{Z}/H'$ is isomorphic to G/H.

[*Hint*: Use the Choquet–Deny theorem.]

(2) Prove that the inclusion in Exercise 2.19 (1) is an equality.

(3) If G is connected, for every bounded measure ν such that $\nu(G) = 0$,

$$\lim_{n}\|\mu^n * \nu\| = 0.$$

Exercise 2.22. (1) Prove that there exist Harris random walks on the group of rigid motions of the Euclidean plane.

(2) Let μ be the law of such a random walk. For every pair (ν_1, ν_2) of probability measures on the plane,

$$\lim_{n}\|\mu^n * \nu_1 - \mu^n * \nu_2\| = 0.$$

(Of course the plane is to be considered as a homogeneous space of the group of rigid motions.)

Exercise 2.23. For resolvents recurrent in the sense of Harris (ch. 3, Exercise 2.22), state and prove results similar to Theorems 2.8 and 2.11.

[*Hint*: One should look for the asymptotic behaviour of αV_α as α tends to zero. For $\alpha < 1$ one can write

$$\alpha V_\alpha = \sum_{n=0}^{\infty} (1 - \alpha)^n \, (V_1)^{n+1}.]$$

3. Quasi-compact transition probabilities and the strong ergodic theorem

Following the usual terminology for convergence of operators on a Banach space, one defines, for the contractions P_n of b$\mathscr{E}$, several types of convergence.

Definition 3.1. The operators P_n are said to converge to a bounded operator T

(i) *uniformly* if

$$\lim_{n \to \infty} \|P_n - T\| = \lim_{n \to \infty} \sup_{\|f\| \leqslant 1} \sup_{x \in E} |P_n f(x) - T f(x)| = 0;$$

(ii) *strongly* if, for every $f \in$ b$\mathscr{E}$,

$$\lim_{n \to \infty} \|P_n f - Tf\| = \lim_{n \to \infty} \sup_{x \in E} |P_n f(x) - T f(x)| = 0;$$

(iii) *weakly* if, for every $f \in b\mathscr{E}$ and every $\nu \in b\mathscr{M}(\mathscr{E})$,

$$\lim_{n \to \infty} \langle \nu, P_n f - Tf \rangle = 0.$$

The weak convergence is equivalent to simple convergence on E of functions $P_n f$.

Orey's theorem asserts that if X is positive recurrent, the operators P_{nd} converge weakly to the operator with finite range $\sum_{i=1}^{d} 1_{C_i} \otimes m_i$. The present section is devoted to the study of the necessary and sufficient conditions for this convergence to be uniform. For this purpose we need the following

Definition 3.2. The transition probability P is said to be *quasi-compact* if there exists a sequence $\{U_n\}$ of compact operators on $b\mathscr{E}$ such that

$$\lim_{n} \|P_n - U_n\| = 0.$$

In the following section, we shall show that with each Harris chain we can associate plenty of quasi-compact operators. We begin with another definition of quasi-compactness.

Proposition 3.3. *The T.P. P is quasi-compact if and only if there exist a compact operator U and an integer n_0 such that*

$$\|P_{n_0} - U\| < 1.$$

Proof. The necessity is obvious. To prove the sufficiency, let us first recall that the set of compact operators is a closed two-sided ideal in the algebra of bounded operators.

Assume that $P_{n_0} = U + Q$, where U is compact and $\|Q\| < 1$. An integer $n > n_0$ may be written $n = mn_0 + l$ in only one way with $m \geqslant 1$ and $0 \leqslant l < n_0$; so

$$P_n = (U + Q)^m P_l = U_n + Q^m P_l,$$

where U_n is compact. Since

$$\|Q^m P_l\| \leqslant \left(\sup_{l < n_0} \|P_l\| \right) \|Q^m\| \xrightarrow[n \to \infty]{} 0,$$

the T.P. P is quasi-compact.

Remark. In Definition 3.2 and Proposition 3.3, one can put "operator with finite range" instead of "compact operator" without altering their validity.

Proposition 3.4. *If there exists an integer d such that P_{nd+k} converges uniformly to an operator with finite range, then P is quasi-compact.*

Proof. Obvious from Proposition 3.3.

We now shall prove that this condition is also sufficient. We call $\mathcal{K}$ the space of Q-harmonic functions on $E \times \mathbf{N}$ which were defined in the last section; the space $\mathcal{K}$ is a Banach sub-space of $b(\mathcal{E} \otimes \mathcal{P}(\mathbf{N}))$, and for $f \in \mathcal{K}$,

$$\|f\| = \lim_n \|f(\,\cdot\,, n)\|.$$

Proposition 3.5. *The following two statements are equivalent:*
(i) *the σ-algebra of equivalence classes of asymptotic events is a.s. finite;*
(ii) *the dimension of $\mathcal{K}$ is finite.*
If these equivalent conditions are satisfied, there exists a finite number of integers d_ρ ($\rho = 1, 2, \ldots, r$) and functions $U_{\rho,\delta}$ in $\mathcal{E}_+$, where δ is an integer taken modulo d_ρ, such that every element f in $\mathcal{K}$ has a unique representation

$$f(\,\cdot\,, n) = \sum_{\rho=1}^{r} \sum_{\delta=1}^{d_\rho} C_{\rho,\delta}\, U_{\rho,\delta+n}$$

where $C_{\rho,\delta} \in \mathbf{R}$. If we set $U_\rho = \sum_{\delta=1}^{d_\rho} U_{\rho,\delta}$, every bounded harmonic function f has a unique representation

$$f = \sum_{\rho=1}^{r} b_\rho U_\rho.$$

Moreover one may choose the functions $U_{\rho,\delta}$ in one and only one way in order that

$$\sum_{\rho=1}^{r} \sum_{d=1}^{d_\rho} U_{\rho,\delta} = 1.$$

Proof. The equivalence of (i) and (ii) is an obvious consequence of Proposition 2.3. Assume now that these conditions are satisfied, and consider a finite partition $\mathcal{P}$ of Ω consisting of atoms of $\mathcal{A}$. For every $A \in \mathcal{P}$ the event $\theta_n^{-1}(A)$ is also an atom of $\mathcal{A}$; otherwise we would have $1_A \circ \theta_n = 1_{B_1} + 1_{B_2}$ with $B_1 \cap B_2 = \emptyset$, hence

$$1_A = 1_B \circ \theta_n^{-1} + 1_{B_2} \circ \theta_n^{-1},$$

and since these two sets are disjoint we would have a contradiction.

Consequently the group θ_n $(n \in \mathbf{Z})$ induces a one-to-one group of transformations of $\mathscr{P}$. One can therefore partition $\mathscr{P}$ into r classes invariant under θ and within each, label the atoms as $A_{\rho,\delta}$ in such a way that $\theta_n^{-1}(A_{\rho,\delta}) = A_{\rho,\delta-n}$. It remains to set $U_{\rho,\delta} = P.[A_{\rho,\delta}]$ to get the desired result.

Proposition 3.6. *If P is quasi-compact, then $\mathscr{K}$ is finite dimensional.*

Proof. A Banach space is finite dimensional if and only if it is locally compact. It suffices therefore to prove that the unit ball $\mathscr{K}_1$ of $\mathscr{K}$ can be covered, for any $\varepsilon > 0$, by a finite number of balls of radius less than ε. This amounts to showing that there exist at most a finite number of points in $\mathscr{K}_1$ such that their pairwise distance is greater than ε.

Fix $\varepsilon > 0$ and choose n such that $\|P_n - U\| < \tfrac{1}{4}\varepsilon$ for a compact operator U. There exist a finite number N of balls of radius $\tfrac{1}{4}\varepsilon$, with centres f_k $(k = 1, 2, \ldots, N)$ which cover $U(\mathscr{K}_1)$. Therefore the N balls with centre f_k and radius $\tfrac{1}{2}\varepsilon$ cover $P_n(\mathscr{K}_1)$ and one cannot find more than N points in $P_n(\mathscr{K}_1)$ whose pairwise distance is greater than ε. Then the same property is true for $\mathscr{K}_1$, since otherwise there would exist $N + 1$ points g_k in $\mathscr{K}_1$ such that, for $k \neq k'$ and m sufficiently large,

$$\|g_k(\,\cdot\,, m) - g_{k'}(\,\cdot\,, m)\| > \varepsilon,$$

but as

$$g_k(\,\cdot\,, m) = P_n g_k(\,\cdot\,, n + m) \in P_n(\mathscr{K}_1),$$

this is impossible.

If P is quasi-compact, we are therefore in the situation described in Proposition 3.5, the notation of which we use below.

Theorem 3.7. *If P is quasi-compact, there exist $d_\rho \geqslant 1$ $(\rho = 1, \ldots, r)$ bounded measurable functions $U_{\rho,\delta}$ $(\delta = 1, 2, \ldots, d)$ such that $\sum_\rho \sum_\delta U_{\rho,\delta} = 1$, and probability measures $m_{\rho,\delta}$ carried by the pairwise disjoint sets $E_{\rho,\delta} = \{U_{\rho,\delta} = 1\}$ such that, if d denotes the least common multiple of the d_ρ, then for every k,*

$$\lim_{n \to \infty} \left\| P_{nd+k} - \sum_{\rho=1}^{r} \sum_{r=1}^{d_\rho} U_{\rho,\delta-k} \otimes m_{\rho,\delta} \right\| = 0.$$

The sets $E_\rho = \bigcup_\delta E_{\rho,\delta}$ are absorbing sets, and the chain induced on E_ρ is a Harris chain with invariant measure $m_\rho = \sum_\delta m_{\rho,\delta}$. The sets $E_{\rho,\delta}$ and the number d_ρ are the corresponding cyclic classes and period.

Proof. We start by showing that the operators P_{nd+k} converge strongly.

Fix $\varepsilon > 0$ and pick an integer k and a compact operator U such that $\|P_k - U\| < \frac{1}{2}\varepsilon$. The image $U(\mathscr{U})$ of the unit ball $\mathscr{U}$ of $b\mathscr{E}$ can be covered by a finite number of balls of radius ε, hence is relatively compact in $b\mathscr{E}$.

Then using the diagonal procedure there exists a sequence n_j such that $g(\cdot, m) = \lim_j P_{n_j d - m} f$ exists for every m in the sense of convergence in the norm of $b\mathscr{E}$. Clearly the function g is in $\mathscr{K}_1$ and by virtue of Proposition 3.5, $g(\cdot, nd + m) = g(\cdot, m)$ for every n and therefore $P_{nd-m} g(\cdot, 0) = g(\cdot, m)$ as long as $nd \geqslant m \geqslant 0$. Consequently, if $nd \geqslant n_j d + m$,

$$\|P_{nd-m} f - g(\cdot, m)\| = \|P_{(n-n_j)d-m}(P_{n_j} f - g(\cdot, 0))\| \leqslant \|P_{n_j d} f - g(\cdot, 0)\|.$$

Letting n, and then n_j, tend to infinity, we get that $P_{nd-m} f$ converges to $g(\cdot, m)$ in $b\mathscr{E}$, and thus the operators P_{nd-m} converge strongly.

We proceed by showing that this convergence is in fact uniform. The preceding discussion allows us to define a contraction S of $b\mathscr{E}$ by setting $Sf = \lim_n P_{nd} f$. For every integer m, $SP_{md} = P_{md} S = S$. Fix $\varepsilon > 0$ and choose an integer $m > 0$ and a compact operator U such that $\|P_{md} - U\| < \varepsilon$. For every $f \in \mathscr{U}$, we have

$$\|P_{(n+m)d} f - Sf\| = \|(P_{nd} - S) P_{md} f\| \leqslant 2\varepsilon + \|(P_{nd} - S) Uf\|;$$

since $U(\mathscr{U})$ is relatively compact, the convergence

$$\lim_{n \to \infty} \|(P_{nd} - S) Uf\| = 0$$

is uniform on $\mathscr{U}$. It follows, upon letting n tend to infinity and then ε to zero, that the convergence $\lim_n P_{nd} = S$ is uniform. This implies that P_{nd+m} also converges uniformly to $P_m S = SP_m$.

By virtue of Proposition 3.5, for every $f \in b\mathscr{E}$ there exist uniquely determined numbers $C_{\rho,\delta}(f)$ such that

$$Sf = \sum_{\rho=1}^{r} \sum_{\delta=1}^{d_\rho} C_{\rho,\delta}(f) \, U_{\rho,\delta}.$$

Since S is the uniform limit of transition probabilities, it is easily seen that the mappings $f \to C_{\rho,\delta}(f)$ are defined by probability measures $m_{\rho,\delta}$, and thus S can be written

$$S = \sum_{\rho=1}^{r} \sum_{\delta=1}^{d_\rho} U_{\rho,\delta} \otimes m_{\rho,\delta}.$$

It follows from $P_d U_{\rho,\delta} = U_{\rho,\delta}$, that $S U_{\rho,\delta} = U_{\rho,\delta}$; hence $\langle m_{\rho',\delta'}, U_{\rho,\delta} \rangle = 1$ or 0 according as $\rho = \rho'$ and $\delta = \delta'$ (mod d_ρ) or not. Finally, the equalities

$$\sum_\rho \sum_\delta (U_{\rho,\delta} \otimes m_{\rho,\delta}) P_n = S P_n = P_n S = \sum_\rho \sum_\delta P_n U_{\rho,\delta} \otimes m_{\rho,\delta}$$

$$= \sum_\rho \sum_\delta U_{\rho,\delta-n} \otimes m_{\rho,\delta} = \sum_\rho \sum_\delta U_{\rho,\delta} \otimes m_{\rho,\delta+n}$$

imply that $m_{\rho,\delta} P_n = m_{\rho,\delta+n}$.

Now denote $E_{\rho,\delta} = \{U_{\rho,\delta} = 1\}$. Clearly $m_{\rho,\delta}(E_{\rho,\delta}) = 1$, and by Proposition 3.5 the sets $E_{\rho,\delta}$ are pairwise disjoint. From the equality

$$1 - U_{\rho,\delta}(x) = \int P(x, \mathrm{d}y) \, (1 - U_{\rho,\delta+1}(y))$$

it follows that $E_{\rho,\delta} = \{x : P(x, E_{\rho,\delta+1}) = 1\}$. The sets E_ρ are therefore absorbing sets, the measure m_ρ is clearly invariant and by the uniform convergence the restriction of X to E_ρ is m_ρ-irreducible and therefore recurrent in the sense of Harris. The last statement is obvious.

3.8. Denote by ν any convex combination of the probability measures $m_{\rho,\delta}$. It is easily seen that P satisfies the following condition, known as *Doeblin's condition: there exist an integer n, two real numbers $\theta < 1$ and $\eta > 0$, and a probability measure ν on $(E, \mathscr{E})$ such that, for $A \in \mathscr{E}$,*

$$\nu(A) > \theta \qquad implies \qquad P_n(\cdot, A) \geqslant \eta \quad on \ E.$$

This condition is in fact also sufficient for P to be quasi-compact. This will be shown at the end of this section for the case $r = 1$ and $E_1 = E$.

For a further study of Harris chains with quasi-compact T.P., we recall a few definitions and facts which are relevant to the general theory of Riesz spaces.

Definition 3.9. A continuous linear functional on $\mathrm{b}\mathscr{E}$ is called a *mean*.

Every mean has a minimal decomposition as a sum of a finite measure and of a *pure mean*; a pure mean is a mean that is singular with respect to all measures. A mean φ is said to be *invariant* if for every $f \in \mathrm{b}\mathscr{E}$, we have $\langle \varphi, f \rangle = \langle \varphi, Pf \rangle$. Finally, if m is bounded we set

$$\mathrm{b}^\circ\mathscr{E} = \{f \in \mathrm{b}\mathscr{E} ; \ m(f) = 0\}.$$

Theorem 3.10. *If X is a Harris chain with invariant measure m, the following statements are equivalent:*

(i) P is quasi-compact;

(ii) $n^{-1} \sum_{k=1}^{n} P_k$ converges uniformly to an operator of rank one;

(iii) there exists no invariant pure mean;

(iii)' there exists no positive invariant pure mean;

(iv) the measure m is bounded and

$$(I - P) \, \mathrm{b}\mathscr{E} = \overline{(I - P) \, \mathrm{b}\mathscr{E}} = \mathrm{b}^\circ \mathscr{E}$$

(v) the measure m is bounded and is the only invariant mean.

Proof. We first observe that (iii)' is equivalent to (iii). Indeed, if φ is an invariant pure mean, call φ^+ and φ^- the positive and negative part of its minimal decomposition. From the equality $\varphi^+ - \varphi^- = \varphi^+ P - \varphi^- P$, it follows that $\varphi^+ \leqslant \varphi^+ P$ and $\varphi^- \leqslant \varphi^- P$; but since $P1 = 1$ these inequalities are in fact equalities. Thus φ^+ and φ^- are positive invariant pure means, and the result follows.

The proof will now be performed according to the following scheme of implications:

$$\text{(i)} \Rightarrow \text{(ii)} \Rightarrow \text{(iii)} \Rightarrow \text{(i)} \Rightarrow \text{(iv)} \Rightarrow \text{(v)} \Rightarrow \text{(iii)}.$$

(i) $\Rightarrow$ (ii) is an easy consequence of Theorem 3.7, and is left to the reader as Exercise 3.13.

(ii) $\Rightarrow$ (iii). If $n^{-1} \sum_1^n P_k$ converges uniformly to an operator of rank 1, it is easily seen that this operator is necessarily $1 \otimes m$. If φ is an invariant pure mean, there exists a set $A \in \mathscr{E}$ such that $m(A) > 0$ and $\varphi(A) = 0$. If φ were invariant, for every n we should have

$$\left\langle \varphi, \, n^{-1} \sum_1^n P_k(\,\cdot\,, A) \right\rangle = 0,$$

and this is impossible since the sequence on the right converges in $\mathrm{b}\mathscr{E}$ to the constant $m(A)$.

(iii) $\Rightarrow$ (i). We begin with the following remark. If P has no invariant pure mean, then P_k, for any integer k, has the same property. Indeed if φ is a pure mean and $\varphi P_k = \varphi$, then the mean $\sum_0^{k-1} \varphi P_n$ is invariant by P, hence is not pure. Consequently, there is an integer $0 < n < k$ such that φP_n is not pure, and then $\varphi P_k = \varphi P_n P_{k-n}$ is not pure either, which yields a contradiction.

By § 1 we know that, X being Harris, there exists an integer n such that P_n is the sum of an integral kernel K and of another kernel. By ch. 1, Theorem 5.7 there exist sets $A_k \in \mathscr{E}$ of arbitrarily large measure such that $I_{A_k} K$ is a compact operator on b$\mathscr{E}$. We may therefore write $P_n = Q + R$, where Q is compact and $m\{R1 < 1\} > 0$. Moreover, we may pick n outside the set of multiples of d in order that m be the only measure invariant by P_n. We will be finished if we show that there exists a k such that $\|R^k\| < 1$.

Let φ be an invariant mean for R and $\varphi = \varphi^+ - \varphi^-$ its minimal decomposition into positive and negative parts. From $\varphi R = \varphi$, we derive $\varphi^+ \leqslant \varphi^+ R \leqslant \varphi^+ P_n$, and since $P_n 1 = 1$, $\varphi^+ = \varphi^+ P_n$. Let $\varphi^+ = \varphi_1 + \varphi_2$, where φ_1 is a measure and φ_2 a pure mean. The equality $\varphi_1 + \varphi_2 = \varphi_1 P_n + \varphi_2 P_n$ implies that $\varphi_1 \geqslant \varphi_1 P_n$, and since X is Harris, $\varphi_1 = \varphi_1 P_n$, and thus $\varphi_2 = \varphi_2 P_n$. Since P_n has no invariant pure mean, $\varphi_2 = 0$ and φ^+ is zero or a multiple of m. In the latter case, since $m\{R1 < 1\} > 0$, we have

$$\langle \varphi^+, 1 \rangle > \langle \varphi^+, R1 \rangle,$$

which is a contradiction. In the same way we prove that $\varphi^- = 0$, so that the kernel R has no invariant mean.

Consequently, by the Hahn–Banach theorem, we have $\overline{(I - R) \, \mathrm{b}\mathscr{E}} = \mathrm{b}\mathscr{E}$, since a mean which is zero on $(I - R) \, \mathrm{b}\mathscr{E}$ is R-invariant. For every $\varepsilon > 0$, there exists therefore a function $g \in \mathrm{b}\mathscr{E}$ such that $\|g - Rg - 1\| < \varepsilon$. Hence

$$\left\| n^{-1} \sum_{k=1}^{n} R^k 1 \right\| \leqslant \left\| n^{-1} \sum_{k=1}^{n} R^k (1 - g + Rg) \right\| + \left\| n^{-1} \sum_{k=1}^{n} R^k (g - Rg) \right\|$$

$$\leqslant \varepsilon + 2\|g\| \, n^{-1};$$

it follows that $n^{-1} \sum_{k=1}^{n} R^k 1$ converges uniformly to zero, and since $R^k 1$ is a decreasing function of k, this proves that $\|R^k 1\| < 1$ for k sufficiently large.

(i) $\Rightarrow$ (iv). We have already seen that if P is quasi-compact, the measure m is bounded. Clearly $(I - P) \, \mathrm{b}°\mathscr{E} \subset \mathrm{b}°\mathscr{E}$. By the spectral theory of quasi-compact operators, the points of the spectrum of P located on the unit circle are eigenvalues; but X, being Harris, has no eigenfunction in $\mathrm{b}\mathscr{E}$; the operator $I - P$ has therefore a bounded inverse on $\mathrm{b}°\mathscr{E}$.

(iv) $\Rightarrow$ (v). The invariant means have value zero on $\overline{(I - P) \, \mathrm{b}°\mathscr{E}}$. If this subspace is equal to $\mathrm{b}°\mathscr{E}$, the measure m is the only invariant mean.

(v) $\Rightarrow$ (iii). Obvious.

Remark. We have shown that for a positive Harris chain $\overline{(I - P) \, \mathrm{b}\mathscr{E}} = \mathrm{b}°\mathscr{E}$ implies $(I - P) \, \mathrm{b}\mathscr{E} = \mathrm{b}°\mathscr{E}$; indeed the former equality implies (v), which implies (iii), which implies that P is quasi-compact, which implies the latter equality.

We now turn to the result announced in § 3.8.

Proposition 3.11. *If X is Harris, the following two statements are equivalent:*
(i) *P is quasi-compact;*
(ii) *P satisfies the Doeblin condition.*

Proof. We have already seen that (i) implies (ii). To show the converse, one can repeat the argument of (ii) $\Rightarrow$ (iii) in the preceding proof with ν instead of m. Hence P has no invariant pure mean, and is therefore quasi-compact.

Exercise 3.12. If E is finite, all T.P.'s on E are quasi-compact. Show by an example that the union of the sets $E_{\rho,\delta}$ may be a proper subset of E.

Exercise 3.13. Set $U_\rho = \sum_{\delta=1}^{d_\rho} U_{\rho,\delta}$, and prove that

$$\lim_{n\to\infty} \left\| n^{-1} \sum_1^n P_k - \sum_{\rho=1}^r U_\rho \otimes m_\rho \right\| = 0.$$

State and prove a similar result for positive Harris chains.

Exercise 3.14. With the notations of Proposition 3.5 and Theorem 3.7 show that

$$A_{\rho,\delta} = \lim_n \{X_n \in E_{\rho,\delta+n}\} \quad \text{a.s.}$$

Prove a similar result for invariant events. Prove that

$$U_\rho(x) = P_x[T_{E_\rho} < \infty].$$

Can one give a similar result for $U_{\rho,\delta}$?

Exercise 3.15. The powers P_n of P converge uniformly to $1 \otimes m$, where m is a probability measure on $(E, \mathscr{E})$ if and only if there exist an integer n, a real number $C > 0$ and a probability measure ν such that $P_n \geqslant C \otimes \nu$. (See also ch. 3, Lemma 2.4.)

Exercise 3.16. In the situation of Proposition 3.5, we set

$$\lambda_{\rho,k} = \exp(2i\pi k/d_\rho), \qquad f_{\rho,k} = \sum_\delta (\lambda_{\rho,k})^\delta U_{\rho,\delta},$$

where k is an integer modulo d_ρ. Prove that $Pf_{\rho,k} = \lambda_{\rho,k}f_{\rho,k}$. Show that for every complex number λ of modulus 1, the space of bounded measurable functions f such that $Pf = \lambda f$ is finite dimensional and admits as a basis the $f_{\rho,k}$ corresponding to those of the $\lambda_{\rho,k}$ equal to λ.

[*Hint*: Notice that $g(\,\cdot\,, n) = \lambda^{-n} f$ is Q-harmonic.]

Exercise 3.17. In Theorem **3.10**(ii), one can use strong convergence instead of uniform convergence.

Exercise 3.18. If a T.P. satisfies Theorem **3.10**(iii), then there exists a bounded invariant measure.

[*Hint*: Make P operate on the convex compact set (for $\sigma(b\mathscr{E}^*, b\mathscr{E})$) of positive invariant means, and apply a fixed point theorem.]

Exercise 3.19. Let M be a compact homogeneous space of a group G. We assume that there exists a continuous cross-section $s: M \to G$. Prove that, if μ is a spread-out probability measure on G, the T.P. $\mu * \varepsilon_x$ $(x \in M)$ is quasi-compact, and derive a convergence theorem. (See example in ch. 5 § 1.10.) In particular, if G is a compact connected group with normalized Haar measure m, and μ a spread-out probability measure on G, then

$$\lim_{n\to\infty} \sup_{x\in G}\|\mu^n * \varepsilon_x - m\| = \lim_{n\to\infty} \sup_{x\in G}\|\varepsilon_x * \mu^n - m\| = 0.$$

Exercise 3.20. Let (V_α), $\alpha > 0$, be a resolvent such that V_1 is quasi-compact. Prove that, as α tends to zero, αV_α converges uniformly to an operator of finite rank. (See also Exercises **2.23** and **4.14**.)

4. Special functions

We proceed with the study of Harris chains. Our goal is twofold: we want to build a potential theory suitable for the recurrent case – in particular we want to solve the Poisson equations – this will be initiated in the next section and achieved in chs. 8 and 9; on the other hand we want to show a general quotient limit theorem generalizing ch. 4, Exercise 3.9, and this will be done in § 6. Throughout this study the class of functions to be defined below will play a prominent role.

Definition 4.1. A function $f \in \mathscr{E}_+$ is said to be *special* if for every non-negligible function $g \in \mathscr{U}_+$, the function $U_g(f)$ is bounded. A set $A \in \mathscr{E}$ is called *special* if its characteristic function 1_A is special.

Proposition 4.2. *The set $\mathscr{S}$ of special functions is a convex hereditary sub-cone of $L^1_+(m)$.*

Proof. Let $g \in \mathscr{U}_+$ and $0 < m(g) < \infty$; by ch. 3, Proposition 2.11,

$$m(f) = m(g\, U_g(f)) \leqslant m(g)\, \|U_g(f)\| < \infty.$$

Moreover, every function dominated by a special function is obviously special.

To give a first characterization of special functions as well as for other important purposes, we need the following:

Proposition 4.3. *There exists a strictly positive function $h \in \mathscr{U}_+$ such that $m(h) < 1$ and $U_h > 1 \otimes m$.*

Proof. The chain is evidently m-irreducible; hence, by ch. 3, Proposition 2.3 and ch. 3, Proposition 2.9, there is a strictly positive function $h_0 \in \mathscr{U}_+$ and a measure m_0 equivalent to m such that $U_{h_0} \geqslant 1 \otimes m_0$. Let f be a strictly positive function such that $m_0 = fm$. The function $h = h_0 f/(1 + f)$ is a strictly positive function of $\mathscr{U}_+$, and

$$U_h > U_{h_0} I_{h_0 - h} U_h$$

$$\geqslant 1 \otimes ((h_0 - h)\, m_0)\, U_h = 1 \otimes (hm)\, U_h = 1 \otimes m$$

by virtue of ch. 3, Proposition 2.11. Since $1 = U_h(h) > m(h)$, the proof is complete.

Proposition 4.4. *Let h_0 be a strictly positive function in $\mathscr{U}_+$ such that $U_{h_0} \geqslant 1 \otimes m_0$ for a positive measure m_0. Then a function $f \in \mathscr{E}_+$ is special if and only if $U_{h_0}(f)$ is bounded on E.*

Proof. The necessity is obvious. Conversely suppose $U_{h_0}(f) \leqslant a$; for $0 < h \leqslant h_0$, we have

$$U_{h_0}(h_0 - h) = 1 - U_{h_0}(h) \leqslant 1 - m_0(h) < 1,$$

and therefore

$$U_h(f) = \sum_{n \geqslant 0} (U_{h_0} I_{h_0 - h})^n\, U_{h_0} f \leqslant a/m_0(h).$$

If h is the function of Proposition 4.3, the function $h' = h \wedge h_0$ has the same properties as h, since $U_{h'} \geqslant U_h$ and $0 < h' \leqslant h_0$, so that $U_{h'}(f) \leqslant a' = a/m_0(h')$. The above argument thus yields, for $g \leqslant h'$ and $m(g) > 0$,

$$U_g(f) \leqslant a'/m(g) < \infty.$$

Finally, if g is any non-negligible function in $\mathscr{U}_+$, the function $g \wedge h'$ satisfies the preceding conditions, and since $U_g(f) \leqslant U_{g \wedge h'}(f)$, we get the desired result.

Remark. Special functions are integrable by the measure m_0.

Corollary 4.5. *The cone $\mathscr{S}$ of special functions is invariant under the operators $I_h U_h$, where $h \in \mathscr{U}_+$ and $m(h) > 0$. In particular, it is invariant under P.*

Proof. Let $f \in \mathscr{S}$; if $0 \leqslant h \leqslant k \leqslant 1$, then $U_h \geqslant U_k$, hence

$$U_{h_0}(hU_h(f)) \leqslant U_{h_0 \wedge h}(hU_h(f)).$$

By the resolvent equation, we have therefore

$$U_{h_0}(hU_h(f)) \leqslant U_{h_0 \wedge h}(f) - U_h(f) + U_{h_0 \wedge h}((h \wedge h_0) U_h(f))$$
$$\leqslant \|U_{h_0 \wedge h}(f)\| + \|U_h(f)\|,$$

and this is finite since f is special.

The following corollary shows that there exist special functions, and that E is the union of an increasing sequence of special sets.

Corollary 4.6. *Every strictly positive function $h_0 \in \mathscr{U}_+$ such that $U_{h_0} \geqslant 1 \otimes m_0$ for a non-zero measure m_0 is special.*

Proof. Since $U_{h_0}(h_0) = 1$ this follows immediately from Proposition 4.3.

It follows from ch. 3 § 2 and ch. 6 § 3 that the T.P. $U_{h_0} I_{h_0}$ is quasi-compact. We shall now show a converse to this result, which will lead to another characterization of special functions.

Lemma 4.7. *Let $h \in \mathscr{U}_+$, c be a real number in $[0, 1[$ and $A \in \mathscr{E}$. For every T.P. on $(E, \mathscr{E})$ the following inequality holds on $\{U_A(1_A) = 1\}$:*

$$U_{ch}(1_A) \geqslant (1 - c) U_A(h).$$

Proof. By ch. 2, Definition 2.8,

$$U_{ch}1_A(x) = E_x\left[\sum_{n>0} (1 - ch(X_1)) \cdots (1 - ch(X_{n-1})) 1_A(X_n)\right]$$
$$\geqslant E_x[(1 - ch(X_1)) \cdots (1 - ch(X_{S_A-1}))].$$

If $U_A 1_A(x) = 1$, the stopping time S_A is P_x-a.s. finite. The inequality $1 - ch(x) \geqslant (1 - c)^{h(x)}$, which holds since c and $h(x)$ are in $[0, 1]$, and Jessen's inequality then imply

$$U_{ch} 1_A(x) \geqslant E_x[(1 - c)^{(h(X_1) + \cdots + h(X_{S_A-1}))}]$$

$$\geqslant (1 - c)^{E_x[h(X_1) + \cdots + h(X_{S_A-1})]}.$$

Since

$$U_A h(x) = E_x[h(X_1) + \cdots + h(X_{S_A})],$$

the proof is complete.

Proposition 4.8. *For every non-negligible bounded special function f and every positive real number c strictly less than $\|f\|^{-1}$, there is a measure μ_c equivalent to m such that $U_{cf} \geqslant 1 \otimes \mu_c$.*

Proof. We may suppose $\|f\| < 1$. The resolvent equation and ch. 3, Lemma 2.2 yield

$$U_{cf} \geqslant U_{cf}(c(1 - f)) U_c \geqslant U_{cf}(c(1 - f) a_c) \otimes b_c m.$$

The function $c(1 - f) a_c$ being strictly positive on E, there is a real $\varepsilon > 0$ and a set A of positive m-measure such that $\varepsilon 1_A \leqslant c(1 - f) a_c$. By Lemma 4.7, we have therefore

$$U_{cf}(c(1 - f) a_c) \geqslant \varepsilon U_{cf}(1_A) \geqslant \varepsilon(1 - c)^{U_A f}.$$

Since f is special, $U_A(f)$ is bounded; hence

$$U_{cf} \geqslant 1 \otimes (\varepsilon(1 - c)^{\|U_A f\|}) b_c m,$$

and it remains to call this measure μ_c to get the desired result.

If we argue as in ch. 3, Theorem 2.7, the preceding proposition implies that $cU_{cf}I_f$ is quasi-compact. This will be used in the following important results.

Proposition 4.9. *If X is Harris, the following two statements are equivalent:*
(i) *P is quasi-compact;*
(ii) *every positive bounded function is special.*

Proof. If f is special for every integer n, the function $f_n = n^{-1} \sum_{k=1}^{n} P_k f$ is special by virtue of Corollary 4.5. If P is quasi-compact the sequence $\{f_n\}$

converges uniformly to $m(f)$. If $m(f) > 0$, there is therefore an integer n such that f_n majorizes a positive constant, and consequently all bounded functions are special.

Conversely if the function 1 is special, Proposition 4.8 implies that for $c \in\ ]0, 1[$ the T.P. cU_c is quasi-compact; hence, by Theorem 3.10, it has no invariant pure mean. By the resolvent equation, $U_c = P + P(1 - c)\,U_c$, if φ is a P-invariant pure mean, then

$$c\varphi U_c = \varphi + \varphi U_c - \varphi U_c = \varphi,$$

which is a contradiction. Thus P has no invariant pure mean and therefore is quasi-compact.

Theorem 4.10. *A non-negligible function $f \in \mathcal{U}_+$ is special if and only if the transition function $U_f I_f$ is quasi-compact.*

Proof. It is known (ch. 3, Proposition 2.11) that the T.P. $Q = U_f I_f$ is Harris, the corresponding invariant measure being fm.

For $h \in \mathcal{U}_+$, the kernel U_h associated with Q will be denoted by U_h^Q, and is equal to

$$U_h^Q = \sum_{n \geqslant 0} (U_f I_f I_{1-h})^n\, U_f I_f = U_{hf} I_f.$$

Let $g \in b\mathscr{E}_+$; fg is special for P and therefore $U_h^Q(g) = U_{hf}(fg)$ is bounded on E. The bounded functions are therefore special for Q; hence Q is quasi-compact.

Conversely, if Q is quasi-compact and if $h_0 \in \mathcal{U}_+$ is such that $U_{h_0} \geqslant 1 \otimes m_0$, then

$$U_{h_0}(f) \leqslant U_{h_0 f}(f) = U_{h_0}^Q(1),$$

which is a bounded function. Thus f is special and the proof is complete.

Exercise 4.11. (1) Prove that, if E is countable, all functions with finite support are special. More generally if E is LCCB and if P is strong Feller, the bounded functions with compact support are special. The result can even be shown for Feller transition probabilities.

(2) For a random walk recurrent in the sense of Harris, all bounded functions with compact support are special.

Exercise 4.12. If $f \in \mathcal{U}_+$ let $Q = U_f I_f$, as in Theorem 4.10. Show that if g is special for Q then fg is special for P. Is the converse true?

Exercise 4.13. Prove that, for every bounded special function f, there is constant c such that $U_{cf}I_{cf}$ is 1-quasi-compact, i.e. there is a compact operator K such that $\|U_{cf}I_{cf} - K\| < 1$.

Exercise 4.14. Let the resolvent $\{V_\alpha\}$ be Harris.

(1) Prove that the set of special functions is the same for all the chains X^α and is equal to the set of functions f such that $V_h(f)$ is bounded whenever $V_h > 1 \otimes m$.

We shall call these functions *the special functions of the resolvent* $\{V_\alpha\}$.

(2) If αV_α is quasi-compact for an $\alpha > 0$, it is quasi-compact for every $\alpha > 0$. (See also Exercise 3.20.)

(3) Prove that f is special if and only if $V_f I_f$ is quasi-compact.

Exercise 4.15. Let P be a T.P. enjoying the two following properties:

(i) There is a measure ν such that $\nu P \ll \nu$ and P induces a conservative and ergodic contraction of $L^1(\nu)$.

(ii) There is a function $f \in \mathscr{U}_+$ such that $U_f I_f$ is quasi-compact. Then prove that there exists an absorbing set F such that $\nu(F^c) = 0$ and that the restriction of P to F is Harris.

[*Hint*: Begin with $f = 1_A$, $A \in \mathscr{E}$.]

5. Potential kernels

In ch. 2 it was shown that for transient chains, the kernel G gives rise to a satisfactory potential theory, and in particular permits us to solve the Poisson equation. In the present situation of Harris chains, the kernel G is no longer proper, and we shall look for another kernel which could be used for similar purposes.

Definition 5.1. A *charge* is a function $f \in b\mathscr{E}$ such that $|f|$ is special and $m(f) = 0$. The set of charges will be denoted by $\mathscr{N}$. A proper kernel Γ is said to be a *potential kernel* if it maps special functions into finite functions and if, for every $f \in \mathscr{N}$,

$$(I - P)\, \Gamma f = f.$$

Theorem 5.2. *With each function h in $\mathscr{U}_+$ such that $U_h > 1 \otimes m$, one can associate a positive proper kernel W such that, for every non-negligible function $g \in \mathscr{U}_+$,*

$$U_g + U_g I_g W = W + \frac{1}{m(h)} U_g(h) \otimes m, \qquad (5.1)$$

$$U_g + W I_g U_g = W + \frac{1}{m(h)} \otimes (hm) U_g. \qquad (5.2)$$

The positive proper kernel $\Gamma = I + W$ *is a potential kernel.*

Proof. For clarity we divide the proof into four parts.

(1) We may write $U_h = V + 1 \otimes m$ with V a strictly positive kernel. Since $U_h(h) = 1$ and $(hm) U_h = m$, we have

$$Vh = 1 - m(h), \qquad (hm) V = (1 - m(h)) m.$$

Recalling the formula

$$U_0 = \sum_{n \geqslant 0} (U_h I_h)^n U_h,$$

we define

$$W = \sum_{n \geqslant 0} (V I_h)^n V = \sum_{n \geqslant 0} V (I_h V)^n.$$

The kernel W is clearly a positive kernel, and setting $q = (1 - m(h))/m(h)$, we have

$$Wh = \sum_{n \geqslant 0} (1 - m(h))^{n+1} = q,$$

and $(hm) W = qm$.

(2) It is easily seen that

$$V = P + P I_{1-h} V - Ph \otimes m.$$

Thus the obvious identity $W = V + V I_h W$ may be written

$$W = P + P I_{1-h} V - Ph \otimes m + P I_h W + P I_{1-h} V I_h W - Ph \otimes (hm) W.$$

But since $(hm) W = qm$, it follows that

$$W = P + P I_h W + P I_{1-h} (V + V I_h W) - Ph \otimes (1 + q) m,$$

and consequently

$$W = P + PW - (Ph/m(h)) \otimes m, \qquad (5.3)$$

which is eq. (5.1) in the special case $g = 1$. From this equation, it is easily derived by induction that, for every integer n,

$$\sum_{1}^{n} P_k + P_n W = W + \left(\sum_{1}^{n} P_k(h) \Big/ m(h) \right) \otimes m.$$

Let c be a real number with $0 < c < 1$; from the last displayed equality we get

$$\sum_{n \geqslant 1} (1 - c)^{n-1} \left(\sum_{1}^{n} P_k \right) + U_c W = c^{-1} W + \sum_{n \geqslant 1} (1 - c)^{n-1} \left(\left(\sum_{1}^{n} P_k h \middle/ m(h) \right) \otimes m \right).$$

Now it is easily calculated that

$$\sum_{n \geqslant 1} (1 - c)^{n-1} \left(\sum_{1}^{n} P_k \right) = c^{-1} U_c,$$

and consequently

$$U_c + c U_c W = W + (U_c h / m(h)) \otimes m, \tag{5.4}$$

which is eq. (5.1) in the special case $g = c$.

In analogous fashion, we get the following special cases of eq. (5.2):

$$P + WP = W + m(h)^{-1} \otimes (hm) P, \tag{5.5}$$

$$U_c + c W U_c = W + m(h)^{-1} \otimes (hm) U_c. \tag{5.6}$$

(3) Now let g be a non-negligible function in $\mathscr{U}_+$, with $\|g\| < 1$. We may write eq. (5.3) in the form

$$P(I + I_g W) + P I_{1-g} W = W + (Ph/m(h)) \otimes m.$$

We repeat p times the following computation: multiply through the above equality to the left by $P I_{1-g}$ and add $P(I + I_g W)$ to both sides. We get

$$\sum_{n \leqslant p} (P I_{1-g})^n P(I + I_g W) + (P I_{1-g})^{p+1} W$$

$$= W + \left(\sum_{n \leqslant p} (P I_{1-g})^n Ph/m(h) \right) \otimes m.$$

Letting p tend to infinity in the resulting inequality

$$\sum_{n \leqslant p} (P I_{1-g})^n P(I + I_g W) \leqslant W + \left(\sum_{n \leqslant p} (P I_{1-g})^n Ph/m(h) \right) \otimes m$$

yields

$$U_g(I + I_g W) \leqslant W + (U_g h/m(h)) \otimes m. \tag{5.7}$$

Pick a number c such that $\|g\| < c < 1$; the function $h' = c U_c h$ is strictly positive, and if we apply h' to the right of both sides of eq. (5.7) we get, on account of eq. (5.6),

$$c U_g U_c h + U_g I_g (Wh - U_c h + m(h)^{-1} (hm) U_c h) \leqslant$$

$$\leqslant U_g h + Wh - U_c h + m(h)^{-1} (hm) U_c h.$$

Using the fact that Wh is constant, this inequality reduces, after cancellation, to

$$cU_gU_ch - U_gI_gU_ch \leqslant U_gh - U_ch;$$

but the left-hand side is equal to $U_gI_{c-g}U_ch$, and by the resolvent equation of ch. 2 § 2, this inequality is in fact an equality. As a result, the inequality (5.7) is an equality, and eq. (5.1) holds in that case.

Finally, if $\|g\| = 1$, we deduce from the preceding discussion and the resolvent equation

$$U_g = U_{cg} + (1 - c) U_gI_gU_{cg},$$

where $0 < c < 1$, that eq. (5.1) is true in full generality.

We now turn to the proof of eq. (5.2). Following the same pattern as above, with right multiplications instead of left multiplications, we get, for any non-negligible function g in $\mathscr{U}_+$,

$$U_g + WI_gU_g \leqslant W + m(h)^{-1} \otimes (hm) U_g.$$

We claim that this inequality is in fact an equality. From eq. (5.6), it follows that $Wh' = cWU_ch \leqslant Wh + \langle h, cU_ch \rangle / m(h)$ is a bounded function. Consequently, if $0 \leqslant f \leqslant h'$, the function

$$k = U_gf + WI_gU_gf - Wf - \langle h, U_gf \rangle / m(h)$$

is bounded. Moreover, k is harmonic; this follows from writing the equalities

$$\begin{aligned}
P + P(U_g + WI_gU_g) &= P + (PI_{1-g}U_g + PI_gU_g) + PWI_gU_g \\
&= (P + PI_{1-g}U_g) + (P + PW) I_gU_g \\
&= U_g + WI_gU_g + (Ph/m(h)) \otimes m
\end{aligned}$$

and

$$P + P(W + m(h)^{-1} \otimes (hm) U_g) = W + m(h)^{-1} \otimes (hm) U_g + (Ph/m(h)) \otimes m$$

and taking their difference. By ch. 3 § 3, the function k is thus constant. On the other hand, combining the two equalities

$$(hm) (U_g + WI_gU_g) = (hm) U_g + qm$$

$$(hm) (W + m(h)^{-1} \otimes (hm) U_g) = qm + (hm) U_g$$

proves, since the measure hm is bounded, that $\langle hm, k \rangle = 0$ and therefore that k is identically zero. The proof of eq. (5.2) is thus complete.

(4) We have already noticed that Wh' is bounded; since h' is strictly positive this implies that W is a proper kernel. Furthermore, if f is special, eq. (5.2) written for $g = h$ yields

$$Wf \leqslant U_h(f) + W(hU_h f)$$

$$\leqslant \|U_h(f)\| (1 + W(h)) = \|U_h f\| / m(h).$$

The kernel W thus maps special functions into bounded functions and $\Gamma = I + W$ maps special functions into finite functions.

Moreover, if $f \in \mathcal{N}$, then by eq. (5.1),

$$f + Wf = f + Pf + PWf,$$

which reads

$$(I - P)\, \Gamma f = f.$$

We observe that Γf is then bounded.

Corollary 5.3. *Let f be a charge; then the Poisson equation*

$$(I - P)\, g = f$$

has a bounded solution, unique up to addition of a constant function.

Proof. By the preceding result, Γf is a bounded solution of the Poisson equation. The difference between two such solutions is a bounded harmonic function, hence a constant function.

The potential kernel Γ is not unique and there are always many potential kernels. Indeed, if φ is a finite function and ν a measure taking finite values on special functions, then the kernel $\Gamma + \varphi \otimes m + 1 \otimes \nu$ is also a potential kernel. In the following result, we prove that in this way we obtain all possible potential kernels. We notice that some of these kernels are not positive.

Proposition 5.4. *Let Γ and Γ' be two potential kernels; then there is a finite function φ and a measure ν taking finite values on special functions such that*

$$\Gamma' = \Gamma + \varphi \otimes m + 1 \otimes \nu.$$

Proof. If $f \in \mathcal{N}$, then Γf and $\Gamma' f$ are two bounded solutions of the Poisson equation and thus differ by a constant. Pick x_0 in E and set

$$\nu = \Gamma'(x_0, \cdot\,) - \Gamma(x_0, \cdot\,);$$

the measure ν takes finite values on special functions and

$$\Gamma' f - \Gamma f = \nu(f).$$

Now pick a special function f_0 such that $m(f_0) = 1$. For every special function f, the function $f - m(f) f_0$ is a charge, and consequently

$$\Gamma'(f - m(f) f_0) - \Gamma(f + m(f_0)) = \nu(f) - m(f)\,\nu(f_0),$$

hence

$$\Gamma' f = \Gamma f + m(f)\,(\Gamma' f_0 - \Gamma f_0 - \nu(f_0)) + \nu(f).$$

It remains to put $\varphi = \Gamma' f_0 - \Gamma f_0 - \nu(f_0)$ to get the desired result, since it is easily seen that two measures equal on special functions are equal.

The case in which Γ and Γ' are associated with positive special functions by Theorem 5.2 is of special interest, since in that case one can compute φ and ν. When necessary to avoid possible misinterpretation, we shall write W_h and Γ_h for the kernels associated in Theorem 5.2 with the function h.

Corollary 5.5. *If h_1 and h_2 are two positive special functions such that $U_{h_i} > 1 \otimes m$ $(i = 1, 2)$, then the kernels W_{h_i} $(i = 1, 2)$ are related by the formula*

$$W_{h_1} + \frac{1}{m(h_1)}\,W_{h_2}(h_1) \otimes m = W_{h_2} + \frac{1}{m(h_2)} \otimes (h_2 m)\,W_{h_1}.$$

Proof. Within the course of this proof let us abbreviate W_{h_i} to W_i. By Proposition 5.4, there is a function φ and a measure ν such that

$$W_1 + \varphi \otimes m = W_2 + 1 \otimes \nu.$$

Since $W_1(h_1) = q_1$ and $(h_2 m)\,W_2 = q_2 m$, by multiplying this equality to the left by $(h_2 m)$ and to the right by h_1 we get

$$\varphi = m(h_1)^{-1}\,(W_2(h_1) + a), \qquad a \in \mathbf{R},$$

$$\nu = m(h_2)^{-1}\,((h_2 m)\,W_1 + bm), \qquad b \in \mathbf{R},$$

and we may write

$$W_1 + m(h_1)^{-1}\,W_2(h_1) \otimes m = (W_2 + m(h_2)^{-1} \otimes (h_2 m)\,W_1) + k1 \otimes m,$$

where k is a real number. As

$$(h_2 m) (W_1 + m(h_1)^{-1} W_2(h_1) \otimes m) (h_1) = m(h_2) q_1 + q_2 m(h_1)$$

and

$$(h_2 m) (W_2 + m(h_2)^{-1} \otimes (h_2 m) (h_1) = q_2 m(h_1) + m(h_2) q_1,$$

it follows that $k = 0$, and we are done.

The existence of potential kernels gives yet another characterization of special functions.

Proposition 5.6. *A positive function f is special if and only if Γf is bounded for any potential kernel*

$$\Gamma = I + W + \varphi \otimes m + 1 \otimes \nu$$

such that φ is bounded.

Proof. The necessity follows from Theorem 5.2 and Proposition 5.4. To prove the sufficiency, we start by noticing that if Γf is bounded, then Wf is bounded, and since (hm) is a bounded measure we have

$$m(f) = q^{-1}(hm) \, Wf < \infty.$$

The result then follows from the inequality

$$U_g(f) \leqslant Wf + m(h)^{-1} U_g(h) \, m(f).$$

Proposition 5.7. *If $f \in \mathcal{N}$, then*

$$\sup_n \left\| \sum_{m=0}^n P_m f \right\| < +\infty.$$

Proof. From $(I - P) \, \Gamma f = f$, it is easily derived that

$$\sum_{m=0}^n P_m f = \Gamma f - P_{n+1} \Gamma f;$$

therefore

$$\left\| \sum_{m=0}^n P_m f \right\| \leqslant 2 \|\Gamma f\|.$$

We now turn to the problem of solving the Poisson equation for measures. For this purpose, we lay down the following

Definition 5.8. A positive measure μ on $(E, \mathscr{E})$ is said to be *special* if there is a bounded measure σ and a non-negligible function $g \in \mathscr{U}_+$, such that $\mu \leqslant \sigma U_g$.

Proposition 5.9. *Let h be a strictly positive function in $\mathscr{U}_+$ such that $U_h > 1 \otimes m$. Then a measure μ is special if and only if there is a bounded measure ρ such that $\mu \leqslant \rho U_h$.*

Proof. The sufficiency is obvious. Conversely assume that $\mu \leqslant \sigma U_g$; since $U_g \leqslant U_{g \wedge h}$, we may assume $g \leqslant h$.

The measure

$$\rho = \sum_{n \geqslant 0} \sigma (U_h I_{h-g})^n$$

is bounded because

$$\rho(E) \leqslant \sigma(E) \sum_{n \geqslant 0} (1 - U_h(g))^n \leqslant \sigma(E) \sum_{n \geqslant 0} (1 - m(g))^n = \sigma(E)/m(g) < \infty.$$

By the resolvent equation,

$$U_g = \sum_{n \geqslant 0} (U_h I_{h-g})^n \, U_h,$$

we get $\rho U_h = \sigma U_g$, which proves the necessity.

Remark. The measure m is special since $m = (hm) \, U_h$.

Corollary 5.10. *Special measures take finite values on special functions. They are thus σ-finite.*

Proof. Let μ and f be special; then

$$\mu(f) \leqslant \langle \sigma U_h, f \rangle \leqslant \sigma(E) \|U_h(f)\| < \infty.$$

The convex cone of special measures is obviously hereditary to the left and we have the following

Proposition 5.11. *The cone of special measures is invariant by the operators $I_h U_h$.*

Proof. Left to the reader as Exercise 5.18.

Proposition 5.12. *For every bounded measure ν such that $\nu(E) = 0$, there is a measure μ such that $|\mu - \nu|$ is special and*

$$\nu = \mu(I - P).$$

The measure μ is unique up to addition of a multiple of m.

Proof. If ρ is a bounded measure, then ρW is special since

$$\rho W \leqslant \left(\sum_{n \geqslant 0} \rho(VI_h)^n\right) U_h,$$

and

$$\sum_{n \geqslant 0} \rho(VI_h)^n (E) = \rho(E)/m(h) < \infty.$$

The measure

$$\mu = \nu \Gamma = \nu + \nu^+ W - \nu^- W$$

is such that $|\mu - \nu|$ is special, and by Theorem 5.2 is the desired measure.

We turn to show the latter half of the statement. Let μ' be another measure with the same properties. Then $\lambda = \mu - \mu'$ is such that $|\lambda|$ is special and $\lambda = \lambda P$, which implies $\lambda^{\pm} \leqslant \lambda^{\pm} P$. It remains to show that the multiples of m are the only special measures λ such that $\lambda \leqslant \lambda P$.

If $\lambda \leqslant \lambda P$, we may obtain inductively the inequality

$$\lambda \leqslant \lambda I_h P \left(\sum_{l < n} (I_{1-h}P)^l\right) + \lambda(I_{1-h}P)^n.$$

Then if $\lambda \leqslant \rho U_h$, we have

$$\lambda(I_{1-h}P)^n \leqslant \rho U_h(I_{1-h}P)^n = \sum_{l \geqslant n} \rho P(I_{1-h}P)^l;$$

as $\rho U_h(h) = \rho(E) < + \infty$, it follows that $\lim_n (I_{1-h}P)^n h = 0$, and since h is strictly positive, $(h\lambda) \leqslant (h\lambda) I_h U_h$. These two measures are bounded since

$$\lambda(h) \leqslant \rho U_h(h) = \rho(E) < \infty$$

and have the same total variation, hence they are equal. The measure $h\lambda$ is thus $U_h I_h$-invariant, and therefore by ch. 3 § 2.11, there is a constant c such that $h\lambda = chm$. Since h is strictly positive, $\lambda = cm$.

Exercise 5.13. Prove that the measure $(hm) U_g$, which appears in eq. (5.2), is majorized by a multiple of m.

Exercise 5.14. If f is special and $m(g) > 0$, the sequence $W(I_{1-g}P)^n f$ converges pointwise to zero as n tends to infinity.

Exercise 5.15. If $f \in \mathcal{N}$, the set $\{U_g(f) : g \in \mathcal{U}_+\}$ is bounded in $b\mathcal{E}$.

Exercise 5.16. For every special set K there is a constant C_K such that, for every bounded charge f vanishing outside K,

$$\sup_n \left\| \sum_{m=0}^n P_m f \right\| \leq C_K \|f\|.$$

Exercise 5.17. Assume X either aperiodic or null, and let f be a charge. Prove that for any pair (ν_1, ν_2) of probability measures on $(E, \mathcal{E})$,

$$\lim_{n \to \infty} \left\langle \nu_1 - \nu_2, \sum_{k=0}^n P_k f \right\rangle = (\nu_1 - \nu_2) \, \Gamma f,$$

where Γ is any potential kernel. Derive that the sequence $WP_n f$ converges pointwise to zero. What can be said for positive periodic X?

Exercise 5.18. Prove Proposition 5.11.

Exercise 5.19. The kernel $I + WI_h$ satisfies the reinforced complete maximum principle. The kernel W satisfies the positive maximum principle, that is,

$$\sup_{x \in E} W f(x) = \sup_{x \in \{f > 0\}} W f(x).$$

Exercise 5.20. In the situation of Theorem 4.10, prove that $I + WI_f$ is a potential kernel for Q. If f is special, it is then a bounded kernel. More precisely, $I + W$ is bounded if and only if P is quasi-compact.

Exercise 5.21 (Potential kernels for Harris resolvents). As for chains, a charge is a function f such that $|f|$ is special and $m(f) = 0$. A potential kernel is a proper kernel W which maps special functions into finite ones, and which is such that, for every charge f and every $\alpha > 0$,

$$(I + \alpha W) \, V_\alpha f = Wf = V_\alpha (I + \alpha W) \, f.$$

(1) Prove that there is a whole family of potential kernels and describe their pairwise relationship.

(2) Define special measures and prove a result similar to Theorem 5.12.

Exercise 5.22. Prove that the kernel W of Theorem 5.2 is the sum of a bounded kernel and of an integral kernel with basis m.

6. The ratio-limit theorem

We now want to sharpen ch. 4, Theorem 3.5, which was obtained by a straightforward application of the Chacon–Ornstein theorem (see also ch. 4, Exercise 3.9). The most general result that one could hope for is the following: for every pair (f, g) of integrable functions and every pair (v_1, v_2) of probability measures on $(E, \mathscr{E})$,

$$\lim_{n\to\infty} \left(\sum_{m=0}^{n} v_1 P_m f \middle/ \sum_{m=0}^{n} v_2 P_m g \right) = m(f)/m(g).$$

Unfortunately, it turns out that this result is not true, but below we shall give several theorems which are very close to it.

Proposition 6.1. *If f and g are special functions and $m(g) > 0$, for every probability measure v on $\mathscr{E}$,*

$$\lim_{n\to\infty} \left(\sum_{m=0}^{n} v P_m f \middle/ \sum_{m=0}^{n} v P_m g \right) = m(f)/m(g).$$

Proof. The function $m(g)\, f - m(f)\, g$ is a charge; thus, by Proposition 5.7, there is a number M such that, for every integer n,

$$\left| m(g) \sum_{m=0}^{n} v P_m f - m(f) \sum_{m=0}^{n} v P_m g \right| \leqslant M < \infty.$$

Since $\sum_{m=0}^{n} v P_m g > 0$ for n sufficiently large,

$$\left| \sum_{m=0}^{n} v P_m f \middle/ \sum_{m=0}^{n} v P_m g - m(f)/m(g) \right| \leqslant M \left(m(g) \sum_{m=0}^{n} v P_m g \right)^{-1},$$

and this converges to zero as n tends to infinity.

In the sequel, we shall use the kernel W associated, as in Theorem 5.2, with a strictly positive function h. We shall denote by λ the bounded measure hm, and put

$$a_n = \|\lambda\|^{-1} \left(\sum_{m=1}^{n} \lambda P_m h \right).$$

Lemma 6.2. *For every $\varepsilon > 0$, there is a constant c_ε such that, for every integer n,*

$$\sum_{m=1}^{n} P_m h \leqslant c_\varepsilon + (1 + \varepsilon)\, a_n.$$

Proof. Set

$$A_n = \left\{ \sum_{m=1}^{n} P_m h < (1 + \varepsilon)\, a_n \right\}.$$

Integrating with respect to λ the two terms of the inequality

$$\sum_{m=1}^{n} P_m h \geqslant (1 + \varepsilon)\, a_n 1_{A_n^c}$$

yields

$$\|\lambda\|\, a_n > (1 + \varepsilon)\, a_n \lambda(A_n^c),$$

and therefore

$$\lambda(A_n) \geqslant \|\lambda\|\, \varepsilon/(1 + \varepsilon).$$

For $f \in \mathscr{U}_+$, it is easy to derive inductively the formula

$$\sum_{1}^{n} P_m + U_f P_n = U_f I_f \left(\sum_{1}^{n} P_m \right) + U_f. \tag{6.1}$$

By applying eq. (6.1) to the function $f_n = h 1_{A_n}$, we get

$$\sum_{1}^{n} P_m h \leqslant U_{f_n} \left(f_n \left(\sum_{m=1}^{n} P_m h \right) \right) + U_{f_n}(h).$$

But

$$f_n \left(\sum_{m=1}^{n} P_m h \right) < (1 + \varepsilon)\, a_n f_n,$$

and, since $U_{f_n}(f_n) = 1$,

$$\sum_{1}^{n} P_m h \leqslant (1 + \varepsilon)\, a_n + U_{f_n}(h).$$

Now, because of the resolvent equation,

$$U_{f_n}(h) = \sum_{k \geqslant 0} (U_h I_{h - f_n})^k\, U_h(h)$$

$$\leqslant \sum_{k \geqslant 0} (1 - m(f_n))^k = m(f_n)^{-1} = \lambda(A_n)^{-1} \leqslant (1 + \varepsilon)\, (\varepsilon \|\lambda\|)^{-1}.$$

The proof is now complete.

Lemma 6.3. *For every* $\delta \in \,]0, 1[$ *and every probability measure* ν, *there are two numbers* α, $\beta > 0$ *such that*

   (i) $U_{\alpha h} I_{\alpha h} \geqslant (1 - \delta) \, \|\lambda\|^{-1} \otimes \lambda$;

   (ii) $\nu U_{\alpha h + \beta}(\alpha h) \geqslant 1 - \delta$.

Proof. If $\alpha < 1$, we have

$$U_{\alpha h} I_{\alpha h} = \sum_{n \geqslant 0} \alpha (1 - \alpha)^n \, (U_h I_h)^{n+1};$$

that is, with the notation of § 5,

$$U_{\alpha h} I_{\alpha h} = \sum_{n \geqslant 0} \alpha (1 - \alpha)^n \, (1 \otimes \lambda + V I_h)^{n+1}.$$

Since

$$(V I_h) \, (1 \otimes \lambda) = (1 \otimes \lambda) \, V I_h = (1 - \|\lambda\|) \, (1 \otimes \lambda),$$

easy computations prove that

$$U_{\alpha h} I_{\alpha h} = (1 - (1 - \alpha) \, (1 - \|\lambda\|))^{-1} \otimes \lambda + \sum_{n \geqslant 0} \alpha (1 - \alpha)^n \, (V I_h)^{n+1}.$$

It is then easily seen that (i) is satisfied for sufficiently small α.

   The number α being chosen, when β decreases to zero the operator $U_{\alpha h + \beta}$ increases to $U_{\alpha h}$ and therefore

$$\lim_{\beta \to 0} \nu U_{\alpha h + \beta}(\alpha h) = \nu U_{\alpha h}(\alpha h) = 1;$$

The condition (ii) is thus satisfied for sufficiently small β.

Lemma 6.4. *For every probability measure* ν *on* $(E, \mathscr{E})$,

$$\lim_n \left(\sum_{m=1}^{n} \nu P_m h \Big/ \sum_{m=1}^{n} \lambda P_m h \right) = \|\lambda\|^{-1}.$$

Proof. Denote by R_n the ratio which occurs in the statement. Because of Proposition 6.2, we have $\overline{\lim}_n R_n \leqslant \|\lambda\|^{-1}$, and we are going to prove the reverse inequality for the inferior limit.

   Let $\delta \in \,]0, 1[$ and set

$$B_n = \left\{ \sum_{1}^{n} P_m h \geqslant (1 - \delta) \, a_n \right\}.$$

The inequality

$$\sum_{1}^{n} P_m h \geqslant (1 - \delta) \, a_n 1_{B_n},$$

together with eq. (6.1), implies

$$\sum_{1}^{n} P_m h \geqslant U_f I_f \left(\sum_{1}^{n} P_m h \right) - U_f P_n h$$

$$\geqslant (1 - \delta) \, a_n U_f(f1_{B_n}) - U_f P_n h. \tag{6.2}$$

With the notation of Lemma 6.3, put $f = \alpha h + \beta$; it follows that

$$\nu U_f(f1_{B_n}) \geqslant \nu U_{\alpha h + \beta}(\alpha h 1_{B_n}) \geqslant \nu U_{\alpha h}(\alpha h 1_{B_n}) - \delta,$$

since by Lemma 6.3(ii),

$$\nu(U_{\alpha h} I_{\alpha h} - U_{\alpha h + \beta} I_{\alpha h}) \, (E) \leqslant \delta.$$

By Lemma 6.3(i), it then follows that

$$\nu U_f(f1_{B_n}) \geqslant (1 - \delta) \, \|\lambda\|^{-1} \lambda(B_n) - \delta.$$

Let us study the asymptotic behaviour of $\lambda(B_n)$. By virtue of Proposition 6.2, we have

$$\sum_{1}^{n} P_m h \leqslant (1 - \delta) \, a_n \qquad \text{on } B_n^c,$$

$$\sum_{1}^{n} P_m h \leqslant c_\varepsilon + (1 + \varepsilon) \, a_n \qquad \text{on } B_n;$$

taking the integral with respect to λ yields

$$a_n\|\lambda\| \leqslant (1 - \delta) \, a_n(\|\lambda\| - \lambda(B_n)) + (c_\varepsilon + (1 + \varepsilon) \, a_n) \, \lambda(B_n),$$

hence

$$\delta a_n\|\lambda\| \leqslant (c_\varepsilon + (\delta + \varepsilon) \, a_n) \, \lambda(B_n).$$

Since $\{a_n\}$ converges to infinity, we find

$$\varliminf_{n} \lambda(B_n) \geqslant \delta\|\lambda\|/(\delta + \varepsilon),$$

and since ε is arbitrary, $\varliminf_n \lambda(B_n) \geqslant \|\lambda\|$; hence $\lim_n \lambda(B_n) = \|\lambda\|$. It then follows that

$$\varliminf_{n} \nu U_f(f1_{B_n}) \geqslant 1 - 2\delta.$$

Finally as $f \geqslant \beta$ and $P_n h \leqslant 1$, for every n we have

$$U_f P_n h \leqslant U_\beta 1 = \beta^{-1}.$$

Returning to eq. (6.2), we see that

$$\varliminf_n R_n \geqslant \|\lambda\|^{-1} (1 - \delta)(1 - 2\delta),$$

and since δ is arbitrary, the proof is complete.

Theorem 6.5. *For every pair (f, g) of special functions with $m(g) > 0$ and every pair (ν_1, ν_2) of probability measures on $(E, \mathscr{E})$*

$$\lim_{n \to \infty} \left(\sum_{m=0}^{n} \nu_1 P_m f \Big/ \sum_{m=0}^{n} \nu_2 P_m g \right) = m(f)/m(g).$$

Proof. Beginning the summations at 0 instead of 1 causes no trouble, since the denominator diverges. By applying Lemma 6.4 with ν_1, and then with ν_2, and taking the ratio, we get

$$\lim_{n \to \infty} \left(\sum_{m=0}^{n} \nu_1 P_m h \Big/ \sum_{m=0}^{n} \nu_2 P_m h \right) = 1.$$

We then apply Proposition 6.1 twice, first to ν_1, f, h, then to ν_2, g, h, and writing

$$\frac{\sum_{m=0}^{n} \nu_1 P_m f}{\sum_{m=0}^{n} \nu_2 P_m g} = \frac{\sum_{m=0}^{n} \nu_1 P_m f}{\sum_{m=0}^{n} \nu_1 P_m h} \times \frac{\sum_{m=0}^{n} \nu_1 P_m h}{\sum_{m=0}^{n} \nu_2 P_m h} \times \frac{\sum_{m=0}^{n} \nu_2 P_m h}{\sum_{m=0}^{n} \nu_2 P_m g},$$

we get the desired result.

In the same way we may obtain

Theorem 6.6. *Let f, g be two functions in $L^1(m)$ with $m(g) > 0$. There exist two negligible sets N_f and N_g depending only on f and g and such that for $x \notin N_f$ and $y \notin N_g$*

$$\lim_{n \to \infty} \left(\sum_{m=0}^{n} P_m f(x) \Big/ \sum_{m=0}^{n} P_m g(y) \right) = m(f)/m(g).$$

Proof. It can be performed by following the pattern of Theorem 6.5, except that instead of Proposition 6.1 we use ch. 4, Theorem 3.5. The set N_f is the negligible set which appears in ch. 4, Theorem 3.5, as applied to f and h.

Remark. One could think of enlarging the scope of validity of the preceding theorems to functions f such that $P_n f$ is special. Exercise 6.7 shows that nothing can be gained in that way.

Exercise 6.7. If f is such that $U_g(f)$ is special for a function $g \in \mathcal{U}_+$, then f is special.

Exercise 6.8. Prove that if there is a Harris random walk on the group G, then G is unimodular.

   [*Hint*: Apply Theorem 6.5 to the left and right random walks with $\nu_1 = \nu_2 = \varepsilon_e$.]

Exercise 6.9. Carry over the result of this section to the case of Harris resolvents.

CHAPTER 7

MARTIN BOUNDARY

The purpose of Martin boundary theory is twofold. From the potential theoretic point of view it is to give an integral representation of harmonic functions which turns them into "potentials" of charges carried by the boundary of the space. We thus wish to generalize the classical Poisson integral representation of harmonic functions in the unit disc, namely that there is a one-to-one correspondence between the non-negative harmonic functions h and the Borel measures μ^h on the circle S^1 given by (with classical notation)

$$ h(re^{i\theta}) = \int_{S^1} \frac{1 - r^2}{1 - 2r \cos (\theta - t) + r^2} \, d\mu^h(t). $$

The function 1 corresponds to the Lebesgue measure m on S^1, and if f is the density of μ^h with respect to m, then Fatou's theorem states that $h(re^{i\theta})$ converges to $f(t)$ whenever $re^{i\theta}$ converges to t non-tangentially.

From the probabilistic point of view we wish to study the asymptotic behaviour of transient Markov chains. If the potential kernel G is proper, the space E is the union of an increasing sequence of transient sets, and one can thus say, loosely speaking, that the chain eventually leaves the space. For example, a transient random walk on $\mathbf{R}$ with positive first moment converges towards $+ \infty$; we can say that it leaves the space on the right. We wish to describe, for any transient chain, how it leaves the space.

1. Regular functions

In this section we shall investigate more thoroughly some of the notions introduced in ch. **3** § **3**. For $f \in \mathscr{E}$ we set

$$ R(f) = \overline{\lim_n} f(X_n), $$

and put $R(1_A) = R(A)$, to be consistent with the notation of ch. **3** § **3**. The random variable $R(f)$ is invariant.

Definition 1.1. A function f in $\mathscr{E}$ is said to be *regular* if $\lim_n f(X_n)$ exists a.s. A set $A \in \mathscr{E}$ is said to be *regular* if 1_A is a regular function. Two regular functions f and g are said to be equivalent if $R(f) = R(g)$ a.s.

Finite superharmonic functions and bounded harmonic functions are regular. Absorbing sets are regular; transient sets are regular and equivalent to the empty set.

Proposition 1.2. *The set $\mathscr{R}$ of regular functions is an algebra (for ordinary pointwise multiplication) and a lattice. The collection of regular sets is a Boolean algebra of sets which will also be denoted by $\mathscr{R}$.*

Proof. Obvious.

We call b$\mathscr{R}$ the sub-algebra of bounded regular functions, $\bar{\mathscr{R}}$ and b$\bar{\mathscr{R}}$ the collections of equivalence classes in $\mathscr{R}$ and b$\mathscr{R}$. We observe that the family of transient sets is an ideal in the Boolean algebra $\mathscr{R}$ and $\bar{\mathscr{R}}$ is the quotient set of $\mathscr{R}$ by this ideal.

Proposition 1.3. *The map $A \rightarrow R(A)$ is an isomorphism of the Boolean algebra $\bar{\mathscr{R}}$ onto the Boolean algebra of equivalence classes of invariant events.*

Proof. Plainly $R(A^c) = R(A)^c$ and $R(A \cup B) = R(A) \cup R(B)$ if A, B are regular; moreover $R(A) = \mathbf{0}$ a.s. if and only if A is transient. Finally, if $\Gamma \in \mathscr{T}$, the set $A = \{x : P_x[\Gamma] > \frac{1}{2}\}$ is regular and $\Gamma = R(A)$, because $\lim_n P_{X_n}[\Gamma] = 1$ according to the reasoning in ch. 3 § 3.

Proposition 1.4. *A function f in b$\mathscr{E}$ is regular if and only if it is the uniform limit of simple functions over the Boolean algebra $\mathscr{R}$.*

Proof. The sufficiency is obvious. Conversely, let $f \in$ b$\mathscr{R}$ and pick an invariant, simple random variable $Y = \sum \alpha_i 1_{\Gamma_i}$ such that $\|Y - \mathscr{R}(f)\| < \varepsilon$. Let A_i be regular sets such that $R(A_i) = \Gamma_i$ a.s., and set $g = \sum \alpha_i 1_{A_i}$; the set $A_\varepsilon = \{|f - g| > \varepsilon\}$ is easily seen to be transient. Let h be any bounded simple function such that $|h - f| < \varepsilon$ on A_ε and set $f_\varepsilon = g\,1_{A_\varepsilon^c} + h\,1_{A_\varepsilon}$; then f_ε is a simple and regular function, and $\|f - f_\varepsilon\| < \varepsilon$, which yields the desired result.

In ch. 3 § 3, we have seen how to establish a one-to-one correspondence between bounded harmonic functions and equivalence classes of a.s. bounded

invariant random variables. We may summarize all these results in the following statement.

Theorem 1.5. *If P is markovian, the following three vector spaces are isomorphic:*
   (i) *the space of bounded harmonic functions;*
  (ii) *the space of equivalence classes of a.s. bounded invariant functions;*
 (iii) *the space* b$\tilde{\mathscr{R}}$.

This theorem has the following corollary. We recall that a positive harmonic
function h is said to be *extremal* if, for every harmonic function h' such that
$0 \leqslant h' \leqslant h$, there is a real number c such that $h' = ch$.

Corollary 1.6. *The extremal bounded harmonic functions are in one-to-one correspondence with the atoms of the Boolean algebra* $\tilde{\mathscr{R}}$.

We are now going to show a particular class of regular functions which will
be basic in the sequel.

The kernel G is henceforth assumed to be proper. There is therefore an
increasing sequence of sets E_n in $\mathscr{E}$ such that the potentials $G(\cdot, E_n)$ are
bounded. We call L_k the last hitting time of E_k, that is

$$L_k(\omega) = \sup\{n \geqslant 0: X_n(\omega) \in E_k\},$$

where the supremum of the empty set is understood to be $+\infty$. Clearly
$L_k \leqslant L_{k+1}$ on $\{L_k < \infty\}$ and $\lim_k L_k = +\infty$ a.s. We define $Y_k = X_{L_k}$ and
$\mathscr{H}_k = \sigma(Y_l, l \leqslant k)$.

Proposition 1.7. *The σ-algebra $\mathscr{T}$ of invariant events is a.s. equal to the σ-algebra*
$\bigcap_k \mathscr{H}_k$.

Proof. Let $\Gamma \in \mathscr{T}$ and set $A = \{x: P_x[\Gamma] > \frac{1}{2}\}$; we already know that

$$\Gamma = \lim_n \{X_n \in A\} \quad \text{a.s.,}$$

and since $\lim_k L_k = +\infty$ a.s., we have also

$$\Gamma = \lim_k \{Y_k \in A\} \quad \text{a.s.}$$

Conversely, it is easily seen that $L_k \circ \theta = L_k - 1$ on the event $\{0 < L_k < \infty\}$
and that $L_k \circ \theta = +\infty$ on $\{L_k = 0\} \cup \{L_k = \infty\}$. Consequently, $Y_k \circ \theta = Y_k$

on $\{0 < L_k\}$, and therefore if $\Gamma \in \mathcal{H}_k$,

$$\theta^{-1}(\Gamma \cap \{0 < L_k\}) = \Gamma \cap \{1 < L_k\}.$$

If $\Gamma \in \bigcap \mathcal{H}_k$, it follows from the fact that $\lim_k L_k = +\infty$ a.s. that $\theta^{-1}(\Gamma) = \Gamma$ a.s., which is the desired conclusion.

Let ν be a probability measure on $\mathscr{E}$ and set $\lambda = \nu G$. The measure λ is σ-finite, and for any probability measure γ on $\mathscr{E}$ we may write $\gamma G = \gamma K \lambda + \gamma G^1$, where γK is a function in $\mathscr{E}_+$ and γG^1 a measure singular with respect to λ. We denote by A_γ a set such that $\lambda(A_\gamma^c) = 0$ and $\gamma G^1(A_\gamma) = 0$; clearly $P_\nu[\bigcup_n \{X_n \in A_\gamma^c\}] = 0$. If $\gamma = \varepsilon_x$, we shall write $K(x, y)$ for $\gamma K(y)$. We shall prove that the sequence $\{\gamma K(X_n)\}$ converges P_ν-a.s. to a limit as n converges to $+\infty$. We begin with some lemmas.

Lemma 1.8. Let $A_0, A_1, \ldots, A_n, B$ be in $\mathscr{E}$ with $A_0 \subset A_\gamma$, and set

$$\Lambda = \{X_{L_B - n} \in A_0, X_{L_B - n + 1} \in A_1, \ldots, X_{L_B} \in A_n\}.$$

Then

$$P_\gamma[\Lambda \cap \{n \leqslant L_B < \infty\}] = E_\nu[\gamma K(X_{L_B - n}) \, 1_\Lambda \, 1_{\{n \leqslant L_B < \infty\}}]$$

Proof. Set $\Lambda' = \Lambda \cap \{n \leqslant L_B < \infty\}$; we have

$$P_\gamma[\Lambda'] = \sum_{p=n}^{\infty} P_\gamma[X_{p-n} \in A_0, \ldots, X_p \in A_n \cap B, X_q \notin B, q > p]$$

$$= \sum_{p=n}^{\infty} \int_{A_0} \gamma P_{p-n}(dx_0) \, P_{x_0}[\Gamma],$$

where

$$\Gamma = \{X_1 \in A_1, \ldots, X_n \in A_n \cap B, X_q \notin B, q > n\}.$$

Since $\gamma G^1(A_0) = 0$, it follows that

$$P_\gamma[\Lambda'] = \int_{A_0} \gamma G(dx_0) \, P_{x_0}[\Gamma] = \int_{A_0} \gamma K(x_0) \, P_{x_0}[\Gamma] \, \lambda(dx_0)$$

$$= \sum_{p=n}^{\infty} \int_{A_0} \nu P_{p-n}(dx_0) \, \gamma K(x_0) \, P_{x_0}[\Gamma]$$

$$= E_\nu[\gamma K(X_{L_B - n}) \, 1_\Lambda \, 1_{\{n \leqslant L_B < \infty\}}].$$

Let μ and ν be two probability measures. The Radon–Nykodim derivative of the restriction of μ to the sub-σ-algebra $\mathscr{B}$ with respect to the restriction of ν to $\mathscr{B}$ will be denoted $(\mathrm{d}\mu/\mathrm{d}\nu)_{\mathscr{B}}$.

Lemma 1.9. *For every k we have*

$$\gamma K(Y_k) = (\mathrm{d}P_\gamma/\mathrm{d}P_\nu)_{\mathscr{H}_k} \quad P_\nu\text{-a.s.}$$

Proof. Let $A_0, A_1, \ldots, A_n$ be in $\mathscr{E}$, and let us compute

$$P_\gamma[\Lambda] = P_\gamma[Y_k \in A_0, Y_{k+1} \in A_1, \ldots, Y_{k+n} \in A_n]$$

$$= \sum_{p \geqslant 0} P_\gamma[L_k = p, Y_k \in A_0, Y_{k+1} \in A_1, \ldots, Y_{k+n} \in A_n].$$

On $\{L_k = p\}_{p > 0}$, one has $L_{k+n} \geqslant L_k = p$; hence

$$L_{k+n} = p + L_{k+n} \circ \theta_p \quad \text{and} \quad Y_{k+n} = Y_{k+n} \circ \theta_p.$$

By applying the Markov property, we get

$$P_\gamma[\Lambda] = \sum_{p \geqslant 0} \int_E \gamma P_p(\mathrm{d}y) \, P_y[\Gamma],$$

where

$$\Gamma = \{L_k = 0, X_0 \in A_0, Y_{k+1} \in A_1, \ldots, Y_{k+n} \in A_n\}.$$

As in the above lemma, it follows that

$$P_\gamma[\Lambda] = \int_E \lambda(\mathrm{d}y) \, \gamma K(y) \, P_y[\Gamma] + \int_{A_\gamma^c} \gamma G(\mathrm{d}y) \, P_y[\Gamma]$$

$$= E_\nu[\gamma K(Y_k) \, 1_\Lambda] + E_\gamma\left[\sum_p 1_{\{X_p \in A_\gamma^c\}} P_{X_p}[\Gamma]\right];$$

since the event $\bigcup \{X_p \in A_\gamma^c\}$ has zero P_ν-measure, we get the desired result.

Corollary 1.10. *One has*

$$\lim_n \gamma K(Y_n) = (\mathrm{d}P_\gamma/\mathrm{d}P_\nu)_{\mathscr{F}} \quad P_\nu\text{-a.s.}$$

Proof. This is a well-known result in the theory of martingales.

We turn to the main result of this section.

Theorem 1.11. *For every probability measure γ on $\mathscr{E}$, we have*

$$\lim_n \gamma K(X_n) = (\mathrm{d}P_\gamma/\mathrm{d}P_\nu)_{\mathscr{F}} \quad P_\nu\text{-a.s.}$$

Proof. Set $L = L_A$, where A is any set in $\mathscr{E}$, and define the random variables Z_n by

$$Z_n = \gamma K(X_{L-n}) \quad \text{on } \{n \leqslant L < \infty\},$$

$$Z_n = 0 \qquad\qquad \text{on } \{L < n\} \cup \{L = \infty\}.$$

We claim that the sequence $\{Z_n\}$ is a supermartingale with respect to the σ-algebras $\mathscr{B}_n = \sigma(X_{L-k}, k \leqslant n)$. Indeed $\mathscr{B}_{n-1}$ is generated by the sets

$$\Lambda = \{X_{L-n+1} \in A_1, \ldots, X_{L-n+j} \in A_j\},$$

where $A_i \in \mathscr{E}$, and we prove that

$$E_\nu[Z_n \, 1_\Lambda] \leqslant E_\nu[Z_{n-1} \, 1_\Lambda].$$

Since $P_\nu[\bigcup \{X_n \in A_\gamma^c\}] = 0$, we may take $A_i \subset A_\gamma$ for every i, and by Lemma 1.8 we then have

$$E_\nu[Z_n \, 1_\Lambda \, 1_{\{n \leqslant L < \infty\}}] = E_\gamma[1_\Lambda \, 1_{\{n \leqslant L < \infty\}}] \leqslant E_\gamma[1_\Lambda \, 1_{\{n-1 \leqslant L < \infty\}}]$$

$$= E_\nu[Z_{n-1} \, 1_\Lambda \, 1_{\{n-1 \leqslant L < \infty\}}] = E_\nu[Z_{n-1} \, 1_\Lambda].$$

Now let a, b be two real numbers with $a < b$, and let $\xi_{a,b}(L)$ denote the number of upcrossings of the interval $]a, b[$ by $\{Z_n\}$. It is known from martingale theory that

$$E_\nu[\xi_{a,b}(L_A)] \leqslant (b - a)^{-1} E_\nu[Z_0] = (b - a)^{-1} P_\gamma[L_A < \infty].$$

The number $\xi_{a,b}$ of upcrossings of $]a, b[$ by the sequence $\{\gamma K(X_n)\}$ is the increasing limit of the sequence $\{\xi_{a,b}(L_k)\}$. Consequently,

$$E_\nu[\xi_{a,b}] \leqslant (b - a)^{-1} \lim_k P_\nu[L_k < \infty] \leqslant (b - a)^{-1}.$$

By the classical argument in martingale theory it follows that $\lim_n \gamma K(X_n)$ exists P_ν-a.s., and the limit variable is identified by means of Corollary 1.10.

Remark. Exercise 1.16 hints at the idea which lies beneath the above proof.

We may now state

Corollary 1.12. *If $P_x \ll P_v$ on $\mathscr{T}$ for every $x \in E$, then γK is a regular function for every probability measure γ.*

Proof. The event

$$\Lambda = \left\{ \lim_n \gamma K(X_n) = (\mathrm{d}P_\gamma/\mathrm{d}P_v)_{\mathscr{T}} \right\}$$

is plainly an invariant event, and by the previous results $P_v[\Lambda^c] = 0$. If $P_x \ll P_v$ on $\mathscr{T}$, we have $P_x[\Lambda^c] = 0$ for every x in E, which is the desired result.

The following result gives a useful criterion to decide whether the condition in the above corollary is satisfied or not. We write, according to ch. 1 § 5,

$$P_n(x, \cdot) = P_n^0(x, \cdot) + P_n^1(x, \cdot)$$

for the Lebesgue decomposition of P_n with respect to v. If $vP \ll v$, it is easily checked that $P_{n+m}^1 \leqslant P_n^1 P_m^1$, and therefore that the sequence $\{P_n^1(\cdot, E)\}$ decreases to a measurable function g. We then have

Theorem 1.13. *If $vP \ll v$, then for any x in E the following two conditions are equivalent*: (i) $P_x \ll P_v$ on $\mathscr{T}$; (ii) $g(x) = 0$.

Proof. We first show that (ii) implies (i). Let Γ be an invariant event such that $P_v[\Gamma] = 0$. The bounded harmonic function $P.[\Gamma]$ vanishes v-a.e., and therefore for every n,

$$P_x[\Gamma] = \int_E P_n(x, \mathrm{d}y) \, P_y[\Gamma] = \int_E P_n^1(x, \mathrm{d}y) \, P_y[\Gamma] \leqslant P_n^1(x, E).$$

It follows that if $g(x) = 0$, then $P_x \ll P_v$ on $\mathscr{T}$.

To prove the converse let us denote by A^n a set in $\mathscr{E}$ such that $v(A^n) = 0$ and $P_n^1(x, (A^n)^c) = 0$, and set $A = \bigcup_n A^n$. We have

$$g(x) = \lim_n P_x[X_n \in A^n] \leqslant P_x[\overline{\lim}\{X_n \in A\}].$$

The event $\Lambda = \overline{\lim}\{X_n \in A\}$ is invariant, and since $v(A) = 0$ we have $vG(A) = 0$; hence $P_v[\Lambda] = 0$. If $P_x \ll P_v$, it follows that $P_x[\Lambda] = 0$, hence that $g(x) = 0$ and thus (i) implies (ii).

Remark 1.14. It is now readily seen that the condition of Corollary 1.12 is satisfied if $P(x, \cdot) \ll \nu$ for every $x \in E$; hence it is satisfied for discrete chains, and also for spread-out random walks if ν is equivalent to a Haar measure.

We now apply the above results in a way which will be useful in the next section. We assume henceforth that X is in duality with a chain $\hat{X}$ with respect to a measure m.

Proposition 1.15. *For every pair f, g of functions in $\mathscr{L}^1_+(m)$, we have*

$$\lim_n \hat{G}f(X_n)/\hat{G}g(X_n) = (\mathrm{d}P_{fm}/\mathrm{d}P_{gm})_{\mathscr{T}} \quad P_m\text{-a.s.},$$

and hence P_ν-a.s. for every $\nu \ll m$.

If, in addition, $P_x \ll P_m$ on $\mathscr{T}$ for every x in E, the convergence holds almost surely.

Proof. Let g' be a strictly positive function in $\mathscr{L}^1(m)$ with $m(g') = 1$, and let f be any function in $\mathscr{L}^1(m)$ with $m(f) = 1$. In Theorem 1.11, we can take $\nu = g'm$ and $\gamma = fm$, and then $\gamma K = \mathrm{d}(fm)\, G/\mathrm{d}(g'm)\, G$. But $(g'm)\, G \ll m$, and $\hat{G}g'$ is a version of the Radon–Nykodim derivative $\mathrm{d}(g'm)\, G/\mathrm{d}m$. By the well-known properties of these derivatives we thus have $\gamma K = \hat{G}f/\hat{G}g'$ and it follows that

$$\lim_n \{\hat{G}f(X_n)/\hat{G}g'(X_n)\} = (\mathrm{d}P_{fm}/\mathrm{d}P_{g'm})_{\mathscr{T}} \quad P_{g'm}\text{-a.s.},$$

and hence P_m-a.s., since g' is strictly positive. Now if g is any function in $\mathscr{L}^1_+(m)$, by considering the ratios $(\hat{G}f/\hat{G}g')/(\hat{G}g/\hat{G}g')$ we get the general result. The last statement is obtained in the same way as Corollary 1.12.

Exercise 1.16. Assume X to be discrete, and retain the notation of Theorem 1.11. Prove that the sequence of random variables $\{\hat{X}_n\}$ defined by

$$\hat{X}_n = X_{L-n} \quad \text{on } \{n \leqslant L < \infty\}, \qquad \hat{X}_n = \varDelta \quad \text{on } \{L < n\} \cup \{L = \infty\}$$

is a homogeneous Markov chain for the probability measure P_ν with starting measure $P_\nu[\hat{X}_0 = x] = \nu G(x)\, g_\varDelta(x)$ (cf. ch. 2, Proposition 2.5) and transition probability $\hat{P}$ defined by the identity

$$\nu G(x)\, \hat{P}(x, y) = \nu G(y)\, P(y, x).$$

The reader will observe that P and $\hat{P}$ are in duality with respect to νG; this will be extensively used in the next two sections.

Exercise 1.17. Let ν be a probability measure such that $P_x \ll P_\nu$ on $\mathcal{F}$ for every x in E.

(1) Prove that the space $\mathcal{L}$ of a.s. bounded invariant random variables is a Banach algebra when endowed with the norm

$$\|Z\| = \sup_{x \in E} \|Z\|_{L^\infty(\Omega, \mathcal{F}, P_x)}.$$

(2) We endow the space $b\mathcal{H}$ of bounded harmonic functions with the following multiplication

$$(h * h')(x) = E_x[R(h) \, R(h')].$$

Prove that $b\mathcal{H}$ is a Banach algebra for the supremum norm. Prove that the map $h \to R(h)$ is a norm-preserving isomorphism between the Banach algebras $b\mathcal{H}$ and $\mathcal{L}$.

Exercise 1.18. Let X be a right random walk of law μ on a group $\mathbf{G}$.

(1) Prove that the results in the preceding exercise are still true even if μ is not spread-out.

(2) Prove that the space $\mathcal{A}$ of left uniformly continuous, harmonic functions is a closed subalgebra of $b\mathcal{H}$, hence a C^*-algebra.

(3) The spectrum of $\mathcal{A}$ is denoted by Π_μ and called the *Poisson space* of μ. It is a compact and metrizable $\mathbf{G}$-space. There is an isometry j from $C(\Pi_\mu)$ onto $\mathcal{A}$. If we set $\langle \nu, f \rangle = j(f)(e)$, then ν is a probability measure on Π_μ called the *Poisson kernel* of μ and

$$j(f)(g) = \int_{\Pi_\mu} f(gx) \, \nu(\mathrm{d}x), \qquad f \in C(\Pi_\mu).$$

The measure ν is invariant by μ ($\mu * \nu = \nu$).

(4) If μ is spread out, then ν is absolutely continuous with respect to some quasi-invariant measure η. Prove that η may be chosen such that the integral formula of (3) defines an isomorphism between the Banach spaces $b\mathcal{H}$ and $L^\infty(\Pi_\mu, \eta)$. If $\mathbf{G} = \mathrm{SL}(2, \mathbf{R})$ and $T_\mu = \mathbf{G}$ then Π_μ is equal to $\mathbf{G}/\mathbf{K} = S^1$, where $\mathbf{K}$ is the compact sub-group of rotations.

2. Convergence to the boundary

In this section the following set of hypotheses will be in force:

(i) the space E is an LCCB;

(ii) there exists a transition probability $\hat{P}$ in duality with P with respect to a Radon measure m;

(iii) $P(C_K) \subset C_0$ and $\hat{P}(C_K) \subset C_0$;

(iv) the potentials Gf and $\hat{G}f$ are bounded continuous functions whenever f is in C_K.

These hypotheses may always be achieved if E is countable, since in that case we can take $m = \nu G$ for any probability measure ν such that $\nu G(x) > 0$ for every x in E, and set

$$\hat{P}(x, y) = \nu G(y)\, P(y, x)/\nu G(x).$$

They are also in force for transient random walks on groups.

Furthermore, we assume that $P1 = 1$, in other words 1 is a harmonic function.

Definition 2.1. A *reference function* is a positive m-integrable function r such that $\hat{G}r$ is bounded, continuous and strictly positive.

By condition (iv) above, there are plenty of reference functions, but we shall prove a more precise result. We recall that a Borel function f is said to be *locally integrable* if, for every compact K, we have $\langle m, |f|\, 1_K \rangle < \infty$. If E is countable, every finite function is locally integrable. For a spread-out random walk all m-a.e. finite superharmonic functions are locally integrable. (See Exercise 2.13.)

Lemma 2.2. *For every locally integrable superharmonic function f, there is a reference function r such that $m(fr) < \infty$.*

Proof. Let $\{\varphi_n\}$ be an increasing sequence in C_K^+ with limit 1 at every point in E. Then let C_n be the maximum among the numbers $m(\varphi_n)$, $m(\varphi_n f)$, $\|\hat{G}\varphi_n\|$; it is easily checked that

$$r = \sum_{n=1}^{\infty} C_n^{-1}\, 2^{-n}\, \varphi_n$$

is the required reference function.

Remark. The particular reference function just constructed is continuous and strictly positive. All rm-integrable functions are then locally integrable.

Proposition 2.3. *If r is a reference function, then for every $f \in C_K^+$, the function $\hat{K}f = \hat{G}f/\hat{G}r$ is bounded and continuous. Furthermore if $\{f_n\}_{n \geqslant 1}$ is dense in C_K*

for the topology of uniform convergence on compacta then $\{\hat{K}f_n\}_{n\geqslant 1}$ *is dense in* $\{\hat{K}f, f \in C_K\}$ *for the topology of uniform convergence.*

Proof. That $\hat{K}f$ is continuous is clear. Since we have $\hat{G}r > 0$, there exists a constant $a > 0$ such that $\hat{G}r \geqslant a$ on $\{f > 0\}$. Consequently

$$\hat{G}f \leqslant a^{-1}\|\hat{G}f\|\,\hat{G}r \quad \text{on } \{f > 0\},$$

and hence everywhere, by the complete maximum principle.

Let now f be in C_K and $\{f_k\}$ a subsequence of $\{f_n\}$ converging uniformly to f and such that the sets $\{f_k > 0\}$ are contained in a fixed compact set K. Since

$$\|\hat{G}(f - f_k)\| \leqslant \|f - f_k\|\,\hat{G}(\cdot, K),$$

for any $\varepsilon > 0$ we may find k such that $\|\hat{G}(f - f_k)\| < \varepsilon$. The latter half of the statement is then easily proved by the same argument as the former half.

We shall denote by $\hat{K}(x, \cdot)$ the kernel $\hat{G}(x, \cdot)/\hat{G}r(x)$. The measures $\hat{K}(x, \cdot)$ are co-excessive Radon measures such that $\langle \hat{K}(x, \cdot), r \rangle = 1$, and it follows from the above proposition that the set $\{\hat{K}(x, \cdot), x \in E\}$ is vaguely relatively compact.

We are now ready to construct the Martin boundary of E. We first choose a metric δ on E, compatible with the topology of E, and such that the Cauchy completion of (E, δ) is obtained by adjoining the Alexandrov's point Δ.

We next choose a reference function r such that $m(r) = 1$, and a sequence $\{f_n\}_{n\geqslant 1}$ dense in C_K. For x, y in E, we set

$$d(x, y) = \sum_{n=1}^{\infty} W_n |\hat{K}\,f_n(x) - \hat{K}\,f_n(y)|,$$

where the positive real numbers W_n are chosen such that $\sum_1^\infty W_n \|\hat{K}f_n\| < \infty$. Then $\delta + d$ is a metric on E.

Definition 2.4. We define E^* to be the Cauchy completion of the metric space $(E, \delta + d)$ and set $M = E^* \backslash E$. The set E^* is called the *Martin space* for X started with distribution rm, the set M the *Martin exit boundary* for X started with distribution rm.

The pseudo-metric d generates the uniformity relative to which all the functions $\hat{K}f, f \in C_K$, are uniformly continuous; consequently the space E^* depends neither on the choice of $\{f_n\}$ nor on the choice of $\{W_n\}$, and each function $\hat{K}f$ may be extended continuously to E^*; the extended function will still be denoted by $\hat{K}f$. Let x be a point in M; a sequence $\{x_n\}$ of points in E converges to x if and only if $x_n \to \Delta$ in the original topology of E and $\hat{K} f(x_n) \to \hat{K} f(x)$ for every $f \in C_K$.

Proposition 2.5. *The space E^* is compact; E is a dense open subset of E^* and its relative topology coincides with the original topology.*

Proof. By the choice of δ, and since the functions $\hat{K}f_n$ are bounded, from every sequence of points in E^* one may, by use of Cantor's diagonal process, extract a subsequence $\{x_k\}$ which is Cauchy for δ and such that $\{\hat{K} f_n(x_k)\}$ is Cauchy in $\boldsymbol{R}$ for every n. The subsequence $\{x_k\}$ is thus Cauchy in $(E^*, \delta + d)$, hence it is convergent, and E^* is a compact metric space.

That E is dense in E^* follows from the definition of E^*; furthermore, since $d + \delta \geqslant \delta$, the original topology is coarser than the relative topology, and E is open in E^*. On the other hand, the functions $\hat{K}f$ being continuous, a sequence of points converging to a point in E in the original topology converges in the relative topology, which proves that the latter is finer than the former. The proof is thus complete.

Remark. The space E^* may depend on the choice of the reference function r; in other words, it may happen that the spaces E^* obtained for two different functions are not homeomorphic.

It is now plain that Borel sets in E are Borel sets in E^*. Furthermore, for every point x in M the map $f \to \hat{K} f(x)$, $f \in C_K$, is clearly a Radon measure on E which will be denoted by $\hat{K}(x, \cdot)$. The extended function $\hat{K}$ is clearly a kernel on E^*, the measures $\hat{K}(x, \cdot)$ vanishing outside E. Finally, if $\{x_n\}$ is a sequence of points in E converging to a point x in M, the measure $\hat{K}(x, \cdot)$ is the limit of the measures $\hat{K}(x_n, \cdot)$ in the vague topology. This entails that $\hat{K}r(x) \leqslant 1$ for every x in E^*, and also

Proposition 2.6. *The measures $\hat{K}(x, \cdot)$, $x \in M$, are co-excessive.*

Proof. For $f \in C_K^+$, $\hat{P}f$ is continuous; hence if $\{\mu_n\}$ is a sequence of Radon measures converging vaguely to a measure μ, then

$$\langle \mu, \hat{P}f \rangle \leqslant \varliminf_n \langle \mu_n, \hat{P}f \rangle.$$

The proposition then follows from the previous discussions.

As a result, if σ is a probability measure on the Borel sets of M, the measure $\sigma\hat{K}$ is a co-excessive Radon measure and $\langle \sigma\hat{K}, r \rangle \leqslant 1$. This will be of significance in the forthcoming results, which are the main results of this section.

We shall call Λ the set of trajectories ω such that the sequence $\{X_n(\omega)\}$ has a limit in E^* as $n \to \infty$. Since E^* is compact and metrizable, it is easily seen that Λ is measurable, and moreover, it is an invariant event. Let us pick an arbitrary point x in M and set

$$X_\infty(\omega) = \lim_n X_n(\omega) \quad \text{if } \omega \in \Lambda, \qquad X_\infty(\omega) = x \quad \text{if } \omega \in \Lambda^c.$$

We thus define an invariant random variable X_∞, and in the sequel the statement $\{X_n\}$ converges to X_∞ P_v-a.s. will mean that $P_v[\Lambda] = 1$. We are now ready to state

Theorem 2.7. *The sequence $\{X_n\}$ converges P_m-a.s. to X_∞ and the image σ of P_{rm} by X_∞ is carried by M. Furthermore $m = \sigma\hat{K}$; in other words, for every $f \in C_K$*

$$m(f) = \int_M \hat{K} f(s) \, d\sigma(s).$$

Finally if $P_x \ll P_m$ on $\mathscr{T}$ for every x in E, the above convergence holds almost surely.

Proof. Since the potentials of compact sets are bounded it follows that $\{X_n\}$ converges almost surely to Λ in the topology of E, hence for the metric δ. The convergence in E^* P_m-a.s. is then a consequence of Proposition 1.15 and of the definition of E^*. The last sentence of the statement is shown in exactly the same way. The equality $m = \sigma\hat{K}$ is shown by the following set of equations, where f ranges through C_K^+:

$$\int_M \hat{K} f \, d\sigma = \int_\Omega \hat{K} f(X_\infty) \, dP_{rm} = \int_\Omega (dP_{fm}/dP_{rm})_{\mathscr{T}} \, dP_{rm} = m(f).$$

Finally σ vanishes on E because $X_\infty \in M$ P_{rm}-a.s.

The preceding theorem may be generalized as follows. In the remainder of this chapter, we shall use "harmonic function" to mean "positive harmonic function". We denote by $\mathscr{H}_r$ the set of harmonic functions h such that $m(rh) \leqslant 1$. For a harmonic function h, we set $E^h = \{h > 0\}$; the set E^h is regular, since it is easily checked that $\{h = 0\}$ is absorbing. We define a new T.P. on $(E^h, E^h \cap \mathscr{E})$ by setting, for $x \in E^h$ and $A \in E^h \cap \mathscr{E}$,

$$P^h(x, A) = h(x)^{-1} \int_A P(x, \mathrm{d}y) \, h(y).$$

Plainly, $(P^h)^n = I_{h^{-1}} P_n I_h$, and a function f is P^h-(super) harmonic if and only if hf is P-(super) harmonic. In particular 1 is P^h-harmonic. It is also easily seen that P^h is in duality with $\hat{P}$ with respect to the measure hm. The functions $\hat{G}f/\hat{G}r$ are therefore the same for P and P^h, and the preceding theorem will be applied to the chains with transition probability P^h.

Such a chain may be constructed on the space $(\Omega, \mathscr{F})$ of the chain X. For any positive measure ν on E^h, we call P^h_ν the measure on $(\Omega, \mathscr{F})$ for which $\{X_n\}$ is a homogeneous Markov chain with transition probability P^h and starting measure $h\nu$. For any finite collection A_i, $0 \leqslant i \leqslant n$, of sets in $\mathscr{E}$, one has

$$P^h_\nu[X_0 \in A_0, X_1 \in A_1, \ldots, X_n \in A_n]$$

$$= \int_{A_0} \nu(\mathrm{d}x_0) \, E_{x_0}[1_{A_1}(X_1) \cdots 1_{A_n}(X_n) \, h(X_n)].$$

In this formula, E_{x_0} is the usual expectation associated with the probability measure P_{x_0}; in other words, if $h = 1$, then $P^h = P$ and $P^h_\nu = P_\nu$. It is clear that $P^h_\nu[X_n \notin E^h] = 0$ for every integer n. Finally, if h and k are two harmonic functions, then $P^{h+k}_\nu = P^h_\nu + P^k_\nu$.

Theorem 2.8. *Let h be a locally integrable function in $\mathscr{H}_r$. The sequence $\{X_n\}$ converges P^h_m-a.s. to X_∞; the image σ^h of P^h_{rm} by X_∞ is carried by M and $hm = \sigma^h \hat{K}$. Finally if $P_x \ll P_m$ on $\mathscr{T}$ for every x in E, the convergence holds P^h_x-a.s. for every x in E^h.*

Proof. We cannot immediately apply the preceding theorem, because E^h is no longer LCCB and P^h is not necessarily a Feller kernel.

By Proposition 1.15 we still have the convergence P^h_{rm}-a.s. of the sequences $\hat{K}f(X_n)$. It remains therefore to prove that X_n converges P^h_{rm}-a.s. to Δ in E. Let K be any compact subset of E; calling G^h the potential kernel of P^h, it is easily seen that $hG^h(\cdot, K) = G(h1_K)$, and therefore, since h is locally integrable,

$$\langle h r, G^h 1_K \rangle_m = \langle r, G(h 1_K) \rangle_m = \langle \hat{G} r, h 1_K \rangle_m < \infty.$$

As a result, $P^h_{rm}[R(K)] = 0$ and $\{X_n\}$ converges P^h_{rm}-a.s. to Δ. The first part of the statement then follows from the definitions of E^* and M; the equality $hm = \sigma^h \hat{K}$ is derived as was the equality $m = \sigma \hat{K}$ of Theorem 2.7.

Finally, by Theorem 1.13, if the condition $P_x \ll P_m$ on $\mathscr{T}$ is satisfied, then the condition $P_x^h \ll P_m^h$ on $\mathscr{T}$ is also satisfied and the second part of the statement follows.

Remarks. (1) The measure σ of Theorem 2.7 thus appears as a special case of σ^h obtained when $h = 1_E$.

(2) The map $h \to \sigma^h$ is an affine map from the cone of locally integrable functions in $\mathscr{H}_r$ into the space of bounded positive measures on M, and if $h \leqslant k$ rm-a.e., then $\sigma^h \leqslant \sigma^k$.

We conclude this section by giving the probabilistic version of the classical Fatou's theorem in the unit disc and some of its applications.

Theorem 2.9. *If Gg is a finite potential, then $\lim_n Gg(X_n) = 0$ a.s. If h is a locally integrable harmonic function in $\mathscr{H}_r$, and if $\sigma^h = u\sigma + \sigma_s^h$ is the Lebesgue decomposition of σ^h with respect to σ, then*

$$\lim_n h(X_n) = u(X_\infty) \quad P_m\text{-a.s.}$$

This convergence holds a.s. if $P_x \ll P_m$ on $\mathscr{T}$ for every x in E.

Proof. Since $Gg(X_n)$ is a positive supermartingale, the limit exists a.s. by martingale theory. Now by Fatou's lemma, for every x in E,

$$E_x[\lim Gg(X_n)] \leqslant \lim E_x[Gg(X_n)] = \lim P_n Gg(x) = 0;$$

the proof of the first part of the statement is thus complete.

For the second part, we begin with a function h such that $\sigma_s^h = 0$. Then $u(X_\infty)$ is P_{rm}-a.s. equal to $(\mathrm{d}P_{rm}^h/\mathrm{d}P_{rm})_{\mathscr{T}}$. Let f be any function in C_K^+; from the identities

$$\int_E fh \, \mathrm{d}m = \int_\Omega \hat{K}f(X_\infty) \, \mathrm{d}P_{rm}^h = \int_\Omega (\mathrm{d}P_{fm}/\mathrm{d}P_{rm})_{\mathscr{T}} \, \mathrm{d}P_{rm}^h = \int_\Omega u(X_\infty) \, \mathrm{d}P_{fm},$$

we deduce that

$$E_m[f(X_0)\, h(X_0)] = E_m[f(X_0)\, u(X_\infty)].$$

Now let v be in C_K^+ with $m(v) = 1$; for every integer n, the function $\hat{P}_n v$ is bounded and continuous; consequently the last displayed equality may be applied to $f\hat{P}_n v$, which yields

$$E_m[f(X_0)\, \hat{P}_n v(X_0)\, h(X_0)] = E_m[f(X_0)\, \hat{P}_n v(X_0)\, u(X_\infty)].$$

This formula may also be written

$$\int f(x) \, \hat{P}_n v(x) \, h(x) \, \mathrm{d}m(x) = \int f(x) \, \hat{P}_n v(x) \, E_x[u(X_\infty)] \, \mathrm{d}m(x),$$

and using the duality between P and $\hat{P}$, we obtain

$$\int v(x) \, P_n(fh) \, (x) \, \mathrm{d}m(x) = \int v(x) \, P_n(fE.[u(X_\infty)]) \, (x) \, \mathrm{d}m(x),$$

which may be written

$$E_{vm}[f(X_n) \, h(X_n)] = E_{vm}[f(X_n) \, E_{X_n}[u(X_\infty)]].$$

Using the Markov property and the fact that X_∞ is an invariant random variable, it follows that

$$E_{vm}[f(X_n) \, h(X_n)] = E_{vm}[f(X_n) \, u(X_\infty)].$$

Consequently,

$$E_{vm}[u(X_\infty) \mid \mathscr{F}_n] = E_{vm}[u(X_\infty) \mid X_n] = h(X_n),$$

and the desired result follows in that case.

Before we proceed to the general case, let us remark that if h is a harmonic function such that $\{h(X_n)\}$ converges to $u(X_\infty)$ P_m-a.e., then $\sigma^h \geqslant u\sigma$. Indeed, for every integer n,

$$m(hf) = m(P_n hf) = E_{fm}[h(X_n)],$$

and by Fatou's lemma

$$m(hf) \geqslant E_{fm}[u(X_\infty)] = \int_\Omega (\mathrm{d}P_{fm}/\mathrm{d}P_{rm}) \, u(X_\infty) \, \mathrm{d}P_{rm} = \int_M \hat{K}f \, u \, \mathrm{d}\sigma,$$

and since the functions $\hat{K}f$, $f \in C_K^+$, separate M, we get $\sigma^h \geqslant u\sigma$. If, moreover, $h = E.[u(X_\infty)]$ with $u \in L^1(\sigma)$, then $\{h(X_n)\}$ is equi-integrable for the measure P_{fm}, and we may pass to the limit above to get $\sigma^h = u\sigma$.

Suppose now that σ_s^h does not vanish. The function $h' = E.[u(X_\infty)]$ is harmonic and

$$\lim_n h'(X_n) = u(X_\infty) \quad P_m\text{-a.s.}$$

We thus have $\sigma^{h'} \leqslant \sigma^h$, whence it follows that $h' \leqslant h$ m-a.e. The function $h' \wedge h$ is superharmonic; let $Gg + h''$ be its Riesz decomposition. Since $m\{h' > h\} = 0$ it is easily derived that

$$\lim_n (h' \wedge h) (X_n) = u(X_\infty) \quad P_m\text{-a.s.},$$

and by the first part of the theorem $\lim_n Gg(X_n) = 0$; consequently

$$\lim_n h''(X_n) = u(X_\infty) \quad P_m\text{-a.s.}$$

Since $h'' \leqslant h$ everywhere, we may write $h = h'' + k$, where k is harmonic, and from the relation $P^h_{rm} = P^{h''}_{rm} + P^k_{rm}$, we derive that $\sigma^k = \sigma^h_s$. To complete the proof of the theorem it suffices to show that if σ^h and σ are mutually singular, then $\{h(X_n)\}$ converges to zero P_m-a.s.

Let h be such that σ and σ^h are mutually singular, and call h' the harmonic part in the Riesz decomposition of $h \wedge 1$. Since $h' \leqslant h$ and $h' \leqslant 1$, we have $\sigma^{h'} \leqslant \sigma^h$ and $\sigma^{h'} \leqslant \sigma$, which entails that $\sigma^{h'} = 0$, hence $h' = 0$ m-a.e. It follows by a simple application of Fatou's lemma that

$$\lim_n h'(X_n) = 0 \quad P_m\text{-a.e.},$$

and by the first part of the theorem,

$$\lim_n (h \wedge 1) (X_n) = 0 \quad P_m\text{-a.e.}$$

As a result, $\lim_n h(X_n) = 0$, and the proof is complete.

Corollary 2.10. *If r is continuous and strictly positive, the map $u \to u(X_\infty)$ is a positive isometry from $L^1(M, \sigma)$ onto $L^1(\Omega, \mathcal{T}, P_{rm})$.*

Proof. Clearly, if u is in $L^1(M, \sigma)$, then $u(X_\infty)$ is in $L^1(\Omega, \mathcal{T}, P_{rm})$ and

$$\|u\|_{L^1(\sigma)} = \|u(X_\infty)\|_{L^1(P_{rm})}.$$

Now let Z be in $L^1_+(\Omega, \mathcal{T}, P_{rm})$; the harmonic function $h = E.[Z]$ is in $L^1(rm)$, hence it is locally integrable, and therefore there exists an element u of $L^1(M, \sigma)$ such that $\sigma^h = u\sigma + \sigma^h_s$. By the previous results, we know that $h(X_n)$ converges to $u(X_\infty)$ P_{rm}-a.s., and on the other hand

$$h(X_n) = E_{X_n}[Z] = E_{rm}[Z \mid \mathcal{F}_n],$$

which by the martingale theorem converges to Z P_{rm}-a.s. It follows that $Z = u(X_\infty)$ P_{rm}-a.s., and the proof is complete.

The following result is important. It asserts that the Banach space of bounded harmonic functions is isomorphic to the space L^∞ of a probability measure defined on a Borel subset of a compact metrizable space. This provides a generalization of what is known for spread-out random walks on groups. (See Exercise 1.18.)

Theorem 2.11. *If $P_x \ll P_m$ on $\mathcal{T}$ for every x in E and, if r is continuous and strictly positive, the Banach space $b\mathcal{H}$ of bounded harmonic functions is isomorphic to the Banach space $L^\infty(M, \sigma)$.*

Proof. It was seen in ch. 3 § 3 that the vector space $b\mathcal{H}$ is isomorphic to the vector space of a.s. bounded invariant random variables. Since $P_x \ll P_{rm}$ on $\mathcal{T}$ for every x in E, the equivalence a.s. for invariant random variables is the same as equivalence P_{rm}-a.s. As a result, $b\mathcal{H}$ is isomorphic to $L^\infty(\Omega, \mathcal{T}, P_{rm})$ under the mapping $h \to R(h)$, whose inverse mapping is $Z \to E.[Z]$. If $|Z| < c$ P_{rm}-a.s., it follows that $|Z| < c$ P_x-a.s. for every x in E, and clearly these two mappings are norm-decreasing; they are therefore Banach isomorphisms.

It remains to prove that the Banach space $L^\infty(\Omega, \mathcal{T}, P_{rm})$ is isomorphic to $L^\infty(M, \sigma)$. This is done by using the map $u \to u(X_\infty)$ in the same way as in the above corollary.

Remark. If we compare this result with Theorem 1.5, we see that there is a one-to-one correspondence between the Borel subsets of M, up to σ-equivalence, and the equivalence classes of regular sets.

We close this section with a few comments on what can be said if 1 is no longer a harmonic function. In that case, the chain may "disappear" at a finite time and is then placed in the cemetery Δ, which we shall consider as an isolated point. If the other hypotheses of this section are in force we may construct E^* and M as before and prove Theorem 2.8; the measure σ^h will be carried by M. The boundary may be viewed as the union of M and the isolated point Δ, and the image of P_{rm} by X_∞ will be equal to $P_{rm}[\zeta < \infty] \varepsilon_\Delta + \sigma^h$, where h is the harmonic part of the Riesz decomposition of 1.

Exercise 2.12. With the notation of Theorem 2.9, prove that the following two conditions are equivalent:

    (i) $h(X_n)$ converges in $L^1(P_{rm})$;
    (ii) the measure σ_s^h vanishes.
These two conditions are satisfied if h is bounded.

Exercise 2.13. Prove that, if X is a spread-out random walk, every a.e. finite superharmonic function is locally integrable.

    [*Hint*: Choose n such that $\mu^n > cm$ on an open set V. For any x in $\mathbf{G}$, there is a point y such that $f(y) < \infty$ and $x \in yV$. Prove that $\int_{yV} f \, dm < \infty$.]

Exercise 2.14. Let X be a right random walk of law μ on a group $\mathbf{G}$.

    (1) Prove that the following two conditions are equivalent:
        (i) there exist reference functions in C_K^+;
        (ii) there exists a compact set K such that $\mathbf{G} = K \, T_\mu$.

    (2) Assume henceforth that the conditions of (1) are satisfied. Prove that the space E^* obtained for different reference functions in C_K^+ are homeomorphic $\mathbf{G}$-spaces. Prove that in Theorem 2.7 the convergence holds a.s. even if X is not spread out.

    (3) Let ν be a probability measure on $\mathbf{G}$ equivalent to m. Call σ_ν the image of P_ν by X_∞ and N the support of σ_ν. Prove that N does not depend on ν and is a compact $\mathbf{G}$-space.

    (4) From now onwards X is assumed to be spread out. Prove that there is an isomorphism $h \to \tilde{h}$ between the Banach spaces $b\mathscr{H}$ of bounded harmonic functions and $L^\infty(N, \sigma_\nu)$ such that

$$\tilde{h}(X_\infty) = \lim h(X_n) \quad \text{a.s.} \quad \text{and } h(g) = \langle g\gamma, \tilde{h} \rangle,$$

where γ is the image of P_e by X_∞. Compare with Exercise 1.18.

    (5) Assume further that $\mu \ll m$, and prove that there exists a function k on $\mathbf{G} \times N$ such that $k(\cdot, x)$ is invariant for σ_ν-almost every x in N, and if $h \in b\mathscr{H}$, then

$$h(g) = \int_N k(g, x) \, h(x) \, d\sigma_\nu(x).$$

Exercise 2.15. (1) Prove that for any pair of points x, y in E, the equality $\hat{K}(x, \cdot) = \hat{K}(y, \cdot)$ holds if and only if $x = y$.

    (2) Prove that there exists a unique (up to homeomorphism) compact metrizable space F such that: (i) E is a dense subset of F and the relative topology of E is coarser than its original topology; (ii) the functions $\hat{K}f, f \in C_K$, extend to continuous functions on F which separate F.

    (3) State and prove a theorem of convergence to the boundary in F.

3. Integral representation of harmonic functions

In the preceding section, we have associated with each positive locally integrable harmonic function h of $\mathcal{H}_r$ a measure σ^h on the boundary. As a result, the co-invariant Radon measure hm had an integral representation as the image of σ^h by the kernel $\hat{K}$. Conversely, if η is a bounded measure on the boundary, $\eta\hat{K}$ is a co-excessive Radon measure such that $\langle \eta\hat{K}, r \rangle < \infty$. We wish to turn this into an integral representation for harmonic functions, recalling the classical Poisson representation in the unit disc. For this purpose, we need some extra condition ensuring that the map $f \to fm$ is an isomorphism between the cones of superharmonic functions and the cone of co-excessive measures. Unfortunately, we do not know of such a condition in a general setting, and we shall have to restrict ourselves to the study of discrete chains. We begin by translating the previous results.

From now on, we assume that X is discrete. Let Π be a probability measure such that the potential ΠG is bounded and strictly positive on E. By setting

$$m = \Pi G \quad \text{and} \quad \hat{P}(x, y) = P(y, x)\, m(y)/m(x),$$

we get a chain $\hat{X}$ in duality with X, and we have the hypotheses of the preceding section. If we set $r(x) = \Pi(x)/\Pi G(x)$, it is easily computed that $\hat{G}r = 1$, and thus r may be used as a reference function. Furthermore, a function is integrable with respect to rm if and only if it is integrable with respect to Π and all finite functions are locally integrable.

We may define the boundary M and the space E^* by using this particular reference function r. In the sequel, we shall use the kernel

$$K(x, s) = \hat{K}(s, x)/\Pi G(x), \qquad s \in E^*, \quad x \in E;$$

it is easily computed that, for $s \in E$, one has $K(x, s) = G(x, s)/\Pi G(s)$.

Theorem 2.8 may now be restated as:

Theorem 3.1. *If h is a Π-integrable harmonic function, then for every x in E, $\{X_n\}$ converges to X_∞ P_x^h-a.s., and*

$$h(x) = \int_M K(x, s)\, d\sigma^h(s),$$

where σ^h is the image of P_Π^h by X_∞. In particular, $\{X_n\}$ converges to X_∞ a.s. and

$$1 = \int_M K(\cdot, s)\, d\sigma(s).$$

Moreover, if A is a Borel subset of M, then for every x in E,

$$P_x^h[X_\infty \in A] = \int_A K(x, s) \, d\sigma^h(s).$$

Proof. Taking $f = 1_{\{x\}}$ in Theorem 2.8 yields

$$\Pi \, G(x) \, h(x) = \int_M \hat{K}(s, x) \, d\sigma^h(s),$$

and the first part of the statement follows at once from the definition of K.

To prove the second part, let us first observe that if $f = 1_{\{x\}}$, then $P_{fm}^h = \Pi \, G(x) \, P_x^h$; then, by the foregoing section, we have

$$K(x, X_\infty) = (dP_x^h/dP_\Pi^h)_{\mathscr{F}} \quad P_\Pi^h\text{-a.s.}$$

It follows that

$$P_x^h[X_\infty \in A] = \int_\Omega K(x, X_\infty) \, 1_{\{X_\infty \in A\}} \, dP_\Pi^h = \int_A K(x, s) \, d\sigma^h(s),$$

and the proof is complete.

In the present setting, for $f = 1_{\{x\}}$, we have $\hat{G}f/\hat{G}r = \hat{G}(x, \cdot)$, and consequently $\hat{K}f = m(x) \, K(x, \cdot)$. The uniformity relative to which the functions $\hat{K}f$, $f \in C_K$, are uniformly continuous is the same as the uniformity relative to which the functions $K(x, \cdot)$, $x \in E$, are uniformly continuous. As a result, E^* could have been defined by using the functions $K(x, \cdot)$ instead of the functions $\hat{K}f$. A sequence $\{s_n\}$ of points in E^* converges to a point s of E^* if and only if either s is in E and $s_n = s$ for n sufficiently large, or s is in M and $K(x, s_n) \to K(x, s)$ for every x in E.

It turns out that the ancillary dual chain used above disappears completely in the statement, and may thus be forgotten in the sequel; of course if X admits a particular dual chain of independent interest, as for instance the dual random walk whenever X is a random walk on a discrete group, we can keep it in mind and apply the results of § 2.

We may now use Theorem 3.1 to state

Theorem 3.2. *Let η be any probability measure on E^*; the function*

$$f(\cdot) = \int_{E^*} K(\cdot, s) \, d\eta(s)$$

is superharmonic and $\Pi(f) \leqslant 1$. Conversely, for any superharmonic Π-integrable function f, there is at least one bounded measure σ^f on E^* such that

$$f(\cdot) = \int_{E^*} K(\cdot, s)\, \sigma^f(\mathrm{d}s).$$

Proof. The functions $K(\cdot, s)$ are easily seen to be superharmonic and $\langle \Pi, K(\cdot, s)\rangle \leqslant 1$ for every s in E^*, so that the first statement is an easy consequence of Fubini's theorem.

Conversely, f has a Riesz decomposition as the sum $Gg + h$ of a potential and a harmonic function h. Since E is discrete, g may be viewed as a measure on E, and by putting $\sigma^f = g + \sigma^h$, we get the desired measure.

We have thus obtained a linear map from the space of bounded positive measures on E^* onto the space of Π-integrable superharmonic functions on E. Counter-examples show that this correspondence is not one to one, and we shall now look for a Borel subset M_e of M such that the correspondence becomes one to one if we restrict ourselves to measures carried by the subset $E \cup M_e$ of E^*.

To get this uniqueness property, we must clearly exclude the points s in M such that the superharmonic function $K(\cdot, s)$ is not harmonic. Indeed if $K(\cdot, s) = Gg + h$, then it corresponds to both ε_s and $g + \sigma^h$.

Proposition 3.3. *The set B of points s in M such that $K(\cdot, s)$ is not harmonic is a Borel subset of M. The set B has σ^h-measure zero for every Π-integrable harmonic function h.*

Proof. Each of the sets

$$B_x = \left\{ s \colon \int P(x, \mathrm{d}y)\, K(y, s) < K(x, s) \right\}$$

is measurable, since $K(x, \cdot)$ is continuous on E^*, and B is the countable union of the sets B_x, where x runs through E.

The second half of the statement is obvious.

Before we proceed, we must introduce the following terminology. We call $\mathscr{S}_\Pi$ the set of superharmonic functions f such that $\Pi(f) \leqslant 1$ and $\mathscr{H}_\Pi$ the set of harmonic functions in $\mathscr{S}_\Pi$. The set $\mathscr{H}_\Pi$ takes the place of the set $\mathscr{H}_r$ of the preceding section.

Lemma 3.4. *The set $\mathscr{S}_\Pi$, endowed with the topology of pointwise convergence, is a compact convex set.*

Proof. That $\mathscr{S}_\Pi$ is a convex set is clear. Let $\{f_n\}$ be a sequence of functions of $\mathscr{S}_\Pi$; for every x in E, we have $0 \leqslant f_n(x) \leqslant \Pi(x)^{-1}$ and consequently, by Cantor's diagonal process, we may extract a sub-sequence converging point-wise to a limit f. By Fatou's lemma, f is in $\mathscr{S}_\mu$, which is thus a compact set.

Definition 3.5. We call *extremal functions* the extremal points of the compact convex set $\mathscr{S}_\Pi$.

The zero function is extremal, and a non-zero function f is extremal if, whenever $f = f_1 + f_2$ with f_1 and f_2 in $\mathscr{S}_\Pi$, there is a real $t \in [0, 1]$ such that $f_1 = tf$ and $f_2 = (1 - t)f$. This is equivalent to saying that if $f' \in \mathscr{S}_\Pi$ and $f - f' \in \mathscr{S}_\Pi$, then there is a real $t \in [0, 1]$ such that $f' = tf$. In particular, if h is harmonic and extremal, and if h' is harmonic and $h' \leqslant h$ then $h' = th$. The reader is invited to return to ch. 2, Exercise 1.27 for the study of the proper order of the cone of Π-integrable superharmonic functions. Finally, we observe that if f is a non-zero extremal function, then $\Pi(f) = 1$. In the sequel we shall use *"extremal function"* to mean *"non-zero extremal function"*.

From the Riesz decomposition theorem, we deduce that an extremal function is either a harmonic function or a potential. Moreover, we have

Lemma 3.6. *A potential is extremal if and only if it is equal to $K(\cdot, y)$ with $y \in E$.*

Proof. The necessity is obvious. Conversely, if $f \in \mathscr{S}_\Pi$ is such that $K(\cdot, y) - f \in \mathscr{S}_\Pi$ with $y \in E$, the harmonic part of f is bounded above by a finite potential and thus vanishes identically. Let $f = Gg$; it follows that $K(\cdot, y) - Gg$ is a potential, hence $(\varepsilon_y(\cdot)/\Pi G(y)) - g(\cdot)$ is a positive function, which implies that g is a multiple of ε_y.

If there is a point s in $M \backslash B$ such that the harmonic function $K(\cdot, s)$ is not extremal, then the uniqueness property that we are looking for cannot hold. Indeed, we could have $K(\cdot, s) = h_1 + h_2$ with $h_1 \neq t K(\cdot, s)$, and $K(\cdot, s)$ would correspond to ε_s as well as to $\sigma^{h_1} + \sigma^{h_2}$. We shall therefore try to restrict the boundary to the set of points s such that $K(\cdot, s)$ is extremal.

Since the functions $h = K(\cdot, s)$, $s \in M \backslash B$, are harmonic and in $\mathscr{H}_\Pi$, one can define the probability measures P_ν^h and measures σ^h as in § 2. To simplify the writing, we shall write P_ν^s and σ^s instead of $P^{K(\cdot, s)}$ and $\sigma^{K(\cdot, s)}$.

Lemma 3.7. *For any $\Lambda \in \mathscr{F}$, the map $s \to P_\nu^s[\Lambda]$ is $\mathscr{E}^*$-measurable, and for $f \in \mathscr{H}_\Pi$,*

$$P_\nu^h[\Lambda] = \int_M P_\nu^s[\Lambda] \, \sigma^h(\mathrm{d}s).$$

For any Borel subset A of M, the map $s \to \sigma^s(A)$ is $\mathscr{E}^*$-measurable and

$$\sigma^h(A) = \int_M \sigma^s(A) \, \sigma^h(\mathrm{d}s).$$

Proof. By § 2, if $\Lambda \in \mathscr{F}_n$ we have

$$P_\nu^s[\Lambda] = E_\nu[1_\Lambda K(X_n, s)] \, ;$$

the measurability of $s \to P_\nu^s[\Lambda]$ is thus clear when $\Lambda \in \mathscr{F}_n$, and the proof is completed by means of the monotone class theorem.

Next, with Λ still in $\mathscr{F}_n$, we have, on account of Theorem 3.1,

$$P_\nu^h[\Lambda] = E_\nu[1_\Lambda h(X_n)] = E_\nu \left[1_\Lambda \int_M K(X_n, s) \, \mathrm{d}\sigma^h(s) \right],$$

and by Fubini's theorem we get

$$P_\nu^h[\Lambda] = \int_M E_\nu[1_\Lambda K(X_n, s)] \, \mathrm{d}\sigma^h(s) = \int_M P_\nu^s[\Lambda] \, \mathrm{d}\sigma^h(s),$$

which is the desired result when $\Lambda \in \mathscr{F}_n$. The general result follows by the monotone class theorem.

The second half of the theorem is an easy consequence of the definition of σ^s and σ^h:

$$\sigma^s(A) = P_\Pi^s[X_\infty \in A], \qquad \sigma^h(A) = P_\Pi^h[X_\infty \in A].$$

We shall need the following:

Lemma 3.8. *If $h \in \mathscr{H}_\Pi$, the map $f \to hf$ is a homogeneous affine map from the compact convex set $\mathscr{S}_\Pi^h$ of $h\Pi$-integrable P^h-superharmonic functions into $\mathscr{S}_\Pi$. If h is an extremal function in $\mathscr{S}_\Pi$, then 1_{E^h} is an extremal function in $\mathscr{S}_\Pi^h$.*

Proof. The first statement is easily checked; we recall that the set $(E^h)^c = \{h = 0\}$ is absorbing for P, and hence that $P(hf)$ vanishes on $(E^h)^c$.

Now, if 1_{E^h} is not extremal, that means that there are two non-constant functions f_1 and f_2 in $\mathscr{S}_\Pi^h$ such that $1_{E^h} = f_1 + f_2$. We then have $h = hf_1 + hf_2$, and hf_i is not a multiple of h, which thus cannot be an extremal function.

Remark. We may also say that h is extremal if and only if the only bounded P^h-harmonic functions are constant.

We now derive

Proposition 3.9. *Let s be in $M \setminus B$; then $h = K(\cdot, s)$ is extremal if and only if $\sigma^h = \varepsilon_s$. Then $P_H^s[X_\infty = s] = 1$.*

Proof. If the function 1 is extremal there exists no non-constant bounded harmonic function. Consequently the σ-algebra $\mathcal{T}$ is a.s. trivial, and therefore the $\mathcal{T}$-measurable random variable X_∞ is constant P_H-a.s. As a result, the measure σ is the unit mass at some point of M.

If $h = K(\cdot, s)$ is extremal, then, by the preceding lemma, the function 1_{E^h} is extremal in $\mathscr{S}_H^h$, and therefore σ^h is the unit mass at some point in M. By Theorem 3.1, this point must be s.

Conversely, if $h = K(\cdot, s)$ is the sum of two harmonic functions h_1 and h_2 which are not multiples of h, then $\sigma^h = \sigma^{h_1} + \sigma^{h_2}$, where σ^{h_1} and σ^{h_2} are not multiples of σ^h. It is then clearly impossible for σ^h to be equal to ε_s.

As a consequence we get

Proposition 3.10. *The set M_e of points s in M such that $K(\cdot, s)$ is harmonic and extremal is a Borel subset of M, and for any $h \in \mathscr{H}_H$ we have $\sigma^h(M_e^c) = 0$.*

Proof. By Proposition 3.9, the set M_e is the set of points s in M such that $\sigma^s = \varepsilon_s$. Let $\{B_n\}_{n \geqslant 0}$ be a countable algebra of sets generating the σ-algebra of Borel subsets of M. Then by the monotone class theorem,

$$M_e = \bigcap_{n=0}^{\infty} \{s : \sigma^s(B_n) = 1_{B_n}(s)\},$$

and by Lemma 3.7, M_e is a Borel set.

Next, from the formula $\sigma^h(A) = \int \sigma^s(A) \, d\sigma^h(s)$ of Lemma 3.7, it follows that

$$\sigma^s(A) = 1_A(s) \sigma^h \quad \text{a.s.}$$

for every Borel subset A of M. Consequently,

$$\sigma^s(B_n) = 1_{B_n}(s) \sigma^h \quad \text{a.s.}$$

for every $n \geqslant 0$; hence by the monotone class theorem, the set of points s such that $\sigma^s \neq \varepsilon_s$ has σ^h-measure zero.

We may now state our main result.

Theorem 3.11. *Let* $f = Gg + h$ *be a superharmonic function in* $\mathscr{S}_{\Pi}$; *the measure* $\sigma^f = g + \sigma^h$ *is the unique measure carried by the subset* $E \cup M_e$ *of* E^* *such that*

$$f(x) = \int_{E \cup M_e} K(x, s) \, \sigma^f(\mathrm{d}s).$$

Proof. By previous discussions, it suffices to show that if η is a probability measure on M_e and $h(x) = \int_{M_e} K(x, s) \, \eta(\mathrm{d}s)$, then $\sigma^h = \eta$.

Let A be a Borel subset of M; by the same argument as in Lemma 3.7 we get

$$P^h_{\Pi}[X_\infty \in A] = \int P^s_{\Pi}[X_\infty \in A] \, \eta(\mathrm{d}s);$$

but since for η-almost all s, $P^s_{\Pi}[X_\infty \in A] = 1_A(s)$, we have $P^h_{\Pi}[X_\infty \in A] = \eta(A)$, and therefore $\sigma^h = \eta$.

From this uniqueness property and the fact that X_∞ is in M_e P^h_x-a.s. for every $h \in \mathscr{H}_{\Pi}$ and x in E, we see that the set M_e is the *useful part* of the boundary of E. Furthermore, it is often easier to describe the set M_e, which is isomorphic to a set of extremal points of a compact convex set, than the whole set M. In applications, the set M will therefore be forgotten, and the enlarged state space will be $E \cup M_e$. It may happen that it is no longer a compact space, but that causes no inconvenience in general.

Exercise 3.12. Prove that, if $A \in M$,

$$P_{\Pi}[X_\infty \in A \mid \mathscr{F}_n] = \int_A K(X_n, s) \, \mathrm{d}\sigma(s).$$

Exercise 3.13 (Fine topology). (1) Prove that, if $s \in M_e$, and if A is a Borel subset of E^* such that $P^s_{\Pi}[\underline{\lim} \{X_n \in A\}] > 0$, then $P^s_{\Pi}[\underline{\lim} \{X_n \in A\}] = 1$.

(2) Prove that one can define a topology on E^* in the following way: if $s \in E^* \backslash M_e$, then $\{s\}$ is open; if $s \in M_e$, then the collection of sets satisfying the condition of (1) is a basis of neighbourhoods of s. Prove that this topology is finer than the topology of E^*; we call it the fine topology.

(3) Using the notation of Theorem 2.9, prove that u is σ-a.s. equal to a finely continuous function.

Exercise 3.14. Let X be the random walk of ch. 3, Exercise 4.15(2).

(1) Observe that in the discussion of the present section we may take $\Pi = \varepsilon_0$ and then all harmonic functions are Π-integrable. Compute K and prove that E^* is obtained by adjoining two points to the space $E = \mathbf{Z}$. Prove that both points correspond to a non-zero extremal function; compute these functions. Give all harmonic functions and compare with ch. 5, Exercise 1.9.

(2) Take now $\Pi(x) = 0$ for $x > 0$ and $\Pi(x) = (p/q)^x ((p - q)/p)$ for $x \leqslant 0$. Do the same work as in (1). Observe that one of the points of the boundary does not correspond to a non-zero extremal harmonic function; thus M_e is different from M in this case.

(3) More generally, if X is any transient random walk on $\mathbf{Z}$, prove that, for any probability measure Π on $\mathbf{Z}$, there is at most one Π-integrable extremal harmonic function other than the function 1.

Exercise 3.15. In § 2, the set M might have been viewed as the *Martin entrance boundary* of the chain $\hat{X}$. Assume that X and $\hat{X}$ are discrete; state and prove for co-excessive measures a result similar to Theorem 3.11.

Exercise 3.16. Let E be the set of lattice points (n, i) in the plane with $0 \leqslant i \leqslant n$, and define P by

$$P((n, i), (n + 1, i)) = P((n, i), (n + 1, i + 1)) = 2^{-1}.$$

A point in E is thus identified with i heads in n tosses of a fair coin.

(1) Observe that the unit mass at $(0, 0)$ is a reference measure, and compute the corresponding kernel K.

(2) Prove that a sequence (n_k, j_k) is Cauchy in the corresponding space E^* if and only if there is a number $s \in [0, 1]$ such that $\lim_k j_k/n_k = s$. Prove that M is homeomorphic to $[0, 1]$ endowed with its usual topology and that for $s \in M$,

$$K((m, i), s) = 2^m s^i (1 - s)^{m-i}.$$

Prove that $M_e = M$.

(3) What is the measure σ corresponding to the harmonic function 1? Describe h and P^h for the case in which σ^h is the Lebesgue measure on M, and that in which $\sigma^h = \varepsilon_s$ for $s \in M$.

Exercise 3.17. Let E be the set of all finite sequences of letters a and b. The empty sequence is taken as the starting state, and is denoted by 0. A transition probability on E is defined in the following way: if x is a finite sequence, and we denote by xa and xb the sequences obtained by adjoining a or b on the right of x, then

$$P(x, xa) = P(x, xb) = \tfrac{1}{2}.$$

(1) Prove that the boundary M is the set of all infinite sequences of letters a and b. Find the topology of M.

(2) Compute the measure σ corresponding to the harmonic function 1.

CHAPTER 8

POTENTIAL THEORY FOR HARRIS CHAINS

In this chapter, we proceed with the study of a potential theory suitable for Harris chains, which was initiated in ch. 6. Special functions will still play an important role, but we shall consider only the bounded ones. Thus, in all statements of this chapter, "special" must be understood as "special and bounded".

1. Harris chains and duality

As was seen in ch. 4 §3, most Harris chains, and actually all the usual ones, have a dual chain, and it was shown in ch. 3 §2 that, up to modification, the dual chain is also Harris.

We shall give below a proof of the latter result that does not rely on the notion of essential irreducibility. Afterwards we shall study the relationship between special and co-special (special for the dual chain) functions.

Theorem 1.1. *If P is Harris and in duality with $\hat{P}$, there is a modification of $\hat{P}$ which is Harris. Furthermore if $h \in \mathcal{U}_+$, $h > 0$ and $U_h > 1 \otimes m$, this modification may be chosen so that $\hat{U}_h(h) = 1$ and $\hat{U}_h > 1 \otimes m$.*

Proof. As m is the only invariant measure for P, the duality between P and $\hat{P}$ holds with respect to m. For $f, g \in \mathcal{E}_+$,

$$\langle \hat{U}_h f, g \rangle = \langle f, U_h g \rangle > m(f)\, m(g),$$

which implies that, for all $f \in b\mathcal{E}_+$, $\hat{U}_h f > m(f)$ m-a.e. By letting f run through a denumerable algebra of sets generating $\mathcal{E}$ we get that there is an m-null set N_1 such that $\hat{U}_h(x, \cdot) > m$ for x outside N_1. Moreover, for every $g \in b\mathcal{E}_+$,

$$\langle \hat{U}_h(h), g \rangle = \langle h, U_h(g) \rangle = (hm)\, U_h(g) = m(g)$$

according to ch. 3, Proposition 2.11. Therefore $\hat{U}_h(h) = 1$ outside an m-null set N_2.

Since m is $\hat{P}$-excessive, one can find, as in ch. 3, Corollary 3.10, an m-null set N containing $N_1 \cup N_2$ and such that N^c is an absorbing set. We then pick a point x_0 in N^c and set

$$\hat{P}'(x, \cdot) = \hat{P}(x, \cdot) \quad \text{for } x \in N^c,$$

$$\hat{P}'(x, \cdot) = \hat{P}(x_0, \cdot) \quad \text{for } x \in N;$$

the T.P. $\hat{P}'$ is a modification of $\hat{P}$ for which the conditions $\hat{U}_h(h) = 1$ and $\hat{U}_h > 1 \otimes m$ hold. It is then clear from ch. 3, Proposition 2.9 that $\hat{P}'$ is Harris, and the proof is complete.

In the following, we do assume that there is at least one T.P. $\hat{P}$ in duality with P.

On account of ch. 6, Corollary 4.6, the function h in the preceding result is both special and co-special. It is natural to ask whether every special function is, as a rule, also co-special (up to a modification of $\hat{P}$). On account of ch. 6, Proposition 4.9, this would imply that, for every quasi-compact T.P., there is at least one quasi-compact modification of $\hat{P}$. This turns out to be false, as is shown in Exercise 1.10, and we shall below describe the set of functions both special and co-special. For this purpose, we need the following classical

Lemma 1.2. *Let $\{a_n\}_{n \in \mathbf{N}}$ be a bounded sequence of real numbers converging to zero in the sense of Cesaro and set $f(s) = \sum_0^\infty a_n s^n$ $(0 \leqslant s < 1)$; then*

$$\lim_{s \to 1} (1 - s) f(s) = 0.$$

Proof. The sequence $U_n = n^{-1} \sum_0^n a_k$ converges to zero, and an easy computation yields

$$(1 - s) f(s) = (1 - s)^2 \sum_0^\infty U_n \frac{s^n}{n}.$$

For $\varepsilon > 0$, there is an integer N such that $|U_n| \leqslant \varepsilon$ for $n \geqslant N$, hence

$$|(1 - s) f(s)| \leqslant (1 - s)^2 \sum_0^{N-1} |U_n| \frac{s^n}{n} + \varepsilon (1 - s)^2 \sum_N^\infty \frac{s^n}{n}.$$

Now, the first term on the right of this inequality can be made arbitrarily small by choosing s near one, and the second term is less than ε, which completes the proof.

Before we proceed, let us remark that if f is special for X and g special for $\hat{X}$, then $f \wedge g$ is special and co-special.

Proposition 1.3. *A function h in $b\mathscr{E}_+$ is special and co-special if and only if there is a real number c such that*

$$U_{ch} > 1 \otimes m \quad \text{and} \quad \hat{U}_{ch} > 1 \otimes m.$$

Proof. The "if" part is obvious. To prove the converse, we start with P and $\hat{P}$ quasi-compact. Since the constant functions are special there is, by virtue of ch. 6, Lemma 4.7, a function $f > 0$ and a constant $a < 1$ such that $U_a > 1 \otimes fm$. For $a' < a$, we have $U_{a'} > (a - a')\, U_a U_{a'}$, and therefore, for all $g \in b\mathscr{E}_+$ and $x \in E$,

$$U_{a'}\, g(x) > (a - a')\, U_a U_{a'}\, g(x)$$

$$> (a - a')\, \langle f, U_{a'} g \rangle = (a - a')\, \langle \hat{U}_{a'} f, g \rangle.$$

Since $\hat{P}$ is quasi-compact, there is, by Lemma 1.2, a number a_0 such that $a' < a_0$ implies $a' \hat{U}_{a'} f \geqslant k > 0$; thus

$$U_{a'} g(x) > \frac{k(a - a')}{a'}\, m(g).$$

This proves that, for a' sufficiently small, $U_{a'} > 1 \otimes m$. Symmetrically, one can find a'' such that $\hat{U}_{a''} > 1 \otimes m$. Then, taking $c = a' \wedge a''$, we get the desired result for constant functions.

Let us now shift to the general case and suppose $h > 0$. The T.P.'s $Q = U_h I_h$ and $\hat{Q} = \hat{U}_h I_h$ are quasi-compact and in duality with respect to the measure hm. Since $U_c^Q = U_{ch} I_h$, the first part of the proof implies that for c sufficiently small,

$$U_{ch} I_h > 1 \otimes hm \quad \text{and} \quad \hat{U}_{ch} I_h > 1 \otimes hm;$$

hence

$$U_{ch} > 1 \otimes m \quad \text{and} \quad \hat{U}_{ch} > 1 \otimes m.$$

Now, any special and co-special function h is majorized by a strictly positive special function k and by a strictly positive co-special function $\hat{k}$. The function $k \wedge \hat{k}$ is strictly positive, special and co-special, and majorizes h. Since U_h increases when h decreases, the proof is complete.

The importance of functions h such that $U_h > 1 \otimes m$ was shown in ch. 6 §5. The above results lead one to think that it is exactly those functions which are both special and co-special. The following results lead in that direction.

Proposition 1.4. *Let h be special; there is a real c such that $U_{ch} > 1 \otimes m$ if and only if there is a modification of $\hat{P}$ such that h is co-special.*

Proof. The sufficiency follows from Proposition 1.3. The necessity may be shown in a way very similar to Theorem 1.1, and is left to the reader as Exercise 1.7.

Corollary 1.5. *Let P be quasi-compact; then there is a quasi-compact modification of $\hat{P}$ if and only if there is real c such that $U_c > 1 \otimes m$.*

Proof. Obvious.

In Proposition 1.4, the modification of $\hat{P}$ may depend on the function h. However, in important cases, one can find a modification of $\hat{P}$ which works for all functions h. To state the corresponding result, we resume the notational device of ch. 1, Lemma 5.3, and write the Lebesgue decomposition of $\hat{P}_n$ with respect to m as

$$\hat{P}_n(x, \cdot) = \hat{P}_n^0(x, \cdot) + \hat{P}_n^1(x, \cdot).$$

It is easily shown that the singular parts $\hat{P}_n^1$ satisfy the inequality $\hat{P}_{n+m}^1 \leqslant \hat{P}_n^1 \hat{P}_m^1$ for all integers n and m; furthermore, for every x in E, $\lim_n \hat{P}_n^1(x, E) = 0$ (cf. ch. 3, Exercise 2.19 and ch. 7, Theorem 1.13). The following statement covers the case where $\hat{P} \ll m$ (hence in particular the case of discrete chains), the case of Harris random walks on groups and homogeneous spaces, and the case of quasi-compact $\hat{P}$.

Proposition 1.6. *If $\lim_n \|\hat{P}_n(\cdot, E)\| = 0$ and if h is special, then there is a real number c such that $U_{ch} > 1 \otimes m$ if and only if h is co-special.*

Proof. Only the necessity requires a proof. Without losing any generality we may assume that $\|h\| = a < 1$ and $U_h > 1 \otimes m$. As in Theorem 1.1, we may prove that for every g in $b\mathscr{E}_+$, we have

$$\hat{U}_h(g) > m(g) \quad m\text{-a.e.}$$

Pick c such that $a < c < 1$. The kernel $\hat{U}_c = \sum_0^\infty (1 - c)^n \hat{P}_{n+1}$ may be written $\hat{U}_c = \hat{U}_c^0 + \hat{U}_c^1$, where $\hat{U}_c^1$ is the singular part. The hypothesis implies that there is a number $\alpha > 0$ such that $\hat{U}_c^0(\,\cdot\,, E) \geqslant \alpha$. By the resolvent equation, we thus have

$$\hat{U}_h g \geqslant \hat{U}_c(c - h)\,(\hat{U}_h g) \geqslant \hat{U}_c^0(c - a)\,\hat{U}_h g,$$

and since $\hat{U}_h g > m(g)$ m-a.e., for every $g \in b\mathscr{E}_+$,

$$\hat{U}_h g > \alpha(c - a)\,m(g).$$

It follows that h is co-special.

Exercise 1.7. Prove the necessity in Proposition 1.4.

Exercise 1.8. Let X and $\hat{X}$ be two Harris chains in duality and h a strictly positive, special and co-special function. If h is sufficiently small, prove that the associated kernels W_h and $\hat{W}_h$ are in duality relative to m. If φ and ψ are bounded functions, the kernels

$$\Gamma = I + W_h + 1 \otimes \varphi m + \psi \otimes m, \qquad \hat{\Gamma} = I + \hat{W}_h + \varphi \otimes m + 1 \otimes \psi m$$

are potential kernels in duality.

Exercise 1.9. Prove that in the results of this section one can avoid the use of modifications of $\hat{P}$ whenever E is an LCCB space, $\hat{P}$ a Feller kernel and h a continuous function.
[*Hint*: Use the results given in §4.]

Exercise 1.10. Let E be the unit interval $[0, 1]$ of the real line, $\mathscr{E}$ the σ-algebra of Borel subsets of E and m the Lebesgue measure on $\mathscr{E}$. Set $i(x) = x$ for $x \in E$, and define a pointwise transformation θ of E by

$$\theta = 2i1_{[0,\frac{1}{4}]} + (i + \tfrac{1}{4})\,1_{]\frac{1}{4},\frac{1}{2}]} + \tfrac{1}{2}(i + 1)\,1_{]\frac{1}{2},1]}.$$

(1) Compute the Lebesgue derivative of $\theta^n(m)$ with respect to m.
(2) Calling φ the derivative $d\theta(m)/dm$, set, for $f \in \mathscr{E}$,

$$Sf = f \circ \theta^{-1}, \qquad \hat{S}f = (f \circ \theta)\,\varphi$$

and

$$P = 2^{-1}S + (1 \otimes \tfrac{1}{2}\varphi)\,m, \qquad \hat{P} = \tfrac{1}{2}\hat{S} + (1 - \tfrac{1}{2}\varphi) \otimes m.$$

Prove that P and $\hat{P}$ are two T.P.'s in duality relative to m, that P is quasi-compact and that no modification of $\hat{P}$ is quasi-compact.

(3) The same example provides a counter-example to the following sharpening of ch. 6, Exercise 2.13: if P is quasi-compact, P_n converges to $1 \otimes m$ in the norm of linear operators on $L^1(m)$.

2. Equilibrium, balayage and maximum principles

In this section we show that for each one of the potential operators Γ defined in ch. 6, Proposition 5.4 one can develop a potential theory which parallels the theory in ch. 2.

Theorem 2.1 (equilibrium principle). *For every set A in $\mathscr{E}$ such that $m(A) > 0$ and every potential kernel Γ, there is one and only one triple (u_A, C_A, v_A) where*
  (i) *$u_A(v_A)$ is a function (measure) vanishing outside A and C_A a constant;*
  (ii) *$\langle m, u_A \rangle = \langle v_A, 1 \rangle = 1$;*
  (iii) *$u_A = C_A$ on A and $v_A\Gamma = C_A m$ on A.*
Moreover, $C_A = v_A \Gamma u_A$, and the following identities are satisfied:
  (i) $P_A = \Gamma(I_A - \Pi_A) + 1 \otimes v_A$; $\qquad\qquad$ (2.1)
  (ii) $H_A = (I_A - \Pi_A)\,\Gamma + u_A \otimes m$; $\qquad\qquad$ (2.2)
  (iii) $\Gamma - G^A = P_A \Gamma + (\Gamma u_A - C_A) \otimes m = \Gamma H_A + 1 \otimes (v_A \Gamma - C_A m)$. $\quad$ (2.3)

Proof. We start with the kernel $\Gamma = I + W$ of ch. 6, Theorem 5.2. By the formulae therein, we have

$$U_A h + WI_A U_A h = Wh + m(h)^{-1}\,(hm)\,U_A h.$$

Restricting this equality to A yields

$$\Gamma I_A U_A h = Wh + m(h)^{-1}\,(hm)\,U_A h$$

on A. Since Wh is a constant function and $\langle m, I_A U_A h \rangle = m(h)$ by virtue of ch. 3, Proposition 2.11, the function $u_A = I_A U_A h / m(h)$ has the desired property, with

$$C_A = m(h)^{-2}\,(1 - m(h) + (hm)\,U_A h).$$

The process is similar for v_A. Integrating the equality

$$U_A I_A + U_A I_A WI_A = WI_A + m(h)^{-1}\,U_A(h) \otimes mI_A$$

with respect to the measure (hm) yields

$$(hm)\,U_A I_A \Gamma I_A = (hm)\,WI_A + m(h)^{-1}\,(hm)\,U_A h\,mI_A,$$

and since $(hm) \, W = ((1 - m(h))/m(h)) \, m$, one gets

$$(hm) \, U_A I_A \Gamma I_A = m(h)^{-1} (1 - m(h) + (hm) \, U_A h) \, m I_A.$$

As $U_A I_A = 1$, we have $\langle (hm) \, U_A I_A, 1 \rangle = m(h)$; the measure $m(h)^{-1} (hm) \, U_A I_A$ has thus the desired property, with the same value for C_A. Thus we have shown the existence of a triple (u_A, v_A, C_A). We turn to showing that it is unique.

From ch. 6, Theorem 5.2 it is easily seen that

$$U_A I_A + W I_A U_A I_A = W I_A + 1 \otimes v_A, \tag{2.4}$$

$$I_A U_A + I_A U_A I_A W = I_A W + u_A \otimes m. \tag{2.5}$$

Moreover, u_A and v_A are positive, and $C_A = v_A \Gamma u_A$.

Let u be a function with the same properties as u_A. Multiplying to the right by u on both sides of eq. (2.5) yields

$$u_A + I_A W u = (I_A U_A I_A) \, \Gamma u.$$

Since $\Gamma u = k$ on A and $U_A I_A = 1$, this may also be written

$$u_A + I_A W u = I_A \Gamma u = I_A u + I_A W u = u + I_A W u,$$

and since $W u$ is finite on A it follows that $u = u_A$. The uniqueness of v_A may be shown in the same way.

The identities of eqs. (2.1) and (2.2) are straightforward consequences from eqs. (2.4) and (2.5) and from the formulae giving P_A, Π_A, H_A as functions of U_A. To prove eq. (2.3), let us recall that $P_A + G^A = I + I_{A^c} U_A$; using this and ch. 6, Theorem 5.2, we find

$$P_A = \Gamma - G^A + m(h)^{-1} I_{A^c} U_A(h) \otimes m;$$

multiplying on the right by u_A the two members of this equality yields, thanks to the properties of u_A,

$$C_A = \Gamma u_A + m(h)^{-1} I_{A^c} U_A(h),$$

which completes the proof, the other equality being shown in a very similar way.

It remains to show that all is still true for a kernel Γ' equal to $\Gamma + 1 \otimes \nu + \varphi \otimes m$. For instance, it is easy to show that if the measure v'_A occurs in eq. (1.1) with Γ' instead of Γ, then $v'_A = v_A - \nu(I_A - \Pi_A)$. By means of eq. (2.5) and of the equality $\nu H_A I_A = \nu I_A$, one may compute $(v_A - \nu(I_A - \Pi_A)) \, \Gamma'$

and find that it is a multiple of m on A; moreover, it is clear that $\langle v_A', 1 \rangle = 1$. In the same way one can show the existence of u_A'.

Remark. The result may be extended to kernels $\Gamma + 1 \otimes \nu + \varphi \otimes m$, where φ is merely finite, if we restrict ourselves to sets A such that $\Pi_A \varphi$ is finite. This will be of significance for Harris random walks.

Definition 2.2. We call $v_A (u_A)$ *the equilibrium measure (function)* of A with respect to Γ. We call C_A the *Robin's constant* of A with respect to Γ.

A probabilistic interpretation of v_A will be seen in the next section under an additional hypothesis. We may already note that v_A is absolutely continuous with respect to m.

Proposition 2.3. *Let Γ and $\hat\Gamma$ be potential kernels for X and $\hat X$ in duality with respect to m. Then for every A in $\mathscr{E}$ such that $m(A) > 0$, we have $C_A = \hat C_A$ and $v_A = \hat u_A m$.*

Proof. For every $g \in \mathscr{E}_+$, vanishing outside A,

$$C_A \, m(g) = \langle g, \Gamma u_A \rangle = \langle \hat\Gamma g, u_A \rangle.$$

Thus, $(u_A m) \, \hat\Gamma = C_A m$ on A, and since $m(u_A) = 1$ we have $u_A m = \hat v_A$ and $C_A = \hat C_A$.

In Exercise 1.8, the reader will find how to get potential kernels in duality. We are now going to use the identities in Theorem 2.1 to prove Potential Theory principles, in a way parallel to ch. 2, Corollary 1.13 and ch. 2, Theorem 3.6 for the transient case.

Theorem 2.4 (balayage principle). *For every A in $\mathscr{E}$ such that $m(A) > 0$, and for every probability measure ν, the probability measure $\nu_A = \nu P_A$ is the only probability measure such that*

$$\nu_A \Gamma = \nu \Gamma + km$$

on A for a constant k.

Proof. In view of eq. (2.3), together with the fact that the measures $G^A(x, \cdot)$ vanish on A, it is clear that ν_A satisfies the required property with $k = \langle \nu, \Gamma u_A - C_A \rangle$.

Now let ν' be another probability measure such that $\nu'\Gamma = \nu\Gamma + k'm$ on A. The measures $H_A(x, \cdot)$ vanish for $x \notin A$, hence

$$v'\Gamma H_A = v\Gamma H_A + k'mH_A,$$

$$v_A\Gamma H_A = v\Gamma H_A + kmH_A,$$

and since by ch. 3, Proposition 2.11, $mH_A = m$, we get

$$v'\Gamma H_A = v_A\Gamma H_A + (k' - k)\, m.$$

Now eq. (1.3), along with the fact that $G^A(x, \cdot)$ vanishes for $x \in A$, implies that

$$v'\Gamma = v_A\Gamma + (k' - k)\, m.$$

Multiplying to the right the two sides of the latter equation by $(I - P)$ yields

$$v' - m(h)^{-1} \otimes (hm)\, P + 1 \otimes \mu(I - P) = v_A - m(h)^{-1} \otimes (him)\, P + 1 \otimes \mu(I - P),$$

provided $\Gamma = I + W + 1 \otimes \mu + \varphi \otimes m$, and consequently $v' = v_A$.

Theorem 2.5 (maximum principle). *Let f be in $\mathcal{N}$ and such that $m(|f|) > 0$. If there is a number k such that $\Gamma f \leqslant k$ on $\{f > 0\}$, then $\Gamma f \leqslant k - f^-$ every-where.*

Proof. Set $A = \{f > 0\}$; we have clearly $m(A) > 0$, and eq. (1.3) implies

$$\Gamma f \leqslant G^A f + P_A \Gamma f;$$

and since $G^A f \leqslant - f^-$ and $P_A \Gamma f \leqslant k$ everywhere, the theorem is established.

Definition 2.6. The kernel Γ is said to satisfy the *reinforced semi-complete maximum principle*.

The maximum principle may be stated in another fashion.

Corollary 2.7. *Let f_1 and f_2 be special and such that $m(f_1) = m(f_2) > 0$. If $\Gamma f_1 \leqslant \Gamma f_2 + k$ on $\{f_1 > 0\}$, then $\Gamma f_1 \leqslant \Gamma f_2 + k$ everywhere.*

Proof. We apply Theorem 2.5 to the function $f = f_1 - f_2$ after noticing that $\{f > 0\} \subset \{f_1 > 0\}$.

Exercise 2.8. If $\Gamma = I + W + 1 \otimes v + \varphi \otimes m$, with v a positive measure, show that in Theorem 2.5 the assumption $m(|f|) > 0$ may be dropped.
   [*Hint*: Set $A = \{\Gamma f \leqslant k\}$ and prove that $m(A) > 0$ even if $m(|f|) = 0$.]

Exercise 2.9. Show that the kernel $\Gamma = I + W$ satisfies the following maximum principle: if f and g are special and such that $m(f) \geqslant m(g)$, then the inequality $\Gamma f \leqslant \Gamma g + k$ holds everywhere if it holds on $\{f > 0\}$.

Exercise 2.10. If f is $\mathcal{N}$ and vanishes outside A, then, as in the transient case, $P_A \Gamma f = \Gamma f$ for every potential kernel Γ.

Exercise 2.11. (1) Assume that there is a point x in E such that the set $\{x\}$ is recurrent (e.g., X is discrete and irreducible recurrent), then the kernel $G^{\{x\}}$ is a potential kernel. A function f is then special if and only if $G^{\{x\}}f$ is bounded.

(2) Let X be the chain with state space $E = \mathbf{N}$ and $P(0, \cdot) = \mu(\cdot)$, $P(n, \cdot) = \varepsilon_{n-1}(\cdot)$, where μ is a probability measure on $\mathbf{N}$. Prove that X is irreducible recurrent; find a necessary and sufficient condition for X to be null, and characterize the special functions.

Exercise 2.12 (capacities). Let $\Gamma = I + W$; then for every A such that $m(A) > 0$ we have $C_A > 0$. Define a set function γ by $\gamma(A) = -C_A$ if $m(A) > 0$, $\gamma(A) = -\infty$ if $m(A) = 0$, and prove that γ is increasing and strongly subadditive.

Exercise 2.13. Prove that for every set A in $\mathscr{E}$ such that $m(A) > 0$, and every special function f,

$$\lim_{N} \sum_{0}^{N} [P_n f - P_A P_n f - P_n H_A f + P_A P_n H_A f] = G^A f.$$

[*Hint*: Use ch. 6, Exercise 5.17.]

Exercise 2.14. Prove that the potential kernels of Harris resolvents satisfy the following *semi-complete maximum principle*: if $f \in \mathcal{N}$ and $k \in \mathbf{R}$, $\{Wf \leqslant k\}$ on $\{f > 0\}$ implies $Wf \leqslant k$ everywhere. Conversely, for every $\alpha > 0$, $I + \alpha W$ satisfies the reinforced semi-complete maximum principle.

3. Normal chains

In ch. 6 §6, we saw that for any pair (f, g) of special functions and any probability measure ν, the ratio of the numbers

$$m(f)^{-1} \sum_0^n \nu P_m f \quad \text{and} \quad m(g)^{-1} \sum_0^n \nu P_m g$$

converges to 1 as n tends to infinity. One could think of sharpening this result by showing that their difference tends to a finite limit. In view of ch. 6, Proposition 5.7, this amounts to showing that for $f \in \mathcal{N}$, the sums $\sum_1^n P_m f$ converge pointwise.

This is also of interest from the potential theoretic point of view, since the above convergence would imply that f has a potential in the sense of ch. 2. As we will see below, such a result permits one to single out from all the kernels exhibited in ch. 6, Proposition 5.4 a subclass of canonical character. Notably, we have as yet not provided recurrent random walks with a potential kernel which is a convolution kernel. The following study is a first step in the search for such a kernel.

Unfortunately the above limit may fail to exist, as is shown in Exercise 3.11, and we shall proceed to what may be said if it exists.

Theorem 3.1. *For a Harris chain the three following statements are equivalent*:

(i) *for every charge f,* $\lim_n \sum_1^n P_m f$ *exists*;

(ii) *for every non-negligible special function h of $\mathcal{U}_+$ there is a probability measure λ_h such that, for every g in $b\mathcal{E}_+$ and x in E,*

$$\lim_n P_n U_h I_h g(x) = \lambda_h(g);$$

(iii) *for every non-negligible special function h of $\mathcal{U}_+$, every x in E and B in $\mathcal{E}$, the sequence $\{P_n U_h I_h(x, B)\}$ has a finite limit as n tends to infinity.*

Whenever $h = 1_A$, we write λ_A in place of λ_h; we then have $\lambda_A = \lim_n P_n P_A$, and λ_A vanishes outside A. Let us also remark that by ch. 6, Proposition 5.7, the convergence in (i) is bounded.

Proof. Obviously (ii) implies (iii). Conversely, for every $B \in \mathcal{E}$ the limit

$$\lambda_h(\cdot, B) = \lim_n P_n U_h I_h(\cdot, B)$$

is a bounded and harmonic, hence constant function, and we can set

$$\lambda_h(B) = \lim_n P_n U_h I_h(\cdot, B).$$

The Vitali–Hahn–Saks theorem then implies that λ_h is a probability measure for which (ii) is satisfied.

We proceed to show that (ii) implies (i). Let $f \in \mathcal{N}$ and h a function in $\mathcal{U}_+$, special, strictly positive and such that $|f|/h$ is bounded (for instance a multiple of $|f| + g$ where g is special and strictly positive). For any kernel W, we have

$$Wf = U_h f + U_h I_h Wf = U_h I_h(f/h + Wf),$$

and since $Wf = \sum_1^n P_m f + P_{n+1} Wf$, this may be written

$$\sum_1^n P_m f = Wf - P_{n+1} U_h I_h(f/h + Wf).$$

The function $f/h + Wf$ is bounded and consequently (ii) implies (i).

Conversely one shows inductively that for $h \in \mathcal{U}_+$,

$$\sum_1^n P_m + P_{n+1} U_h = U_h + \sum_1^n P_n I_h U_h.$$

Assume h special and non-negligible, and let g be in $b\mathscr{E}_+$. The function $f = hg - h\, U_h(hg)$ is a charge because $|f| \leqslant 2h\|g\|$ and

$$m(f) = \langle hm, g \rangle - \langle hm, U_h I_h g \rangle = 0$$

by ch. 3, Proposition 2.11.

The above formula yields

$$\sum_1^n P_m f = U_h(hg) - P_{n+1} U_h I_h g,$$

and it follows that (i) implies (iii) and therefore (ii).

Definition 3.2. A Harris chain satisfying the equivalent conditions of Theorem 3.1 will be called *normal*.

Proposition 3.3. *A chain X is normal if and only if the pointwise limit $\lim_n P_n Wf$ exists for every function f such that $|f|$ is special and any kernel W. It suffices that the limit exists for f in $\mathcal{N}$.*

Proof. The identity

$$Wf = \sum_1^n P_m f + P_{n+1} Wf,$$

which holds for $f \in \mathcal{N}$, shows that if the limit exists, then X is normal and that it suffices to this end that it exists for f in $\mathcal{N}$.

Conversely if X is normal, then $P_{n+1}Wf$ converges for f in $\mathcal{N}$. Let f be special and h be the function used to construct W; the function $m(h)\,f - m(f)\,h$ is in $\mathcal{N}$, hence

$$P_nW(m(h)\,f - m(f)\,h) = m(h)\,P_nWf - m(f)\,(1 - m(h))/m(h)$$

has a limit when n tends to infinity, which completes the proof.

Theorem 3.4. *If X is normal, there exists a potential kernel Γ such that for every $f \in \mathcal{N}$,*

$$\lim_n \sum_0^n P_mf = \Gamma f \quad and \quad \lim_n P_n\Gamma f = 0.$$

Moreover, the probability measure λ_A of Theorem 3.1(ii) is the equilibrium measure of A with respect to Γ.

Proof. By the preceding proof, it suffices to show that there is a measure ν such that, for every special function f, $\nu(f) = \lim_n P_nWf$. The kernel $\Gamma = I + W - 1 \otimes \nu$ will then satisfy the first part of the statement.

The function $\lim_n P_nWf$ is bounded and harmonic and therefore constant. Let h_1 be special and > 0; the sequence of bounded measures $P_nWI_{h_1}$ converges on every bounded function by eq. (2.3), so that, by the Vitali–Hahn–Saks theorem, there is a bounded measure ν_1 such that for f with $|f| < h_1$,

$$\lim_n P_nWf = \nu_1(f).$$

Let h_2 be another function with the same properties and ν_2 the corresponding measure. The measures ν_1 and ν_2 agree on the positive functions less than $h_1 \wedge h_2$, hence are equal. Since every special function is majorized by a strictly positive special function, there is indeed a measure ν such that

$$\lim_n P_nWf = \nu(f)$$

for every special function f.

Now let v_A be the equilibrium measure of A with respect to Γ. By eq. (2.1) we have, for A special and non-negligible,

$$P_A = \Gamma(I_A - \Pi_A) + 1 \otimes v_A.$$

For f in $b\mathscr{E}$ the function $(I_A - \Pi_A)\,f$ is in $\mathcal{N}$, and passing to the limit in

$$P_nP_Af = P_n\Gamma(I_A - \Pi_A)\,f + v_A(f)$$

yields $v_A(f) = \lambda_A(f)$.

By ch. 6, Proposition 5.4 if Γ and Γ' are two kernels with the properties stated in Theorem 3.4, then $\Gamma - \Gamma' = \varphi \otimes m$, where φ is a finite function. The equilibrium measures are the same for the two kernels but the Robin's constants are different. If we assume that $\hat{X}$ is also normal we may narrow still further the class of potential kernels with a canonical character.

Proposition 3.5. *If X and $\hat{X}$ are normal, there is a pair of kernels Γ and $\hat{\Gamma}$ in duality with respect to m and such that $\Gamma(\hat{\Gamma})$ is a potential kernel for $X(\hat{X})$ satisfying the conditions of Theorem 3.4.*

Proof. We first show that the measure ν in the proof of Theorem 3.4 is absolutely continuous with respect to m. Indeed if f is special and $m(f) = 0$ we have for every $g \in \mathscr{L}_+^1$

$$\nu(f) = \lim_n m(g)^{-1} \langle P_n W f, g \rangle = \lim_n m(g)^{-1} \langle f, \hat{W} \hat{P}_n g \rangle = 0.$$

We can thus choose a finite measurable function $\hat{\gamma}$ such that $\nu = \hat{\gamma} m$.

By §1, we may choose W such that, for the function h used in its construction, we have also $\hat{U}_h > 1 \otimes m$. Then $\hat{W}$ is in duality with W. If $\hat{X}$ is normal, then $\hat{P}_n \hat{W}$ converges to $1 \otimes \hat{\nu}$, and by the above discussion we can choose a finite function γ such that $\hat{\nu} = \gamma m$. The kernels

$$\Gamma = I + W - 1 \otimes \hat{\gamma} m - \gamma \otimes m,$$

$$\hat{\Gamma} = I + W - 1 \otimes \gamma m - \hat{\gamma} \otimes m$$

thus have the desired properties. We notice that they map special functions into finite ones but not always into bounded ones.

The functions γ and $\hat{\gamma}$ are defined up to equivalence. In the next chapter we shall see that for random walks there is a canonical choice for these functions. They are also uniquely determined for discrete chains, where for instance

$$m(y)\, m(x)\, \hat{\gamma}(x) = \lim_n \hat{W} \hat{P}_n(x, y)$$

for any $y \in E$. We recall (ch. 6, Exercise 4.11) that all functions with finite support are special, a result which will be generalized in the next section. In these cases, the pair $(\Gamma, \hat{\Gamma})$ is unique up to addition of the same multiple of $1 \otimes m$, so that the Robin's constant, which is the same for Γ and $\hat{\Gamma}$, is determined up to addition of a constant which is the same for all sets. For a further study of Robin's constant see Exercises 3.13 and 4.18.

Normality is a rather stringent condition, and one could think of demanding the convergence of $\{P_n Wf\}$ only for functions f in subclasses of $\mathscr{S}$. Actually if these subclasses are rich enough, one can develop the same theory as above with the obvious changes. One can even solve the Poisson equation with second member the opposite of a special function. This will be sketched for discrete chains in the next section, and studied for random walks in ch. 9.

Unfortunately, Exercise 3.11 shows that there are chains for which the convergence fails to be true for any reasonable subclass. It is therefore a natural task to find out whether all "classical" chains are normal in a more or less stringent sense. Here is a first easy result.

Proposition 3.6. *All aperiodic positive chains are normal.*

Proof. The proposition is an obvious consequence of Orey's theorem of ch. 6 §2.

In the following chapter, we shall prove results of this kind for Harris random walks on abelian groups, and the reader will also find examples of normal chains in Exercise 4.17.

Exercise 3.7. If $f \in \mathscr{L}^1(m)$ and $\sum_1^n P_m f$ has a finite limit when n tends to infinity, then $m(f) = 0$. If $g \in b\mathscr{E} \cap \mathscr{L}^1(m)$ and $f = (I - P) g$, then $\sum_1^n P_m f$ tends to a finite limit when n tends to infinity. Prove that the functions of this form are not always charges.

Exercise 3.8. If X is normal, prove that for any $f \in \mathscr{U}_+$ and g special, the limit $\lim_n P_n U_f g$ exists.

Exercise 3.9. A set $A \in \mathscr{E}$ is said to be *small* if there is a probability measure λ_A such that for all g in $b\mathscr{E}$,
$$\lim_n P_n P_A g = \lambda_A(g).$$

(1) Prove that a subset B of a small set A is small and that $\lambda_B = \lambda_A P_B$. Then show that for a positive chain all sets are small and that $\lambda_A = mP_A$.

(2) If X is normal, special sets are small sets, but the converse is not true. Show that the union of a small set and a special set is small.

Exercise 3.10. Assume that $\hat{X}$ is normal and show that in ch. 6, Theorem 6.5 one may assume that f and g in $\mathscr{L}^1(m)$ provided that ν_1 and ν_2 are absolutely continuous with respect to m, the Radon–Nykodim derivatives being co-special.

Exercise 3.11. Let X be discrete and irreducible recurrent.

(1) Show that if $\hat{X}$ is normal, then for every pair (x, y) of points in E the limit

$$\lim_{N} \sum_{n=0}^{N} (P_n(y, y) - P_n(x, y))$$

exists and is finite.

(2) Pick two points a and b in E and set $F = \{a, b\}$ and for $t \in [0, 1[$

$$A(t) = \sum_{n=1}^{\infty} t^n P_a[S_F = n], \qquad B(t) = \sum_{n=1}^{\infty} t^n P_b[S_F = n].$$

Show that if $\hat{X}$ is normal, the following limit exists:

$$\lim_{t \to 1} R(t) = \lim_{t \to 1} (1 - A(t))/(1 - B(t)).$$

[*Hint*: Express the sums $\sum_0^{\infty} P_n(x, y) \, t^n$ as functions of

$$\sum_1^{\infty} t^n P.[\{S_F = n\} \cap \{X_n = \cdot\}],$$

and then use (1).]

(3) Assume now that the states are labelled

$$a_0 = a, a_1, a_2, \ldots, a_n, \ldots$$

$$b_0 = b, b_1, b_2, \ldots, b_n, \ldots$$

and that the transition probability is given by

$$P(a, a_i) = p_i = P(a_i, b), \quad P(a_i, a_i) = q_i = 1 - p_i,$$

$$P(b, b_i) = p_i' = P(b_i, a), \quad P(b_i, b_i) = q_i' = 1 - p_i',$$

with $\sum_i p_i = \sum_i p_i' = 1$, all other entries being 0. The chain X is irreducible recurrent, as is easily checked.

Let $\{n_k\}$ and $\{n_k'\}$ be two increasing sequences of integers such that $n_k < n_k' < n_{k+1}$. The numbers p_i are chosen in the following way: the first n_1 of them are equal to $\varepsilon_1 = (2n_1)^{-1}$, the n_2 following ones are equal to $\varepsilon_2 = (2^2 n_2)^{-1}$, and so forth; there are therefore n_k consecutive p_i's equal to $\varepsilon_k = (2^k n_k)^{-1}$. The same pattern is followed for the numbers p_i', but with the use of $\{n_k'\}$ in place of $\{n_k\}$.

Show that one can choose the sequences $\{n_k\}$ and $\{n'_k\}$ in such a way that

$$\lim_{n \to \infty} R(1 - \varepsilon_n) \neq \lim_{n \to \infty} R(1 - \varepsilon'_n),$$

and deduce that the corresponding chain $\hat{X}$ is not normal.

(4) By a slight modification of the above example, prove that the limit in (1) may exist for $\hat{X}$ and fail to exist for X.

Exercise 3.12. If X is normal, prove that W is the sum of an integral kernel and of the kernel $\sum_1^\infty P_n^1$, where P_n^1 is the singular part of P_n.

Exercise 3.13 (capacities). (1) Let X and $\hat{X}$ be two normal chains in duality, Γ and $\hat{\Gamma}$ two potential kernels as in Proposition 3.5. For every non-negligible special set A, show that there is a measure ν^A absolutely continuous with respect to m and such that

$$\lim_n P_n G^A = 1 \otimes \nu^A, \qquad \lambda_A \Gamma = C_A m + \nu^A.$$

(2) Let A, B be special and L be any special set containing $A \cup B$, then

$$C_B - C_A = \langle \nu^A - \nu^B, u_L \rangle.$$

(3) Show that $C_A \leqslant C_B$ if $A \subset B$.

For a negligible set A, we shall set $C_A = -\infty$. Then show that for any special sets $A_i, \ldots, A_n$,

$$C_{\cap_{i=1}^n A_i} \leqslant \sum_{i=1}^n C_{A_i} - \sum_{i \neq j} C_{A_i \cup A_j} + \cdots + (-1)^{n+1} C_{A_1 \cup A_2 \ldots \cup A_n}.$$

Exercise 3.14. Extend the definitions and results in this section to Harris resolvents.

4. Feller chains and recurrent boundary theory

Throughout this section, E is an LCCB and the transition probabilities P and $\hat{P}$ are Feller kernels. Since $P1 = 1$, in order that P be Feller it suffices that P maps C_K into C_b.

Since the topology of E has a countable basis, it is readily checked that there is a largest open set O such that $m(O) = 0$. We leave to the reader as Exercise 4.14 the task of showing that O^c is an absorbing set. The set O

is thus of no significance in the study of X, and in the sequel we shall always assume that the following condition is satisfied.

Condition 4.1. For every open set U we have $m(U) > 0$. This condition is naturally satisfied for all the usual chains such as discrete chains and Harris random walks.

Proposition 4.2. *There exists a special function which is strictly positive and continuous.*

Proof. Let h be a strictly positive special function. There exists a number a such that $\infty > m(\{h \geqslant a\}) > 0$. The set $\{h \geqslant a\}$ contains a compact set K with $m(K) > 0$, and K is special.

For $0 < c < 1$, the function $U_c(\cdot, K)$ is upper-semi-continuous, strictly positive and special. The space E is the union of the closed sets $\{U_c(\cdot, K) \geqslant n^{-1}\}$. By Baire's theorem one of these sets has a non-empty interior; there exists a non-zero function φ in C_K^+ that has support in this set and so is special. By Condition 4.1 we have $m(\varphi) > 0$, and therefore $U_c\varphi$ is special, continuous and strictly positive.

This proposition has the following obvious corollary:

Corollary 4.3. *Every function in* $b\mathscr{E}_+$ *with compact support is special. The measure m is a Radon measure.*

Let $f(\hat{f})$ be continuous, special (co-special) and strictly positive. Then by Proposition 1.3, there exists a multiple, say h, of $f \wedge \hat{f}$ such that $U_h > 1 \otimes m$ and $\hat{U}_h > 1 \otimes m$. The function h is continuous and strictly positive. For any non-zero function in C_K^+ there is a multiple, say g, such that $U_g > 1 \otimes m$ and $\hat{U}_g > 1 \otimes m$. In the sequel h and g will always stand for functions enjoying the above properties.

Proposition 4.4. *If $f \in C_b$ and $|f| < ch$ for a positive number c (in particular if $f \in C_K$) then $U_h(f)$ and $W_h(f)$ are bounded and continuous. Furthermore $W_g(f)$ is bounded and continuous for every g.*

Proof. If suffices to consider a function f such that $0 \leqslant f \leqslant h$. Then $U_h(f)$ is lower semi-continuous because it is defined by a series of positive continuous functions. Since $h - f \leqslant h$, $U_h(h - f) = 1 - U_h(f)$ is also lower semi-continuous; hence $U_h(f)$ is continuous. The same argument works for $W_h(f)$, because $W_h(h)$ is constant and therefore continuous. Finally, by ch. 6 §5, we have

$$W_g(f) = W_h(f) - \frac{m(f)}{m(g)} W_h(g) + \frac{1}{m(h)} \langle h, W_g f \rangle,$$

and the latter part of the statement follows from the former.

In §3, we saw that positive chains are normal. This was due to the fact that the powers P_n of the T.P. converge to the bounded invariant measure m. We are now going to give for null chains a result relating normality to some kind of convergence of the powers P_n.

Let $\Gamma = I + W$ be a potential kernel, where W is associated with one of the functions h or g above. Choose a denumerable set $\{f_n\}_{n \geqslant 1}$ of functions dense in C_K for the topology of uniform convergence on compact sets. By the above proposition the functions Γf_n are bounded and continuous. As in ch. 7 §2, we choose a metric δ on E, compatible with the topology of E and such that the Cauchy completion of (E, δ) is obtained by adjoining the Alexandrof's point Δ. Furthermore, for x, y in E we set

$$d(x, y) = \sum_{n=1}^{\infty} |\Gamma f_n(x) - \Gamma f_n(y)| / 2^n \|\Gamma f_n\|.$$

Then $d + \delta$ is a metric on E, and we lay down

Definition 4.5. We define E^* to be the Cauchy completion of the metric space $(E, d + \delta)$ and set $M = E^* \backslash E$. The set M is called the *recurrent boundary* of E for X.

For every compact subset K of E, there is a number M_K such that if $f, g \in b\mathscr{E}$ and vanish outside K, then

$$|\Gamma(f - g)| \leqslant M_K \|f - g\|.$$

As a result, the sequence $\{\Gamma f_n\}$ is dense in the set $\{\Gamma f, f \in C_K\}$ for the topology of uniform convergence, and Γf is uniformly continuous on $(E, d + \delta)$ for every $f \in C_K$. These functions thus extend continuously to E^*; the extended functions will still be denoted by Γf. If x is a point in M, the map $f \to \Gamma f(x)$ defines clearly a Radon measure on E which will be denoted by $\Gamma(x, \cdot)$.

Let us observe that a sequence $\{x_n\}$ of points in E converges to a point x in M, if and only if $\{x_n\}$ converges to Δ in the original topology of E and if the measures $\Gamma(x_n, \cdot)$ converge vaguely to $\Gamma(x, \cdot)$. The metric $d + \delta$ is also extended to E^* by using the extended kernel Γ.

The space E^* may depend on the particular function h or g used in defining Γ. In the following proposition, we accordingly write E_g^* and E_h^*.

Proposition 4.6. *Up to homeomorphism, the space E_g^* does not depend on the particular function g, and there is a continuous map from E_h^* onto E_g^*.*

Proof. From the identity

$$W_g(x, \cdot) + \frac{1}{m(g)} W_h g(x) \otimes m = W_h(x, \cdot) + \frac{1}{m(h)} 1 \otimes (hm) W_g,$$

it follows that if $\{x_n\}$ is a sequence of points in E converging to Δ and such that $W_h(x_n, \cdot)$ converges vaguely, then $W_g(x_n, \cdot)$ converges vaguely. We define the map j from E_h^* to E_g^* by setting $W_g(j(x), \cdot) = \lim W_g(x_n, \cdot)$ if $W_h(x, \cdot) = \lim W_h(x_n, \cdot)$. If $\{x_n\}$ converges to x in E_g^*, one may extract a subsequence $\{x_m\}$ from $\{x_n\}$ such that $W_h(x_m, \cdot)$ converges; consequently the map j is onto. It is also clearly continuous, and that E_g^* does not depend on g is now evident.

Remark. If x and y are two points in E_h^* such that $j(x) = j(y)$, the kernels $W_h(x, \cdot)$ and $W_h(y, \cdot)$ are equal up to addition of a multiple of $1 \otimes m$. This will be useful in the following chapter, where E^* will be computed in the case of random walks.

From now on, E^* will denote the Cauchy completion of E obtained for a function $g \in C_K \cap \mathcal{U}_+$ and such that $U_g > 1 \otimes m$. We observe that if x and y are two points in E such that $\Gamma(x, \cdot) = \Gamma(y, \cdot)$, then, by ch. 6, Theorem 5.2, we have

$$W(x, \cdot) + m(g)^{-1} \otimes (gm) P = W(y, \cdot) + m(g)^{-1} \otimes (gm) P,$$

and since $W = \Gamma - I$, it follows that $x = y$. If x and y are in M and $\Gamma(x, \cdot) = \Gamma(y, \cdot)$, the sequence whose terms are alternately x and y is a Cauchy sequence and thus $x = y$. But it may happen that for a point x in E and a point s in M we have $\Gamma(x, \cdot) = \Gamma(s, \cdot)$. In order to get the following results in a nicer form, we shall assume below that the following hypothesis is in force:

Condition 4.7. The functions Γf, $f \in C_K$, separate the points of E^*.

We may now turn to the result we were aiming at.

Definition 4.8. The chain X is said to be *weakly normal* if the sequences $\sum_1^n P_k f$ have a finite limit whenever n converges to $+\infty$, for every $f \in \mathcal{N} \cap C_K$.

Theorem 4.9. *If the chain X is null, then it is weakly normal if and only if for every x in E the sequence of probability measures $P_n(x, \cdot)$ converges vaguely on E^* to a measure β independent of x and carried by the boundary M.*

The measure β has the following intuitive interpretation. Assume E to be discrete and let K be a finite set; then $P_n P_K(x, y)$ may be viewed as the probability that the chain started at x at time $-n$ enters K at point y after time zero. If λ_K is the probability measure defined in Theorem 3.1, then $\lambda_K(y)$ appears as the probability that the chain started at time $-\infty$ enters K at point y after time zero. If we let K swell to E, then λ_K must converge to an entrance distribution for the chain. It will be seen in Exercise 4.16 that the limit of λ_K is precisely the measure β. That β is an entrance distribution is also well seen from the discussion in Propositions 4.10–12.

Proof. If Γ has been associated with a function $g \in C_K^+$, the reasoning of Proposition 3.3 shows that X is weakly normal if and only if $\{P_n \Gamma f\}$ has a limit for every f in C_K. Now by Condition 4.7, the closed algebra generated by the functions $\{\Gamma f, f \in C_K\}$ and the function 1_{E^*} is $C(E^*)$ itself; the equivalence in the statement follows readily.

Next if $\{P_n(x, \cdot)\}$ converges on E^* to a measure $\beta(x, \cdot)$, for every $f \in C(E^*)$, the function $x \to \langle \beta(x, \cdot), f \rangle$ is clearly harmonic, hence constant, and $\beta(x, \cdot) = \beta$ for every x in E. That β vanishes outside M is a straightforward consequence of ch. 6, Theorem 2.11, and of the fact that m is a Radon measure.

Remark. If the equivalent conditions in the above theorem holds, the sequences $\{P_n \Gamma f\}$ converge for every function f such that Γf extends to a function in $C(E^*)$. We will see in the next chapter that, even for random walks, the class of such functions does not always include all special and continuous functions.

In the remainder of this section we shall assume that X is a recurrent irreducible discrete chain and we shall try to further the results of this and the previous sections. In the following chapter a similar study will be performed for Harris random walks on abelian groups.

In the sequel, e will stand for an arbitrary but fixed point in E. By the above discussions, we may define $\Gamma = I + W$ by taking as function g a suitable multiple of $1_{\{e\}}$. To lighten the notation we shall drop the brackets and write 1_e for the characteristic function of the set $\{e\}$ and $G^e(x, \cdot)$ instead of $G^{\{e\}}(x, \cdot)$.

From ch. 3, Theorem 1.10 it is known that $H_e(x, y) = 0$ if $x \neq e$ and $H_e(e, y) = m(y)/m(e)$. It follows then from Theorem 2.1 that

$$\Gamma = G^e + \frac{\Gamma(\cdot, e)}{m(e)} \otimes m + 1 \otimes (v_e \Gamma - C_e m);$$

but $\Gamma(\cdot, e) = 1_e + W(1_e)$, and $W(1_e)$ is a constant function; hence

$$\Gamma = G^e + \frac{1_e}{m(e)} \otimes m + 1 \otimes v,$$

where $v = km + v_e \Gamma - C_e m$ for a constant k. This will be used to prove

Proposition 4.10. *The space E^* is isomorphic to the Martin space of the transient chain $\hat{Y}$ whose T.P. is defined by $\hat{Q}(x, y) = \hat{P}(x, y)$ if $y \neq e$ and $\hat{Q}(x, e) = 0$, started with distribution $\Pi = \varepsilon_e$.*

Proof. The chain $\hat{Y}$ is clearly transient, and is in duality relative to m with the chain Y whose T.P. is given by $Q(x, y) = P(x, y)$ if $x \neq e$ and $Q(e, y) = 0$. The potential of Y is easily computed and is equal to

$$G^Y(x, \cdot) = G^e(x, \cdot) + 1 \otimes \varepsilon_e.$$

Furthermore $G^Y 1_e = 1$ so that $1_e/m(e)$ may be used as a reference function for $\hat{Y}$. Now the space E^* is homeomorphic to the closure of the set $\{\Gamma(x, \cdot), x \in E\}$ for the vague topology, but this is also homeomorphic to the closure of the set $\{G^e(x, \cdot), x \in E\}$, which in turn is homeomorphic to the closure of the set $\{G^Y(x, \cdot), x \in E\}$, and the proof is completed.

We may thus apply to E^* and $\hat{Y}$ the representation theorems of ch. 7 §3. We must before find out the significance of $\hat{Q}$-harmonic functions for the chain $\hat{X}$.

Proposition 4.11. *A finite positive function f with $f(e) = 1$ is $\hat{Q}$-harmonic if and only if it is a solution of the Poisson equation*

$$(I - \hat{P}) f = - \hat{P}(\cdot, e).$$

Proof. By definition of $\hat{Q}$, the equation $\hat{Q}f = f$ reads

$$\sum_{y \neq e} \hat{P}(x, y) f(y) = f(x);$$

in other words

$$\hat{P}f(x) - \hat{P}(x, e) = f(x),$$

and the result follows.

We thus see that $\hat{Q}$-harmonic functions are co-subharmonic functions and provide solutions of the Poisson equation with second member the opposite of a multiple of $\hat{P}(\cdot, e)$. The function $\hat{P}(\cdot, e)$ is co-special and if k is another co-special function, then $\varphi = m(k)\,\hat{P}(\cdot, e) - k\,m(e)$ is a co-charge and the Poisson equation $(I - P)f = \varphi$ has the solution $\hat{\Gamma}\varphi$. If f is $\hat{Q}$-harmonic, such that $f(e) = m(k)$, then $\hat{\Gamma}\varphi + f$ is a solution of the Poisson equation $(I - \hat{P})f = -k$. As a result, if there exists a $\hat{Q}$-harmonic function, one can solve the above Poisson equation whatever be the co-special function k. It is not obvious that there exist $\hat{Q}$-harmonic functions, but it is so if X is weakly normal.

Proposition 4.12. *If X is weakly normal, there exist solutions for the Poisson equation* $(I - \hat{P})f = -\hat{P}(\cdot, e)$.

Proof. If $f \in C_K^+(E)$, $\Gamma P f$ extends continuously to a function in $C(E^*)$. Indeed if g is the multiple of 1_e used to define Γ, we have

$$\Gamma P f = \Gamma f - f + \langle g, Pf \rangle / m(g),$$

and the result follows easily.

Consequently, if X is weakly normal, we have

$$\beta \Gamma P f = \beta \Gamma f + \langle g, Pf \rangle / m(g)$$

on E^* for every $f \in C_K^+(E)$. Now for $s \in M$, $\Gamma(s, \cdot)$ is of course absolutely continuous with respect to m; if we call $\hat{\gamma}^s(\cdot)$ the corresponding density and set $\hat{\gamma} = \int_M \hat{\gamma}^s \, d\beta(s)$, we have

$$\hat{P}\hat{\gamma} = \hat{\gamma} + \hat{P}g / m(g);$$

since clearly $\hat{P}g / m(g) = \hat{P}(\cdot, e)$ we get the desired result.

Remark. The function $\hat{\gamma}$ has been used in Proposition 3.5 to give potential kernels of canonical character, and will be used again to this end in the following chapter.

In the sequel, we denote by M_e the set of points in the boundary M which corresponds to an extremal $\hat{Q}$-harmonic function. If s is a point in M, it is easily seen, by taking a sequence $\{x_n\}$ of points in E converging to s and using the equation $P + WP = W + m(h)^{-1} \otimes (hm) P$ that

$$\hat{P}\hat{\gamma}^s \leqslant \hat{\gamma}^s + \hat{P}(\cdot, e).$$

If s is an extremal point, this inequality must be an equality. Furthermore it is easily seen that for every s, $\hat{\gamma}^s(e)$ is equal to the constant $\alpha = ((1 - m(g))/m(g))\, m(e)$. By comparing with Proposition 4.11 and using the integral representation of ch. 7 §3, we may state

Theorem 4.13. *If X is null and weakly normal for every positive solution f of the equation $(I - \hat{P})\, f = -\, \hat{P}(\cdot, e)$ such that $f(e) = \alpha$, there is a unique probability measure β^f, carried by M_e and such that*

$$f = \int_M \hat{\gamma}^s \, \mathrm{d}\beta^f(s):$$

This raises the problem of describing M_e for classical recurrent chains; that will be done in the next chapter for Harris random walks on abelian groups.

Exercise 4.14. Let O be the largest open set of measure zero. Prove that O^c is an absorbing set.

Exercise 4.15. Call F the Cauchy completion of E with respect to the metric d in the text. Prove that X is weakly normal if and only if the sequences $P_n(x, \cdot)$ converge vaguely on F. Is the corresponding measure β still carried by the boundary?

Exercise 4.16. Let X be weakly normal and $\{f_k\}$ a sequence of functions in C_K^+ increasing to 1_E; let $\lambda_k = \lim_n P_n U_{f_k} I_{f_k}$ (cf. Theorem 3.1), and prove that, under Condition 4.7, the sequence $\{\lambda_k\}$ converges vaguely on E^* to the measure β.

Exercise 4.17. Assume that X is an irreducible null recurrent discrete chain on $E = \mathbf{N}$ such that $P(k, l) = 0$ if $k \geqslant l + 2$. (See, for instance, ch. 3, Exercise 1.18.)

(1) Prove that m is the only invariant measure for P even if we allow the measures to take negative values.

(2) Prove that from every sequence of integers converging to infinity one may extract a sub-sequence such that, for all pairs (x, y) of points in E,

$$\lim_{j} P_{n_j} W_h(x, y) = \nu(y)$$

exists. Notice that Pf has finite support if f has, and prove that

$$\nu P = \nu + \frac{(hm)\,P}{m(h)}.$$

Then derive that X is weakly normal.

Exercise 4.18 (degenerate discrete chains). We use this term for discrete, weakly normal chains such that the value C_A of the Robin's constant is the same for all finite non-empty sets A.

(1) Assume that $\hat{X}$ is also normal in the same sense and show that the kernels Γ and $\hat{\Gamma}$ in Proposition 3.5 may be chosen in such a way that $C_A = 0$ for every finite non-empty set A, and that in that case $\Gamma(x, x) = \hat{\Gamma}(x, x) = 0$ for all x in E.

(2) Let (x, y) be any pair of points in E and set $A = \{x, y\}$. Prove that either

$$\Gamma(y, x) = 0, \qquad \Gamma(x, y) > 0, \qquad \lambda_A(y) = 1, \qquad \lambda_A(x) = 0$$

or

$$\Gamma(y, x) > 0, \qquad \Gamma(x, y) = 0, \qquad \lambda_A(y) = 0, \qquad \lambda_A(x) = 1.$$

(3) Let $y < x$ stand for $\Gamma(y, x) = 0$, and show that $<$ is an ordering on E. Show that if $z < y < x$, then $P_z[T_y < T_x] = 1$, and conclude that in moving to the right, the chain can move at most at one step at a time.

(4) Prove that the ordering of states must be that of the integers, the positive integers, or the negative integers.

(5) Let X be the chain with state space the non-negative integers and T.P.

$$P(x - 1, x) = p_x > 0 \quad \text{for } x > 0,$$

$$P(x - 1, 0) = 1 - p_x.$$

Find the condition under which it is null recurrent, and prove that it is then weakly normal and degenerate. Other important examples of degenerate chains will be given in the next chapter.

CHAPTER 9

RECURRENT RANDOM WALKS

This chapter is devoted to the study of Harris random walks. Although everything may be carried over to non-abelian groups, we shall deal here only with abelian groups, in order to avoid some technicalities and keep within reasonable bounds. Throughout this chapter, we thus study a Harris random walk with law μ on an abelian locally compact metrizable group G. To save space, we shall use the multiplicative notation in G. When G is compact, all the results are either trivial or meaningless, and we shall therefore always assume G to be non-compact. Finally, a Harris random walk being a Feller chain, we shall use freely the results of ch. 8, items 4.1–4.4.

1. Preliminaries

In the sequel, τ will stand for any translation operator in G, and we shall write τ_a when we want to emphasize the relevant element a in G, namely $\tau_a f(x) = f(xa)$. We write τ^{-1} for the inverse of τ.

Lemma 1.1. *For any function $h \in \mathcal{U}_+$ and such that $U_h > 1 \otimes m$, the function τh has the same properties and*
$$W_{\tau h} = \tau W_h \tau^{-1}.$$

Proof. Left to the reader as Exercise 1.16.

We shall first construct a function h with particularly nice properties.

Lemma 1.2. *Let $f \in C_0$ and K be a compact set in G; the function $g : x \to \inf_{b \in K} f(xb)$ is in C_0.*

Proof. Since the function f is uniformly continuous, for every $\varepsilon > 0$ there is a neighbourhood V of e such that if $xy^{-1} \in V$; then for all b in G,

$$|f(xb) - f(yb)| < \varepsilon.$$

Thus

$$f(xb) < f(yb) + \varepsilon,$$

and taking the infimum over $b \in K$, first in the left member then in the right, yields

$$g(x) < g(y) + \varepsilon.$$

The inequality $g(y) < g(x) + \varepsilon$ may be shown in the same way, and thus the proof is complete.

Proposition 1.3. *There is a strictly positive symmetric function f in $\mathcal{U}_+ \cap C_0$ and such that*
(i) $U_h > 1 \otimes m$ *and* $\hat{U}_h > 1 \otimes m$;
(ii) $\lim_{b \to e} \|W_h(\tau_b h - h)\| = \lim_{b \to e} \|\hat{W}_h(\tau_b h - h)\| = 0.$

Proof. Let u be a symmetric non-negligible function in C_K^+. Since X is Harris, the function

$$h_1 = \alpha \sum_0^\infty 2^{-n} P_n u = \alpha(u + 2^{-1} U_{2-1} u),$$

where $\alpha \in \mathbf{R}_+$, is strictly positive, in C_0, and special.
In the same way put

$$\hat{h}_1 = \alpha \sum_0^\infty 2^{-n} \hat{P}_n u;$$

by ch. 8, Proposition 1.3, if we take α small enough, then $h_2 = h_1 \wedge \hat{h}_1$ is symmetric, in $C_0 \cap \mathcal{U}_+$ and $U_{h_2} > 1 \otimes m$, $\hat{U}_{h_2} > 1 \otimes m$.
Let V be a symmetric compact neighbourhood of e and set

$$h(x) = \inf_{b \in V} h_2^2(xb).$$

We will show that h satisfies (ii), and since it clearly satisfies all the other requirements it is the desired function.
Pick $\varepsilon > 0$ and call K the compact set $\{h \geq \varepsilon\}$. Since V is symmetric, for every x in $\mathbf{G}$ and b in V we have $h(xb) < h_2^2(x)$; hence $|h(x) - h(xb)| < h_2^2(x)$, and it follows that, for x in K^c and b in V,

$$|h(x) - h(xb)| < \varepsilon h_2(x).$$

On the other hand, $h_2 \geq C > 0$ on K, and since h is uniformly continuous, there is a neighbourhood $V' \subset V$ such that, for $b \in V'$ and $x \in K$,

$$\left| h(x) - h(xb) \right| \leqslant C\varepsilon \leqslant \varepsilon h_2(x).$$

Combining the two inequalities yields, for every $b \in V'$,

$$\left| \tau_b h - h \right| < \varepsilon h_2.$$

Consequently $\left\| W_{h_2}(\tau_b h - h) \right\| < \varepsilon m(h_2)/((1 - m(h_2))$, and since, by ch. 6, Corollary 5.5,

$$W_h(\tau_b h - h) = W_{h_2}(\tau_b h - h) - m(h)^{-1} \langle h, W_{h_2}(\tau_b h - h) \rangle,$$

it follows that $\lim_{b \to e} \left\| W_h(\tau_b h - h) \right\| = 0$. The dual result is obtained in the same way.

Throughout the sequel we shall use the kernels W_h and $\hat{W}_h$ (and we often write simply W and $\hat{W}$) associated with the particular function h. For every τ, the function τh has similar properties, and we shall also use the kernels $W_{\tau h}$ and $\hat{W}_{\tau h}$. They satisfy the following

Lemma 1.4. *For every special function φ and $a \in G$,*

$$m(h) \left\| W_h \varphi - W_{\tau_a h} \varphi \right\| \leqslant m(\varphi) \left(\left\| \hat{W}_h(\tau_a h - h) \right\| + \left\| W_h(\tau_a^{-1} h - h) \right\| \right).$$

Proof. By ch. 6, Corollary 5.5,

$$W_h \varphi - W_{\tau h} \varphi = m(h)^{-1} \left[\langle \tau h, W_h \varphi \rangle - m(\varphi) W_{\tau h} h \right],$$

and since by ch. 6, Theorem 5.2 we have $W_h(h) = W_{\tau h}(\tau h)$, it follows that

$$W_h \varphi - W_{\tau h} \varphi = m(h)^{-1} \left[\langle \hat{W}_h(\tau h - h), \varphi \rangle - m(\varphi) W_{\tau h}(h - \tau h) \right].$$

The desired result is then a consequence of Lemma 1.1.

We now proceed to the key technical results.

Lemma 1.5. *For any x in G and $f \in C_K^+$, the set of numbers $\{ W_h(\tau_a f) (x), a \in G \}$ is bounded.*

Proof. Let V be a compact neighbourhood of e, and choose $f' \in C_K^+$ such that $\tau_b f' \geqslant f$ for every $b \in V$. Then

$$W_h(\tau_a f') (xb) = W_{\tau_b h}(\tau_{ab} f') (x) \geqslant W_{\tau_b h}(\tau_a f) (x).$$

Suppose there exists a sequence $\{a_n\}$ converging to $\varDelta$, and such that $W_h(\tau_{a_n}f)\,(x)$ converges to $+\infty$; the formula

$$W_{\tau_b h}(\tau_{a_n}f)\,(x) + \frac{m(f)}{m(h)}\,W_h(\tau_b h) \geqslant W_h(\tau_{a_n}f)\,(x)$$

then implies that

$$\lim_n W_{\tau_b h}(\tau_{a_n}f)\,(x) = +\infty,$$

hence that

$$\lim_n W_{\tau_b h}(\tau_{a_n}f')\,(y) = +\infty,$$

the convergence being uniform in $y \in xV$. It follows that if $g \in C_K^+$ and $g \geqslant 1_{xV}$, then using Lemma 1.4,

$$\lim_n \int g\, W_h(\tau_{a_n}f')\,\mathrm{d}m = +\infty;$$

but since

$$\langle g, W_h(\tau_{a_n}f')\rangle \leqslant \|\hat W_h(g)\|\,\|f'\|_1 < \infty,$$

we have a contradiction.

Proposition 1.6. *For $f \in C_K$, the sets of functions*

$$\{W(\tau_a f),\ a \in \boldsymbol{G}\} \quad \text{and}\ \{WP_n f,\ n \in \boldsymbol{N}\}$$

are equi-uniformly continuous on every compact set in $\boldsymbol{G}$.

Proof. Pick x in $\boldsymbol{G}$. For any $b \in \boldsymbol{G}$, we have

$$A(b) = W_h(\tau_a f)\,(xb) - W_h(\tau_a f)\,(x) = W_{\tau_b h}(\tau_{ab}f)\,(x) - W_h(\tau_a f)\,(x)$$

$$= W_{\tau_b h}(\tau_{ab}f)\,(x) - W_h(\tau_{ab}f)\,(x) + W_h(\tau_a(\tau_b f - f))\,(x)$$

$$= \frac{1}{m(h)}\,(hm)\,W_{\tau_b}h(\tau_{ab}f) - \frac{m(f)}{m(h)}\,W_h(\tau_b h)\,(x) + W_h(\tau_a(\tau_b f - f))\,(x)$$

$$= \frac{1}{m(h)}\,\langle \hat W_h(\tau_b^{-1}h), \tau_a f\rangle - \frac{m(f)}{m(h)}\,W_h(\tau_b h)\,(x) + W_h(\tau_a(\tau_b f - f))\,(x).$$

Let K be the compact support of f, H a symmetric compact neighbourhood of e and f' a function in C_K^+ equal to 1 on HK. For $\varepsilon > 0$, one can find a neighbourhood V of e such that, for $b \in V$,

$$|\tau_b f - f| < \varepsilon f'.$$

By the choice of h, we may now assert that there is a neighbourhood V' of e such that, for $b \in V'$,

$$|A(b)| \leqslant \varepsilon + \varepsilon W_h(\tau_a f') (x).$$

By the preceding lemma, the functions $W_h(\tau_a f)$ are thus equi-uniformly continuous on a neighbourhood of x, and this implies the result by the Heine–Borel property.

For the set $\{WP_n f, n \in \mathbf{N}\}$, the conclusion follows readily from the first one and the fact that

$$WP_n f(x) = \int W(\tau_a f) (x) \mu^n(\mathrm{d}a).$$

Symmetrically, we have

Proposition 1.7. *For $f \in C_K$, the set of functions $\{P_n Wf, n \in \mathbf{N}\}$ is equi-uniformly continuous on every compact set in $\mathbf{G}$.*

Proof. This is much simpler owing to the fact that $P_n Wf \leqslant \|Wf\|$ for every n, and it is left to the reader as Exercise 1.17.

The next result is a first step towards normality theorems.

Proposition 1.8. *Let f be special; for every pair (x, y) of points in $\mathbf{G}$,*

$$\lim_{n \to \infty} (P_n W f(x) - P_n W f(y)) = 0.$$

Proof. Let $\mathfrak{U}$ be an ultrafilter finer than Frechet's filter. Since Wf is bounded for every x in $\mathbf{G}$, $L(x) = \lim_{\mathfrak{U}} P_n W f(x)$ exists. Moreover, for k fixed,

$$L(x) = \lim_{\mathfrak{U}} P_{n+k} W f(x).$$

Indeed

$$P_n W f(x) - P_{n+k} W f(x) = \sum_{i=1}^{k} P_{n+i}[f - (m(f) \, h/m(h))]$$

and since $f - (m(f) \, h/m(h))$ is bounded and m-integrable, by ch. 6, Theorem 2.11 the right member converges to zero as n tends to infinity.

To simplify the notation, we write φ_n below in place of $P_n Wf$. The measure μ being spread out, for k sufficiently large we have $\mu^k = \alpha + \beta$, where $\alpha = gm$. But

$$\varphi_{n+k}(x) = \langle \alpha * \varepsilon_x, \varphi_n \rangle + \langle \beta * \varepsilon_x, \varphi_n \rangle,$$

and therefore

$$\left| \varphi_{n+k}(x) - \int \varphi_n(y)\, g(yx^{-1})\, \mathrm{d}y \right| \leqslant \|Wf\|\, \|\beta\|.$$

The sequence $\{\varphi_n\}$ is bounded; hence it admits a limit ψ along $\mathfrak{U}$ in $\sigma(L^\infty, L^1)$. (As usual we shall not distinguish between functions and equivalence classes.) Passing to the limit in the last inequality, we thus get

$$\left| L(x) - \int \psi(y)\, g(yx^{-1})\, \mathrm{d}y \right| \leqslant \|Wf\|\, \|\beta\|,$$

which implies

$$|L(x) - P_k\, \psi(x)| \leqslant 2\|Wf\|\, \|\beta\|.$$

As k tends to infinity, $P_k\psi$ converges uniformly to L, which is therefore measurable and invariant, hence constant. The proof is then easily completed.

The following result is the key to the whole of the sequel.

Proposition 1.9. *Every sequence of integers converging to infinity contains a subsequence $s = \{n_j\}$ with the following property: for every f in C_K, the four sequences $\{WP_{n_j}f\}$, $\{P_{n_j}Wf\}$, $\{\hat{W}\hat{P}_{n_j}f\}$, $\{\hat{P}_{n_j}\hat{W}f\}$ converge uniformly on every compact subset as j tends to infinity.*

Moreover, the sequence of measures $\varepsilon_x WP_{n_j}$ converges vaguely to a multiple $\gamma^s(x)\, m$ of the Haar measure. The function γ^s is positive, uniformly continuous, and such that

$$P\gamma^s = \gamma^s + m(h)^{-1}\, Ph,$$

and for every τ, the function $(I - \tau)\,\gamma^s$ is bounded.

Of course, the same result holds for $\varepsilon_x \hat{W}\hat{P}_{n_j}$.

Proof. The group G being metrizable, the space C_K contains a dense countable subset. It suffices to prove the first statement for the functions of this subset; but this follows from Propositions 1.6–1.7 and from repeated applications of Cantor's diagonal process.

We turn to the second part of the proposition. From the first part, it is plain that the sequence $\{\varepsilon_x WP_{n_j}\}$ converges vaguely to a Radon measure ν^x and that the map $x \to \nu^x(f)$ is continuous. For $g \in C_K$, we have

$$\int \nu^x(f)\, g(x)\, m(\mathrm{d}x) = \lim_j \langle WP_{n_j}f, g \rangle = \lim_j \langle f, \hat{P}_{n_j}\hat{W}g \rangle,$$

so that if $m(f) = 0$, then $\nu^x(f) = 0$ which shows that $\nu^x = \gamma^s(x)\ m$. We thus have $\gamma^s(x) = \lim_j \hat{W} \hat{P}_{n_j} f(x)$ if f is any function in C_K^+ with $m(f) = 1$. Let f be such a function; then $\tau^{-1}f$ is also such a function, and we have

$$\tau \gamma^s = \lim_j \tau W P_{n_j} \tau^{-1} f = \lim_j W_{\tau h} P_{n_j} f.$$

By Lemma 1.4, we thus have

$$\|(I - \tau)\, \gamma^s\| \leqslant m(h)^{-1} \left(\|\hat{W}(\tau h - h)\| + \|W_h(\tau^{-1}h - h)\| \right);$$

by the choice of h the function γ^s is therefore uniformly continuous, and we see also that $(I - \tau)\, \gamma^s$ is the bounded limit of $(I - \tau)\, WP_{n_j} f$; hence it is bounded for every τ.

We proceed to show that γ^s satisfies the equality in the statement. First passing to the limit in the relation

$$P_{n+j}f + PWP_{n_j}f = WP_{n_j}f + m(h)^{-1}\, Ph$$

yields, by mean of Fatou's lemma, that

$$P\gamma^s \leqslant \gamma^s + m(h)^{-1}\, Ph.$$

Next, by the bounded convergence above, $P(I - \tau)\, WP_{n_j}f$ converges to $P(I - \tau)\, \gamma^s$. It follows that, for every τ,

$$P(I - \tau)\, \gamma^s = (I - \tau)\, \gamma^s + m(h)^{-1}\, (I - \tau)\, Ph,$$

and since all the functions herein are finite, we may rewrite this as

$$\gamma^s - P\gamma^s + m(h)^{-1}\, Ph = \tau(\gamma^s - P\gamma^s + m(h)^{-1}\, Ph).$$

There is consequently a number $k \geqslant 0$ such that

$$P\gamma^s = \gamma^s + m(h)^{-1}\, Ph - k,$$

which implies

$$P_n\gamma^s = \gamma^s + m(h)^{-1} \sum_1^n P_k h - nk.$$

The function h being integrable, the term on the right converges to $-\infty$ if $k > 0$, and this contradicts the fact γ^s is positive. Hence $k = 0$ and

$$P\gamma^s = \gamma^s + m(h)^{-1}\, Ph.$$

The following result will be important in the sequel.

Proposition 1.10. *Every co-special function is integrable by the measure $\gamma^s m$. In particular,*

$$\int h\gamma^s \, dm = m(h)^{-1} \, (1 - m(h)) = q.$$

Proof. Let g be co-special and f in C_K^+ with $m(f) = 1$. By Fatou's lemma

$$\int g\gamma^s \, dm \leqslant \varliminf_j \langle g, WP_{n_j}f \rangle = \varliminf_j \langle \hat{P}_{n_j}\hat{W}g, f \rangle \leqslant \|\hat{W}_h(g)\|,$$

which proves the first conclusion. Since $\hat{W}_h(h) = q$ we also have

$$\int h\gamma^s \, dm \leqslant q. \tag{1.1}$$

If g is in C_K^+, since the convergence of $WP_{n_j}f$ is uniform on compact sets, we actually have

$$\int g\gamma^s \, dm = \lim_j \langle \hat{P}_{n_j}\hat{W}_hg, f \rangle = \lim_j \hat{P}_{n_j}\hat{W}_hg,$$

since this last limit is a constant function. The same equality is true for all functions $\hat{P}_kg$. Indeed

$$\int \hat{P}g\gamma^s \, dm = \int gP\gamma^s \, dm = \int g\gamma^s \, dm + m(h)^{-1} \int gPh \, dm$$

$$= \lim_j \hat{P}_{n_j}\hat{W}g + m(h)^{-1} \int \hat{P}gh \, dm,$$

which by ch. 6, Theorem 5.2 may be written

$$\int \hat{P}g\gamma^s \, dm = \lim_j \hat{P}_{n_j}\hat{W}(\hat{P}g) + \lim_j \hat{P}_{n+j}g,$$

and the last term is zero, by ch. 6, Theorem 2.11. Inductively we get the result for all k's. Now set $\varphi = \sum_0^\infty 2^{-k}\hat{P}_kg$; we have

$$\int \varphi\gamma^s \, dm = \sum_0^\infty 2^{-k}\left(\lim_j \hat{P}_{n_j}\hat{W}(\hat{P}_kg) \right),$$

but for every j, ch. 6, Theorem 5.2 implies that

$$\hat{P}_{n_j}\hat{W}(\hat{P}_kg) \leqslant \|\hat{W}g\| + k\|g\|,$$

so that we can interchange summation and passage to the limit to get

$$\int \varphi \gamma^s \, dm = \lim_j \hat{P}_{n_j} \hat{W} \varphi.$$

By the way h was chosen, we can manage to have $\varphi \geqslant h$. Yet another application of Fatou's lemma then gives

$$\int (\varphi - h) \, \gamma^s \, dm \leqslant \lim_j \hat{P}_{n_j} \hat{W}(\varphi - h) = \int \varphi \gamma^s \, dm - q.$$

Combining this with eq. (1.1) yields the desired result.

Clearly if γ^s were the only solution of the equation $Pf = f + m(h)^{-1} Ph$, the measures $\varepsilon_x W P_n$ would converge vaguely to a limit, and using the duality it would not be difficult to derive a theorem of normality for random walks. That is why we shall now study the uniqueness of the solutions of the above equation. In what follows a *real character* of G will be a homomorphism of G into $\mathbf{R}$.

Proposition 1.11. *Let g be a special function and f_1, f_2 two functions in $\mathscr{E}_+$ such that*

$$Pf_1 - f_1 = Pf_2 - f_2 = g.$$

If for every $\tau \in G$, the function $(I - \tau)(f_1 - f_2)$ is bounded, then $f_1 - f_2 = k + \chi$ where k is a constant and χ a continuous real character of G such that $P|\chi| - |\chi|$ is m-integrable.

Proof. Set $f = f_1 - f_2$; plainly

$$P(I - \tau) f - (I - \tau) f = 0,$$

and since $(I - \tau) f$ is bounded it follows that for every $a \in G$, there is a constant $C(a)$ such that for all x in G,

$$f(x) - f(xa) = C(a).$$

Making $x = e$ in this equation yields $C(a) = f(a) - f(e)$; hence

$$f(xa) = f(x) + f(a) - f(e).$$

It remains to set $k = f(e)$ and $\chi(x) = f(x) - f(e)$ to get the desired constant and character. Since the character χ is measurable, it is also continuous.

It is easily checked that $P\chi = \chi$, which implies $P|\chi| \geqslant |\chi|$. If the functions $v = P|\chi| - |\chi|$ were not m-integrable, by the Chacon–Ornstein theorem (ch. 4, Theorems 3.2 and 3.5) the sequence $\sum_1^n P_k v / \sum_1^n P_k g$ would converge to infinity with n. But since $|\chi| \leqslant k + f_1 + f_2$ for every n,

$$P_n|\chi| \leqslant k + f_1 + f_2 + 2 \sum_1^n P_k g,$$

and we would have a contradiction.

The existence of a non-trivial character demands that the group G as well as the law μ satisfy some stringent conditions that we describe below.

Proposition 1.12. *If there is a non-trivial real continuous character χ such that $P|\chi| - |\chi|$ is m-integrable, the group G is isomorphic to $\mathbf{R} \oplus \mathbf{K}$ or $\mathbf{Z} \oplus \mathbf{K}$, where $\mathbf{K}$ is a compact abelian group. Moreover χ is unique up to multiplication.*

Proof. The kernel Ker χ of the character χ is a closed subgroup of G. Let us call m_1 and m_2 Haar measures on Ker χ and $G/\text{Ker } \chi$. For any $f \in \mathscr{E}_+$, the integral

$$I(g) = \int_{\text{Ker}\,\chi} f(gx_1)\,\mathrm{d}m_1(x_1)$$

is constant on the co-sets of Ker χ, and therefore we may write

$$\int_G (P|\chi| - |\chi|)\,\mathrm{d}m = \int_{G/\text{Ker}\,\chi} \mathrm{d}m_2(x_2) \int_{\text{Ker}\,\chi} (P|\chi| - |\chi|)\,(x_2 x_1)\,\mathrm{d}m_1(x_1),$$

if m_1 and m_2 are suitably chosen. Now the function $P|\chi| - |\chi|$ is constant on the co-sets of Ker χ, because if $g \in$ Ker χ,

$$P|\chi|\,(xg) = \int |\chi|\,(yxg)\,\mu(\mathrm{d}y) = P|\chi|\,(x),$$

and of course $|\chi|(xg) = |\chi|(x)$. Consequently, we have

$$\int_G (P|\chi| - |\chi|)\,\mathrm{d}m = m_1(\text{Ker }\chi) \int_{G/\text{Ker}\,\chi} (P|\chi| - |\chi|)\,(x_2)\,\mathrm{d}m_2(x_2).$$

If the last integral vanishes, then $P|\chi| = |\chi|$. But this implies that $|\chi|$ is harmonic and hence constant, which is impossible since χ is non-trivial. It follows then from the hypothesis that $m_1(\text{Ker }\chi) < \infty$, and therefore that Ker χ is a compact sub-group of G.

Now the group $G/\mathrm{Ker}\,\chi$ is isomorphic to a sub-group of $\mathbf{R}$, and is locally compact for a topology finer than the topology of $\mathbf{R}$. By the structure theorem, $G/\mathrm{Ker}\,\chi$ has an open sub-group isomorphic to $\mathbf{R}^n \oplus K$, where K is compact; since χ is one-to-one on $G/\mathrm{Ker}\,\chi$, it follows that $G/\mathrm{Ker}\,\chi$ is either isomorphic to $\mathbf{R}$ or discrete. In the latter case, a moment's thought proves that $P|\chi| - |\chi|$ is the restriction to $G/\mathrm{Ker}\,\chi$ of a continuous function on $\mathbf{R}$; hence is greater than a number $k > 0$ on a neighbourhood of e in $\mathbf{R}$. Consequently the integral of this function with respect to the Haar measure of the sub-group is not finite unless there is only a finite number of elements of the sub-group in this neighbourhood of e. But this implies that the sub-group is isomorphic to $\mathbf{Z}$.

The group G is therefore compactly generated, hence isomorphic to $\mathbf{R}^n \oplus \mathbf{Z} \oplus K$, with K a compact group. By the above argument it is either $\mathbf{R} \oplus K$ or $\mathbf{Z} \oplus K$. The uniqueness property in the statement is now clear.

From now on, when we deal with such a group, it will always be assumed that its Haar measure m is the product of the Lebesgue measure by the normalized Haar measure on the compact factor. Moreover, a point in G will be a pair (x, k), where x is in $\mathbf{R}(\mathbf{Z})$ and k is in K, and χ will denote the character such that $\chi(x, k) = x$. It is then known, by ch. 3 §5, that $\int_G \chi\, \mathrm{d}\mu = 0$ if the integral is meaningful, and we define

$$\sigma^2 = \int_G \chi^2\, \mathrm{d}\mu.$$

We have

Theorem 1.13. *There is a non-trivial real continuous character such that $P|\chi| - |\chi|$ is m-integrable if and only if the group G is of the above type and $\sigma^2 < +\infty$.*

Proof. Call $\tilde{\mu}$ the image of μ by the mapping χ and $\tilde{P}$ the T.P. on $G/\mathrm{Ker}\,\chi$ associated with $\tilde{\mu}$. Since χ^2 and $P|\chi| - |\chi|$ are constant on the co-sets of $\mathrm{Ker}\,\chi$, it is easily seen that

$$\sigma^2 = \int_G \chi^2\, \mathrm{d}\mu = \int_{G/\mathrm{Ker}} x^2\, \mathrm{d}\tilde{\mu}(x),$$

$$I = \int_G (P|\chi| - |\chi|)\, \mathrm{d}m = \int_{G/\mathrm{Ker}\,\chi} (\tilde{P}|\chi| - |\chi|)\, \mathrm{d}m_2.$$

It suffices therefore to prove that $I = \sigma^2$ when $G = \mathbf{R}$ or $\mathbf{Z}$. We do it for $\mathbf{R}$, the proof for $\mathbf{Z}$ being identical.

Let χ^+ and χ^- be the positive and negative parts of χ. From the equality $P\chi = \chi$, we deduce that $P\chi^+ - \chi^+ = P\chi^- - \chi^-$, whereupon

$$P|\chi| - |\chi| = 2(P\chi^+ - \chi^+) = 2(P\chi^- - \chi^-).$$

Since χ^+ vanishes on $\mathbf{R}_-$ and χ^- on $\mathbf{R}_+$ it follows that

$$I = 2 \int_{-\infty}^{0} P\chi^+(x) \, dx + 2 \int_{0}^{+\infty} P\chi^-(x) \, dx,$$

and using the dual random walk,

$$I = 2 \int_{-\infty}^{+\infty} \chi^+(x) \, \hat{P} 1_{]-\infty, 0]}(x) \, dx + 2 \int_{-\infty}^{+\infty} \chi^-(x) \, \hat{P} 1_{]0, +\infty[}(x) \, dx$$

$$= 2 \int_{0}^{+\infty} x \, \hat{P} 1_{]-\infty, 0]}(x) \, dx - 2 \int_{-\infty}^{0} x \, \hat{P} 1_{]0, +\infty[}(x) \, dx$$

$$= 2 \int_{0}^{+\infty} x \, \mu([x, \infty[) \, dx - 2 \int_{-\infty}^{0} x \, \mu(]-\infty, x[) \, dx.$$

We may apply Fubini's theorem in each of the two integrals, since the functions therein have constant signs, and we get the desired result.

Definition 1.14. The random walk is of *type II* if the conditions of the preceding theorem hold. Otherwise it is of *type I*.

In the sequel, when we deal simultaneously with type I and type II random walks, the character χ occurring in the formulae will be understood as identically zero in the former case.

If the random walk is of type II we shall set

$$G^+ = \{x \in G : \chi(x) \geqslant 0\} \quad \text{and} \quad G^- = (G^+)^{-1}.$$

We shall need the following.

Lemma 1.15. *If the random walk is of type II, for every $a \in G$ the sequence $(I - \tau_a) P_n |\chi|$ converges boundedly to zero.*

Proof. Pick x and a in G; we may write

$$|\chi| \, (yxa) - |\chi| \, (yx) = \alpha 1_{G^+}(y) - \alpha 1_{G^-}(y) + \psi(yx),$$

where α is equal to $|\chi|$ (a) and ψ is a function with compact support which depends on x but is majorized by a constant which depends only on a. (The reader is invited to draw the graph of $(I - \tau_a) |\chi|$ when $G = \mathbf{R}$.) It follows that

$$(I - \tau_a) P_n|\chi|\,(x) = \alpha\,\mu^n(G^+) - \alpha\,\mu^n(G^-) + P_n\,\psi(x).$$

Since $\sigma^2 < \infty$, we may use the central limit theorem to the effect that

$$\lim_n \mu^n(G^+) = \lim_n \mu^n(G^-) = \tfrac{1}{2},$$

and by ch. 6, Theorem 2.11 we have $\lim_n P_n\,\psi(x) = 0$, which completes the proof.

Exercise 1.16. Prove Lemma 1.1.

Exercise 1.17. Prove Proposition 1.7.

Exercise 1.18. Extend all the results of this section to non-abelian groups. [*Hint*: In Proposition 1.6 use left translations instead of right translations.]

2. Normality and potential kernels

In this section we prove a first result of normality, from which we derive the construction of convolution kernels that are potential kernels in the sense of ch. 8. We start by showing that the function γ^s in Proposition 1.9 does not depend on s.

Theorem 2.1. *There is a uniformly continuous positive function γ such that $P\gamma - \gamma = m(h)^{-1}\,Ph$, and such that, for every f in C_K,*

$$\lim_n WP_n\,f(x) = m(f)\,\gamma(x)$$

uniformly on compact sets.

If we want to emphasize the dependence of γ on h we shall write γ_h.

Proof. Let $s = \{n_j\}$ and $s' = \{n'_j\}$ be two sequences such that the sequences $\{WP_{n_j}\}$ and $\{WP_{n'_j}\}$ converge vaguely to $\gamma^s \otimes m$ and $\gamma^{s'} \otimes m$ with $\gamma^s \neq \gamma^{s'}$. By Propositions 1.9–1.11, there are two constants α and β such that $\gamma^s - \gamma^{s'}$

$= \alpha + \beta \chi$, where χ vanishes if the random walk is of type I. By Proposition 1.10, we have

$$\int h \gamma^s \, dm = \int h \gamma^{s'} \, dm = (1 - m(h)/m(h));$$

hence

$$\alpha \int h \, dm + \beta \int h \chi \, dm = 0;$$

since h is symmetric, $\int \chi h \, dm = 0$ and therefore $\alpha = 0$, and the proof is completed for type I random walks.

Now let χ be type II and g a function in C_K^+ such that $m(g) = 1$; then

$$\beta \chi = \lim_j (WP_{n_j}g - WP_{n'_j}g).$$

By taking sub-sequences, we may assume that $n_j \leqslant n'_j$. Let a be in $\mathbf{G}$ outside Ker χ; from the equality

$$WP_n g = Wg + m(h)^{-1} \langle h, Pg + \cdots + P_n g \rangle - (Pg + \cdots + P_n g),$$

we derive that

$$- \beta \chi(a) = \beta(I - \tau_a) \chi = \lim_j \sum_{n_j}^{n'_j} (I - \tau_a) P_k g.$$

By ch. 6, Proposition 5.7, the sequence on the right is bounded, and since $\hat{P}|\chi| - |\chi|$ is m-integrable, we have

$$- \beta \chi(a) \sigma^2 = \int (I - \tau_a) \chi (\hat{P}|\chi| - |\chi|) \, dm$$

$$= \lim_j \int \left(\sum_{n_j}^{n'_j} (I - \tau_a) P_k g \right) (\hat{P}|\chi| - |\chi|) \, dm$$

$$= \lim_j \left\langle g, \int (I - \tau_{a^{-1}}) (\hat{P}_{n'_j+1}|\chi| - \hat{P}_{n_j+1}|\chi|) \, dm \right\rangle,$$

and this limit is zero, by Lemma 1.15. It follows that $\beta = 0$, which completes the proof.

Remark. Of course, the symmetric result holds for the dual chain, and we call $\hat{\gamma}$ the corresponding function. It is easily seen that $\hat{\gamma}(x) = \gamma(x^{-1})$.

The following result of normality will be sharpened at the end of the section.

Theorem 2.2. *For every positive function f majorized by a multiple of h, we have*

$$\lim_n P_n Wf = \int \hat{\gamma} f \, dm, \qquad \lim_n \hat{P}_n \hat{W} f = \int \gamma f \, dm.$$

Proof. It suffices to prove the result for the dual chain and for $f \leqslant h$.

By Proposition 1.8, we may find a sequence n_j such that

$$\lim_{n_j} \hat{P}_{n_j} \hat{W} f = \varlimsup_n \hat{P}_n \hat{W} f,$$

and this limit is a constant function. Let g be in C_K^+, with $m(g) = 1$; passing to the limit in the equality

$$\langle \hat{P}_{n_j} \hat{W} f, g \rangle = \langle f, W P_{n_j} g \rangle,$$

we get, using Fatou's lemma, that

$$\varlimsup_n \hat{P}_n \hat{W} f \geqslant \int \gamma f \, dm.$$

But $h - f$ is also positive and less than h, and therefore

$$\varlimsup_n \hat{P}_n \hat{W}(h - f) \geqslant \int \gamma(h - f) \, dm.$$

Since $\hat{P}_n \hat{W} h = \int \gamma h \, dm$, it follows that

$$\varlimsup_n \hat{P}_n \hat{W} f \leqslant \int \gamma f \, dm,$$

which completes the proof.

We turn to the construction of a potential kernel.

Theorem 2.3. *The kernel*

$$A = I + W - 1 \otimes \hat{\gamma} m - \gamma \otimes m$$

is a convolution kernel which has the following properties:

(i) *it maps special functions into functions finite and bounded above, and maps charges into bounded functions;*

(ii) *if f is a charge such that* $|f| \leqslant h$, *then*

$$\lim_n \sum_0^n P_k f = Af \quad \text{and} \quad \lim_n P_n Af = 0;$$

(iii) *for every special function f, we have*

$$(I - P) \, Af = f.$$

Proof. If f is a charge, it is easily seen that

$$\sum_1^n P_k f = Wf - P_{n+1} Wf.$$

If, in addition, $|f| \leqslant h$, the preceding result yields

$$\lim_n \sum_0^n P_k f = f + Wf - \int \hat{\gamma} f \, dm = Af,$$

and it is obvious that $\lim_n P_n Af = 0$.

We proceed to show that A is a convolution kernel. Let f be a positive function majorized by a multiple of h and such that $m(f) = 1$. The function $\varphi = f - m(h)^{-1} h$ satisfies the above condition, and thus, using Proposition 1.10, we have

$$\lim_n \sum_1^n P_k \varphi = W\varphi - \int \hat{\gamma} f \, dm + m(h)^{-2} \, (1 - m(h)).$$

On the other hand,

$$WP_n f = Wf + m(h)^{-1} \left\langle h, \sum_1^n P_k \varphi \right\rangle + m(h)^{-2} \left\langle h, \sum_1^n P_k h \right\rangle - \sum_1^n P_k f.$$

Letting n tend to infinity, it follows that

$$\lim_n \left[\sum_1^n P_k f - m(h)^{-2} \left\langle h, \sum_1^n P_k h \right\rangle \right] = Wf - \gamma \, m(f) + m(h)^{-1} \langle h, W\varphi \rangle$$
$$- \int \hat{\gamma} f \, dm + m(h)^{-2} \, (1 - m(h)).$$

Since

$$\langle h, W\varphi \rangle = \langle \hat{W}h, \varphi \rangle = 0,$$

by setting

$$C_n = m(h)^{-2} \, (1 - m(h)) + m(h)^{-2} \left\langle h, \sum_1^n P_k h \right\rangle,$$

we get

$$Af = (I + W - \gamma \otimes m - 1 \otimes \hat{\gamma}m) f = \lim_n \left[\sum_0^n P_k f - C_n m(f) \right]$$

$$= \lim_n \left(\sum_0^n P_k - C_n(1 \otimes m) \right) f,$$

which proves that A is a convolution kernel.

Finally, A satisfies (iii) because, for special f, since γ and $P\gamma$ are finite, Af and PAf are also finite. Thus

$$(I - P) Af = f - Pf + (I - P) Wf - \gamma m(f) + P\gamma m(f),$$

and since

$$(I - P) Wf = Pf - m(h)^{-1} Ph \, m(f) \quad \text{and } P\gamma = \gamma + m(h)^{-1} Ph,$$

we get

$$(I - P) Af = f.$$

Of course the same results are true for the dual chain, and we have the following:

Corollary 2.4. *The kernel*

$$\hat{A} = I + \hat{W} - \hat{\gamma} \otimes m - 1 \otimes \gamma m$$

is a convolution kernel in duality with A, and has the same property with respect to $\hat{X}$ as A has with respect to X.

Proof. Straightforward.

Definition 2.5. If f is special we say that Af is the *potential* of f.

We shall denote by α the Radon measure such that $A(x, \cdot) = \alpha * \varepsilon_x$. If $\hat{\alpha}$ is the image of α by the mapping $x \to x^{-1}$, we also have $\hat{A}(x, \cdot) = \hat{\alpha} * \varepsilon_x$ and

$$\alpha - \alpha * \mu = \hat{\alpha} - \hat{\alpha} * \hat{\mu} = \varepsilon_e.$$

We have shown that the kernel A provides us with a solution to the Poisson equation with special second member. We now turn to the problem of knowing to what extent it is the only kernel with such a property.

Theorem 2.6. *Let A' be a convolution kernel satisfying properties* (i) *through* (iii) *in Theorem 2.3; then there is a constant c such that $A' = A + c \otimes m$. Let A' be a convolution kernel satisfying only* (i) *and* (ii) *in Theorem 2.3; then if X is type I, there is a constant c such that $A' = A + c \otimes m$, and if X is type II, there are two constants c and d such that*

$$A' = A + c \otimes m + d(1 \otimes \chi m - \chi \otimes m).$$

Remarks. The kernel $1 \otimes \chi m - \chi \otimes m$ is a convolution kernel, since it may be written $(\chi m) * \varepsilon_x$.

In order that (i) be satisfied, the constant d must lie in the interval $[-\sigma^{-2}, \sigma^{-2}]$, as will be shown in the next section.

Proof. If A' is a convolution kernel satisfying (i), then for every τ in G and f special, $(I - \tau) A'f = A'(I - \tau) f$ is bounded. If A' also satisfies (iii), it follows from Proposition 1.11 that

$$Af - A'f = a(f) + \chi \, b(f),$$

where $a(f)$ and $b(f)$ are constants. If we set $x = e$ in this equality we get

$$a(f) = \int A(e, \mathrm{d}y) \, f(y) - \int A'(e, \mathrm{d}y) \, f(y),$$

thus $a(f) = \int f \, \mathrm{d}\nu_1$ for a measure ν_1. If, in the same way, we set $x = x_0$, where x_0 is not in Ker χ, we get that $b(f) = \int f \, \mathrm{d}\nu_2$ for a measure ν_2. Thus $A' = A + 1 \otimes \nu_1 + \chi \otimes \nu_2$. But since A and A' are convolution kernels, for every a we must have

$$1 \otimes \nu_1\tau_a + \chi \otimes \nu_2\tau_a = 1 \otimes \nu_1 + \tau_a\chi \otimes \nu_2,$$

that is

$$1 \otimes \nu_1\tau_a + \chi \otimes \nu_2\tau_a = 1 \otimes \nu_1 + \chi(a) \otimes \nu_2 + \chi \otimes \nu_2;$$

this implies that for every a in G, $\nu_2\tau_a = \nu_2$, so that $\nu_2 = dm$ for some constant d. It follows that for every a,

$$\nu_1\tau_a = \nu_1 + d\chi(a) \, m.$$

Setting $\nu_1' = \nu_1 + d\chi m$ we get at once that $\nu_1'\tau_a = \nu_1'$, and therefore that $\nu_1 = cm - d\chi m$. We thus have

$$A' = A + c(1 \otimes m) + d(\chi \otimes m - 1 \otimes \chi m),$$

and the proof is now easily completed.

As a result, we see that if we take another function h, the corresponding kernel will differ from A only by a multiple of $1 \otimes m$.

We end this section by strengthening the normality theorem (2.2). One might hope that random walks were normal in the sense of ch. 8 §3; actually this is not always true, and we shall prove a slightly less general result. We need some preliminary results and notation. We define

$$\gamma'(a) = m(h)^{-1} \int h\tau_a\gamma \, dm;$$

the function γ' is positive, uniformly continuous and unbounded. Furthermore, from $\hat{\gamma}(x) = \gamma(x^{-1})$ it is easily derived that $\hat{\gamma}'(x) = \gamma'(x^{-1})$.

Lemma 2.7. *For every x and a in G,*

$$m(h)^{-1} \, W(\tau_a h) \, (x) = \gamma(x) - \gamma(xa) + \gamma'(a).$$

Proof. Choose f in C_K^+ such that $m(f) = 1$; then

$$\tau_a\gamma = \lim_n \tau_a W P_n f = \lim_n W_{\tau_a h} P_n(\tau_a f),$$

so that by ch. 6, Corollary 5.5,

$$\tau_a\gamma = \gamma - m(h)^{-1} \, W(\tau_a h) + m(h)^{-1} \lim_n \langle h, \, W_{\tau_a h} P_n(\tau_a f) \rangle.$$

But

$$\langle h, \, W_{\tau_a h} P_n(\tau_a f) \rangle = \langle \hat{P}_n \hat{W}(\tau_a^{-1} h), \, f \rangle,$$

and by the argument in Proposition 1.10 we could, by choosing $\varphi \geqslant \tau_a^{-1} h$, find a subsequence $\{n_j\}$ such that $\{\hat{P}_{n_j}\hat{W}(\tau_a^{-1} h)\}$ converges boundedly to $\int \gamma \tau_a^{-1} h \, dm$. Consequently

$$\lim_n \langle h, \, W_{\tau_a h} P_n(\tau_a f) \rangle = \int \tau_a \gamma h \, dm,$$

which completes the proof.

Proposition 2.8. *For every x and a in G,*

$$\gamma(xa) \leqslant \gamma(x) + \gamma'(a) \quad \textit{and } \gamma'(xa) \leqslant \gamma'(x) + \gamma'(a).$$

Proof. The first part follows immediately from the preceding lemma, and implies in turn that

$$m(h)^{-1} \int h(y)\, \gamma(yxa)\, \mathrm{d}m(y) \leqslant m(h)^{-1} \int h(y)\, \gamma(yx)\, \mathrm{d}m(y) + \gamma'(a),$$

which is the second conclusion in the statement.

Lemma 2.9. *The function $\gamma - \gamma'$ is bounded.*

Proof. Choose a function f in C_K^+ such that $m(f) = 1$ and integrate the equality in Lemma 2.7 with respect to the measure fm. We get

$$\langle f,\, m(h)^{-1} W(\tau_a h) \rangle = \int f\gamma\, \mathrm{d}m - \int \tau_a \gamma f\, \mathrm{d}m + \gamma'(a);$$

since the left-hand side is a bounded function of a, it remains to prove that $\gamma(a) - \int \tau_a \gamma f\, \mathrm{d}m$ is bounded; but this is equal to

$$\int f(x)\, (I - \tau_x)\, \gamma(a)\, \mathrm{d}m(x),$$

so that the result follows from the fact that $(I - \tau_x)\, \gamma(a)$ is bounded uniformly for x in a compact set.

The following result is the key technical one.

Proposition 2.10. *There exists a constant C such that, for every a in $\mathbf{G}$,*

$$m(h)^{-1} W(\tau_a h) \leqslant \gamma + \hat{\gamma} + C.$$

Proof. In view of the two preceding results, there is a constant C' such that

$$m(h)^{-1} W(\tau_a h)\, (x) \leqslant \gamma(x) + \gamma(a) - \gamma(ax) + C'.$$

In addition,

$$\gamma(a) = \gamma(axx^{-1}) \leqslant \gamma(ax) + \gamma'(x^{-1}),$$

in view of Proposition 2.8; hence

$$m(h)^{-1} W(\tau_a h)\, (x) \leqslant \gamma(x) + \gamma'(x^{-1}) + C' = \gamma(x) + \hat{\gamma}'(x) + C',$$

and another application of the preceding lemma yields the desired conclusion.

We turn to our main result on normality.

Theorem 2.11. *For every special and co-special function* f,

$$\lim_n P_n W f = \int \hat{\gamma} f \, dm.$$

Proof. We first observe that by integrating the inequality of the preceding proposition, written for $\hat{X}$, with respect to $\hat{\mu}^n(da)$, we get

$$m(h)^{-1} \hat{W} \hat{P}_n h \leqslant \gamma + \hat{\gamma} + C$$

for every integer n. The left-hand side tends to $\hat{\gamma}$ as n tends to infinity and a special and co-special function f is integrable by the measure $(\gamma + \hat{\gamma} + C) \, m$; we may thus apply the Lebesgue theorem to obtain

$$\lim \langle P_n W f, m(h)^{-1} h \rangle = \lim \langle f, m(h)^{-1} \hat{W} \hat{P}_n h \rangle = \int \hat{\gamma} f \, dm.$$

We now conclude the proof by using Proposition 1.8.

If the special functions are also co-special (in particular if $\mu = \hat{\mu}$), then X is normal in the sense of ch. 8 §3. It will also be shown in §4 that all type II random walks are normal in the sense of ch. 8 §3.

With the obvious changes we may now apply the results of ch. 8 §§2 and 3. For instance, if K is a special and co-special set, then $P_n P_K$ has a limit λ_K which is the equilibrium measure of K with respect to A. In the same way, we may define the Robin's constant. The reader will have no difficulty in translating the results of ch. 8 to the present situation.

Exercise 2.12. Prove that $\lim WP_n f(x) = \gamma(x) m(f)$ for every special function f.

[*Hint*: Use ch. 6, Exercise 5.17.]

Exercise 2.13. Prove that $\gamma(x^{-1}) = \hat{\gamma}(x)$.

Exercise 2.14. If f is in C_K^+, then Af is continuous.

Exercise 2.15. (1) Let $\mathbf{G}$ be discrete, and prove that the kernel

$$A(x, y) = \lim_{N \to \infty} \sum_0^N (P_n(x, y) - P_n(e, e))$$

exists and is finite and that $A(x, y) \leqslant 0$ for every pair (x, y) of points in $\mathbf{G}$. Furthermore, if f is a charge with finite support, then

$$\lim_{N} \sum_{0}^{N} P_n f(x) = A f(x);$$

hence A is a potential kernel.

(2) Prove that

$$G^{\{e\}}(x, y) = A(x, y) - A(x, e) - A(e, y).$$

(3) Set, according to Definitions 2.5, $\alpha(x) = A(e, x)$. Prove that $\alpha(x) < 0$ for every $x \neq e$ and that $\alpha(x + y) \geqslant \alpha(x) + \alpha(y)$.

(4) Prove that $f \in b\mathscr{E}_+$ is special and co-special if and only if

$$\sum (|\alpha(x)| + |\hat{\alpha}(x)|) f(x) < \infty.$$

Exercise 2.16. (1) Prove the following generalization of the non-positivity property in Exercise 2.15. There is a positive bounded measure α_1 such that $\alpha - \alpha_1$ is absolutely continuous with respect to m, and with a density p bounded above.

(2) Denote by β_n the singular part of μ^n; then prove that the singular parts of the kernels A and W are the convolution kernels $\varepsilon_x * \sum_{0}^{\infty} \beta_n$ and $\varepsilon_x * \sum_{1}^{\infty} \beta_n$.

Exercise 2.17. For every special and co-special function h', there is a function $\gamma_{h'}$ such that $\lim_{n} W_{h'} P_n f = m(f) \gamma'$ for every f in C_K. Check the properties of $\gamma_{h'}$.

Exercise 2.18. If $g \in C_K^+ \cap \mathscr{U}$, there exists a function L_g such that $\lim_{n} U_g P_n f = L_g m(f)$ for every f in C_K and

$$\lim_{n} \hat{P}_n \hat{U}_g f = \int L_g f \, dm.$$

Exercise 2.19. Prove that the kernel A determines μ uniquely.

[*Hint*: Prove that A determines Π_K for any compact set K and prove that $P = \lim_{n} \Pi_{K_n}$, where K_n is an increasing sequence of compact sets whose interiors cover E. The reader should also refer to ch. 10 §3.]

Exercise 2.20 (Fourier criterion for recurrence). Let G be countable and resume the notations of ch. 3 §5. The random walk X is assumed to be recurrent.

(1) Prove that for every x in G, the function

$$\gamma \to 2(1 - \operatorname{Re} \gamma(x))/\operatorname{Re}(1 - \varphi(\gamma))^{-1}$$

is integrable on Γ. We will call its integral $I(x)$.

[*Hint*: For every x in G, there is an integer $n = n(x)$ such that $\mu^n(x) = c > 0$; then $1 - \operatorname{Re} \varphi(\gamma)^n \geqslant c(1 - \operatorname{Re} \varphi(\gamma))$.]

(2) With the notation of Exercise 2.15 we have

$$- I(x) = \alpha(x) + \alpha(- x) = G^{\{e\}}(x, x).$$

(3) Prove that

$$B = \int_\Gamma \operatorname{Re}(1 - \varphi(\gamma))^{-1} \, d\gamma = + \infty.$$

[*Hint*: If the integral were finite then we would have $- I(x) \leqslant B < \infty$, and this is impossible since it may be shown that

$$\lim_{x \to \varDelta} G^{\{e\}}(x, x) = + \infty.$$

For the latter point see, for instance, §4 below.]

(4) Try to extend the above result to arbitrary abelian groups.

Exercise 2.21. (1) Compute the potential kernel of the Bernoulli random walk on $\mathbf{Z}$ ($\mu(1) = \mu(- 1) = 2^{-1}$) by means of Exercise 2.20.

(2) Compare with Exercise 4.14.

Exercise 2.22. Extend the results of this section to non-abelian groups.

3. Martin boundary

As has been shown in ch. 8 §4, the boundary points of G for X are in one-to-one correspondence with the cluster points for the vague topology of the sets $\{W(x, \cdot), x \in G\}$. We are therefore going to study these cluster points, and we shall find that there are either one or two such points, according to whether the random walk is of type I or II.

Our first result parallels Proposition 1.8.

Proposition 3.1. *For every special function f such that $\lim_{x \to \varDelta} Pf(x) = 0$ (in particular $f \in C_0$), and every x in G,*

$$\lim_{a \to \varDelta} (W f(xa) - W f(a)) = 0.$$

Proof. Set $\varphi_a = \tau_a W f$ and $B = \|W f\|$. Let $\mathfrak{U}$ be an ultrafilter finer than the filter of neighbourhoods of Δ, and define

$$L(x) = \lim_{\substack{\mathfrak{U} \\ a \to \Delta}} \varphi_a(x).$$

Since

$$P_n W f = W f - \sum_0^n P_{k+1} f + m(h)^{-1} \sum_0^n P_{k+1} h \, m(f),$$

for fixed n we have

$$\lim_{a \to \Delta} (P_n \varphi_a - \varphi_a) = \lim_{a \to \Delta} \left(-\tau_a \sum_0^n P_{k+1} f + m(h)^{-1} \sum_0^n P_{k+1} h \, m(f) \right) = 0,$$

owing to the assumed property of f.

If n is sufficiently large, $\mu^n = g_n m + \beta_n$, where g_n is a non-zero function in $L^1_+(m)$, and

$$\left| P_n \varphi_a(x) - \int \varphi_a(yx) \, g_n(y) \, m(\mathrm{d}y) \right| \leqslant B \|\beta_n\|.$$

Pick a Borel function ψ within the equivalence class of the limit of φ_a along $\mathfrak{U}$ in $\sigma(L^\infty, L^1)$; clearly

$$\left| L(x) - \int \psi(yx) \, g_n(y) \, m(\mathrm{d}y) \right| \leqslant B \|\beta_n\|,$$

and consequently

$$|L(x) - P_n \psi(x)| \leqslant 2B \|\beta_n\|.$$

By letting n tend to infinity, it follows that $L = \lim_n P_n \psi$, hence that L is a constant function, and that $\lim_{\mathfrak{U}:a \to \Delta} (\varphi_a(x) - \varphi_a(e)) = 0$; the desired conclusion is then easily obtained.

Remark. The reader will notice without difficulty that the condition on f is also necessary.

Proposition 3.2. *Every sequence converging to Δ contains a sub-sequence $\{a_n\}$ such that, for every f in C_K, the sequence $\{W(\tau_{a_n} f)\}$ converges uniformly on compact sets to $\Gamma(x) \, m(f)$, where Γ is a continuous function.*

Proof. By Lemma 1.5, for any x in $\boldsymbol{G}$ the mappings

$$\mu_a^x : f \to W(\tau_a f) \, (x)$$

form a vaguely relatively compact set of positive Radon measures. Next, by Proposition 1.6, and by the Cantor diagonal process, every sequence converging to Δ contains a sub-sequence $\{a_n\}$ such that the sequence $\{W(\tau_{a_n} f_i)\}$ converges uniformly on compact sets for every function f_i in a denumerable dense subset of C_K. As a result, the measures $\mu^x_{a_n}$ converge vaguely to a measure ν^x, and for every $f \in C_K$ the function $x \to \nu^x(f)$ is continuous.

Let f, g be in C_K and b in $\mathbf{G}$. We have

$$\int \nu^x(f - \tau_b f)\, g(x)\, \mathrm{d}m(x) = \lim_n \int W_h(\tau_{a_n}(f - \tau_b f))\, g\, \mathrm{d}m$$

$$= \lim_n \int \tau_{a_n}(f - \tau_b f)\, \hat{W}g\, \mathrm{d}m$$

$$= \lim_n \int f(x)\, (Wg(a_n^{-1}x) - Wg(b^{-1}a_n^{-1}x))\, \mathrm{d}m(x) = 0,$$

in view of Proposition 3.1. It follows that ν^x is translation invariant, hence that $\nu^x = \Gamma(x)\, m$, where Γ is continuous.

As in the preceding sections, we observe that if Γ did not depend on the sub-sequence we would obtain a limit theorem; we therefore study the function Γ.

Proposition 3.3. *There are two constants α and β such that $\Gamma = \gamma + \alpha + \beta\chi$.*

Proof. It is easily seen from the definition of Γ that $P\Gamma \leqslant \Gamma + m(h)^{-1}\, Ph$. Define $C = \Gamma - \gamma$; if $f \in C_K^+$ and $m(f) = 1$, then

$$C(x) = \lim_n W(\tau_{a_n} - P_n)\, f(x),$$

so that for $b \in \mathbf{G}$,

$$C(x) - C(bx) = \lim_n (I - \tau_b)\, W(\tau_{a_n} - P_n)\, f(x)$$

$$= \lim_n (I - \tau_b)\, W_{\tau_x h}(\tau_{a_n} - P_n)\, \tau_x f(e).$$

But $(\tau_{a_n} - P_n)\, \tau_x f$ is a charge, and if g is a charge, then $(I - \tau_b)\, (W_{\tau_x h} - W_h)\, g = 0$ by ch. 6, Corollary 5.5; consequently,

$$\lim_n (I - \tau_b)\, W_{\tau_x h}(\tau_{a_n} - P_n)\, \tau_x f(e) = \lim_n (I - \tau_b)\, W(\tau_{a_n} - P_n)\, \tau_x f(e),$$

and since $m(\tau_x f)$ is still equal to 1, this limit is equal to $C(e) - C(b)$. It follows that $C = \alpha + \tilde{\chi}$, where $\tilde{\chi}$ is a real character. As $|\tilde{\chi}| \leqslant \Gamma + \gamma + \alpha$, it follows that $P|\tilde{\chi}| < +\infty$ and

$$P_n|\tilde{\chi}| \leqslant \Gamma + \gamma + 2m(h)^{-1}(Ph + \cdots + P_nh),$$

hence that $\lim n^{-1}P_n|\tilde{\chi}| = 0$. Next, if

$$P\tilde{\chi} - \tilde{\chi} = \int \tilde{\chi}\, d\mu = \beta,$$

then

$$P_n\tilde{\chi} = \tilde{\chi} + n\beta \quad \text{and} \quad n^{-1}P_n\tilde{\chi} = n^{-1}\tilde{\chi} + \beta;$$

by letting n tend to infinity it follows that $\beta = 0$, hence $P\tilde{\chi} = \tilde{\chi}$ and

$$P\Gamma = \Gamma + m(h)^{-1}Ph;$$

as in Proposition 1.11 we may now prove that $P|\tilde{\chi}| - |\tilde{\chi}|$ is m-integrable. The proof is then complete.

Proposition 3.4. *From every sequence converging to Δ, we may select a subsequence $\{a_n\}$ such that the measures $W(a_n, \cdot)$ converge vaguely to $(\hat{\gamma} + \beta\chi)\, m$, where β is a constant.*

Proof. Since the set $\{W(x, \cdot), x \in G\}$ is vaguely relatively compact it is clear that we may find a sub-sequence $\{a_n\}$ such that the sequence $W(a_n, \cdot)$ converges. In view of Proposition 3.1, for every f in C_K, $Wf(a_nx)$ converges then to a constant C.

For g in C_K we have therefore

$$C\, m(g) = \lim\langle Wf(a_n \cdot), g\rangle$$
$$= \lim\langle f, \hat{W}(\tau_{a_n}^{-1}g)\rangle = m(g)\int (\hat{\gamma} + \alpha + \beta\chi)\, f\, dm,$$

and it follows that $C = \int (\hat{\gamma} + \alpha + \beta\chi)\, f\, dm$.

Now if f is C_0 and if $Wf(a_n)$ converges to $\int (\hat{\gamma} + \alpha + \beta\chi)\, f\, dm$, the same property is true for Pf, because by ch. 6, Theorem 5.2,

$$W\, Pf(a_n) = Wf(a_n) - Pf(a_n) + m(h)^{-1}\int hPf\, dm,$$

and thus the right-hand side has a limit which is equal to

$$\int (\hat{\gamma} + \alpha + \beta\chi) f \, dm + m(h)^{-1} \int \hat{P}hf \, dm$$

$$= \int (\hat{\gamma} + \alpha + \beta\chi) f \, dm + \int (\hat{P}\hat{\gamma} - \hat{\gamma}) f \, dm$$

$$= \int \hat{P}\hat{\gamma}f \, dm + \int \alpha f \, dm + \int \beta\chi f \, dm = \int (\hat{\gamma} + \alpha + \beta\chi) \, Pf \, dm.$$

If $v \in C_K^+$, this property is still true for $\varphi = \sum 2^{-n}P_n v$, because the series $\sum 2^{-n}WP_n v$ converge uniformly, and we can manage to choose v so that $\varphi \geqslant h$. By an argument of lower semi-continuity it follows that

$$\varliminf W(\varphi - h)(a_n) \geqslant \int (\hat{\gamma} + \alpha + \beta\chi)(\varphi - h) \, dm$$

and

$$\varliminf Wh(a_n) \geqslant \int (\hat{\gamma} + \alpha + \beta\chi) h \, dm,$$

so that

$$\lim Wh(a_n) = \int (\hat{\gamma} + \alpha + \beta\chi) h \, dm.$$

Since $Wh = \int \hat{\gamma}h \, dm$ and $\int \chi h \, dm = 0$, it follows that $\alpha = 0$, and the proof is thus complete. Actually, using lower-semi-continuity we can show a bit more, namely that $Wf(a_n)$ converges to $\int (\hat{\gamma} + \beta\chi) f \, dm$ for every continuous function dominated by a multiple of h.

Definition 3.5. If the random walk is of type II, we say that x tends to $\pm \infty$ if $\chi(x)$ tends to $\pm \infty$.

The following theorem is the main result of this section. It states that for type I random walks, the Martin compactification is obtained by adjoining one point to the group G, whereas for type II random walks one must adjoin two points, one at each "end" (in the obvious sense) of the group G. In view of the remark below ch. 8, Proposition 4.6, the compactification thus obtained is the same as if W had been associated with a function $h \in C_K^+$.

Theorem 3.6. *If the random walk is of type I, the measures* $W(x, \cdot)$ *converge vaguely to* $\hat{\gamma}m$ *when* x *tends to* Δ. *If the random walk is of type II, the measures* $W(x, \cdot)$ *converge to* $\hat{\gamma}m \pm \sigma^{-2}\chi m$ *when* x *tends to* $\pm \infty$.

Proof. For type I random walks, there is nothing to prove, in view of the preceding result.

Consider a type II random walk, and let $\{a_n\}$ and $\{a'_n\}$ be two sequences such that $\{W(a_n, \cdot)\}$ and $\{W(a'_n, \cdot)\}$ converge vaguely. By the above proposition, there is a constant β such that

$$\lim(W(a_n, \cdot) - W(a'_n, \cdot)) = \beta\chi m.$$

Pick f in C_K and $b \notin \operatorname{Ker} \chi$; on account of Proposition 3.1,

$$W(I - \tau_b) f(xa_n) - W(I - \tau_b) f(xa'_n)$$

converges boundedly to

$$\beta \int \chi(I - \tau_b) f \, dm = \beta\chi(b) \, m(f).$$

If $v = P|\chi| - |\chi|$, we have therefore

$$\lim\langle v, W(I - \tau_b) f(\cdot a_n) - W(I - \tau_b) f(\cdot a'_n)\rangle = \beta\chi(b) \, m(f) \, m(v). \qquad (3.1)$$

Now, $(I - \tau_b)f$ is a charge with compact support, so that by §2,

$$W(I - \tau_b) f - \int \hat{\gamma}(I - \tau_b) f \, dm = \lim_N \sum_1^N P_n(I - \tau_b) f,$$

and the convergence is bounded; consequently

$$\langle v, W(I - \tau_b) f(\cdot a_n) - W(I - \tau_b) f(\cdot a'_n)\rangle$$

$$= \lim_N \left\langle v, \sum_1^N P_n(I - \tau_b) f(\cdot a_n) - \sum_1^N P_n(I - \tau_b) f(\cdot a'_n)\right\rangle$$

$$= \lim_N \langle \hat{P}_{N+1}|\chi| - \hat{P}|\chi|, (I - \tau_b)(f(\cdot a_n) - f(\cdot a'_n))\rangle$$

$$= \lim_N \langle \hat{P}_{N+1}(I - \tau_b^{-1})|\chi| - \hat{P}(I - \tau_b^{-1})|\chi|, f(\cdot a_n) - f(\cdot a'_n)\rangle,$$

and, by use of Proposition 1.15, this limit is equal to

$$- \langle \hat{P}(I - \tau_b^{-1})|\chi|, f(\cdot a_n) - f(\cdot a'_n)\rangle$$

$$= - \langle Pf, (I - \tau_b^{-1})|\chi|(\cdot a_n^{-1}) - (I - \tau_b^{-1})|\chi|(\cdot a_n'^{-1})\rangle. \qquad (3.2)$$

From the form of the function $(I - \tau_b^{-1}) \, |\chi|$ which was described in §1, it follows that if $\{a_n\}$ and $\{a_n'\}$ either both converge to $+\infty$ or both converge to $-\infty$, the above limit is zero. As a result $\beta = 0$, and therefore the measures $W(x, \cdot)$ have a limit when x converges either to $+\infty$ or to $-\infty$.

The functions Wf thus have a limit at each end of the group G, and since $P_n W$ converges to $\hat{\gamma}m$ and

$$\lim P_n 1_{G+} = \lim P_n 1_{G-} = \tfrac{1}{2},$$

it follows that if $W(x, \cdot)$ converges to $\hat{\gamma}m + \lambda\chi m$ as $x \to +\infty$, then $W(x, \cdot)$ converges to $\hat{\gamma}m - \lambda\chi m$ as $x \to -\infty$. It remains to compute λ.

Let $\{a_n\}$ be a sequence converging to $+\infty$ and $\{a_n'\}$ a sequence converging to $-\infty$. If we resume the above calculations it is seen that $\beta = 2\lambda$ and that the limit in eq. (3.2) is equal to $2\,m(f)\,\chi(b)$. Comparing with eq. (3.1), it follows that $\lambda\,m(v) = 1$; that is, $\lambda = \sigma^{-2}$, and the proof is complete.

As remarked at the end of the proof of Proposition 3.4, the above convergences hold not only for functions in C_K but also for continuous functions majorized by a multiple of h. Actually, the scope of validity of the preceding theorem may be still further enlarged by the use of the same device as in Theorem 2.11.

Theorem 3.7. *If f is both special and co-special, and if $\lim_{a \to \Delta} Pf(a) = 0$, then*

$$\lim_{x \to \Delta} Wf(x) = \int \hat{\gamma}f \, \mathrm{d}m$$

if X is type I, and

$$\lim_{x \to \pm\infty} Wf(x) = \int (\hat{\gamma} \pm \sigma^{-2}\chi)\,f \, \mathrm{d}m$$

if X is type II.

Proof. Let us write down the proof for type I walks, leaving to the reader the obvious changes needed for type II. Let g be a function in C_K^+ with $m(g) = 1$; from Proposition 3.2 and Theorem 3.6, it is easily derived that $\lim_{a \to \Delta} W(\tau_a g) = \gamma$, and by Proposition 2.10, there is a constant D such that $W(\tau_a g) \leqslant D(\gamma + \hat{\gamma} + C)$.

Now on account of Proposition 3.1, from every sequence converging to Δ we may select a sub-sequence $\{a_n\}$ such that $Wf(a_n x)$ converges boundedly to a constant ρ. Then

$$\rho = \lim_n \langle \tau_{a_n} Wf, g \rangle = \lim_n \langle f, \hat{W}(\tau_{a_n}^{-1}g) \rangle = \int \hat{\gamma} f \, dm,$$

by applying the preceding remarks to the dual chain.

The above results may also be stated for the potential kernel A.

Corollary 3.8. *If f is a charge such that $\lim_{a \to \Delta} P|f|\,(a) = 0$, then*

$$\lim_{x \to \Delta} Af(x) = 0$$

for type I random walks, and

$$\lim_{x \to \pm\infty} Af(x) = \pm \sigma^{-2} \int \chi f \, dm$$

for type II random walks.

Proof. Straightforward.

Exercise 3.9. If $g \in C_K^+ \cap \mathcal{U}$, then for type I random walks,

$$\lim_{x \to \Delta} U_g f(x) = \int L_g f \, dm$$

(L_g was defined in Exercise 2.18). For type II random walks there exist two functions $L_g^{\pm}$ such that $2L_g = L_g^+ + L_g^-$ and

$$\lim_{x \to \pm\infty} U_g f(x) = \int L_g^{\pm} f \, dm.$$

4. Renewal theory

In the preceding section, we have studied the asymptotic behaviour of potentials Af when f is a charge. We want now to fulfil the same task when $f \geqslant 0$. Clearly this amounts to studying the asymptotic behaviour of functions γ. Since these functions are positive and sub-harmonic, they are unbounded; therefore when x tends to Δ, $\gamma(x)$ has always $+\infty$ as a cluster point. The problem is to find out whether it is the only one, and in that case to compute the speed of convergence of γ to $+\infty$. We shall find that type I and type II random walks have quite different features with regard to this problem, and require different proofs. We start, however, with some applications of the preceding section, which concern both types.

Proposition 4.1. *If f is in C_K^+ and $m(f) = 1$, then for any a in $\mathbf{G}$,*

$$\lim_{x \to \Delta}(I - \tau_a)\, Af(x) = \lim_{x}(I - \tau_a)\, \gamma(x) = 0$$

for type I random walks, and

$$\lim_{x \to \pm\infty}(I - \tau_a)\, Af(x) = -\lim_{x \to \pm\infty}(I - \tau_a)\, \gamma(x) = \pm\, \sigma^{-2}\, \chi(a)$$

for type II random walks. Moreover, the convergence is uniform for a in a compact set.

Proof. Since

$$(I - \tau_a)\, Af(x) = (I - \tau_a)\, f(x) + (I - \tau_a)\, Wf(x) - (I - \tau_a)\, \gamma(x),$$

it follows from Theorem **3.6** that the two limits are opposite. Indeed for type II random walks x and ax converge to the same end of the group whatever a is.

On the other hand, since A is a convolution kernel, we have $(I - \tau_a)\, Af = A(I - \tau_a)\, f$, and therefore by Corollary **3.8**, the limit is zero in the former case, and

$$\pm\, \sigma^{-2} \int \chi(I - \tau_a)\, f \; \mathrm{d}m = \pm\, \sigma^{-2}\, \chi(a)$$

in the latter. The last conclusion follows from the uniform continuity of functions γ.

Corollary 4.2. *Let a be a point in $\mathbf{G}$ such that a^n converges to Δ; then*

$$\lim_{n} n^{-1}\gamma(a^n) = 0$$

for type I random walks, and

$$\lim_{n} n^{-1}\gamma(a^n) = \sigma^{-2}|\chi|\, (a)$$

for type II random walks.

Proof. By the preceding result, the differences $\gamma(a^n) - \gamma(a^{n-1})$ converge to the assigned limits; since Cesaro convergence is weaker than ordinary convergence, the proof is complete.

For a while we shall deal only with type II random walks. The asymptotic behaviour of γ is then completely settled by the following.

Theorem 4.3. *For type II random walks,*

$$\lim_{x \to \Delta} \gamma(x)/|\chi|(x) = \sigma^{-2}.$$

Proof. When a is in Ker χ, the functions $(I - \tau_a)\,\gamma$ are uniformly bounded; it suffices thus to prove the result when G is either **R** or **Z**. Since the function γ' is subadditive (Proposition 2.8), it is a classical result that $\gamma'(x)/|\chi|(x)$ has a limit whenever $|\chi|(x)$ tends to infinity, or equivalently x tends to Δ. As the difference $\gamma' - \gamma$ is bounded (Lemma 2.9), it follows that $\gamma(x)/|\chi|(x)$ also has a limit. This limit is σ^{-2}, since by Corollary 4.2, $\gamma(na)/|\chi|(na)$ tends to σ^{-2} as $n \to \infty$. This result may be restated in terms of potentials.

Corollary 4.4. *Let f be special, then*

$$\lim_{x \to \Delta} Af(x)/|\chi|(x) = -\sigma^{-2}\,m(f).$$

Proof. Obvious.

This result enables us to complete Theorem 2.6 by stating

Proposition 4.5. *The constant d which appears in Theorem 2.6 must lie in the interval* $[-\sigma^{-2}, \sigma^{-2}]$.

Proof. Consider the kernel $A' = A + c(1 \otimes m) + d(1 \otimes \chi m - \chi \otimes m)$ and let f be a special function; in the right-hand side of the equality

$$A'f = f + Wf + c\,m(f) - \int \hat{\gamma}f \, dm + d \int \chi f \, dm - (\gamma + d\chi)\,m(f),$$

all the summands are bounded but the last one. It is now plain that $A'f$ cannot be bounded from above unless d lies in the interval $[-\sigma^{-2}, \sigma^{-2}]$.

We now turn to type I random walks, for which the situation as well as the proofs are much more intricate.

Proposition 4.6.

$$\lim_{x \to \Delta}(\gamma(x) + \gamma(x^{-1})) = \lim_{x \to \Delta}(\gamma'(x) + \gamma'(x^{-1})) = +\infty.$$

Proof. Since $\gamma - \gamma'$ is bounded, it suffices to prove the result for γ'. If the result were false, there would exist a sequence $\{a_n\}$ and a constant C such that $\gamma'(a_n) + \gamma'(a_n^{-1}) \leqslant C < \infty$. But as γ' is subadditive for every x in $\mathbf{G}$, we have

$$\gamma'(x) = \gamma'(x a_n a_n^{-1}) \leqslant \gamma'(x a_n) + \gamma'(a_n^{-1}),$$

and since $\gamma'(x a_n) - \gamma'(a_n)$ converges to zero as $n \to \infty$ (cf. Proposition 4.1) the function γ' would be bounded, which is a contradiction.

Remark. The above result may also be stated as

$$\lim(\gamma(x) + \hat{\gamma}(x)) = \lim(\gamma'(x) + \gamma'(x^{-1})) = +\infty,$$

and also if f is special as

$$\lim(Af(x) + Af(x^{-1})) = \lim(Af(x) + \hat{A}f(x)) = -\infty.$$

We now turn to the main result for type I random walks. The proof is somewhat similar to a proof given for transient random walks.

Theorem 4.7. *If the functions γ do not converge to $+\infty$, there is one and only one finite number L for which there exist sequences $\{x_n\}$ such that $\lim_n \gamma(x_n) = L$, and then $\lim_n \gamma(x_n^{-1}) = +\infty$.*

Proof. The last conclusion follows at once from Proposition 4.6. To prove the first one, consider a function f in C_K^+ with support V, and set $\varphi = -Af$. For any a in $\mathbf{G}$, we have

$$(\tau_a - I)\,\varphi = (I + W)\,(I - \tau_a)\,f + \text{constant}.$$

Since $(I - \tau_a)f$ is a charge, we may apply the semi-complete maximum principle (ch. 8 §2) to infer that there exists $\xi \in V$ such that, for all x in $\mathbf{G}$,

$$\varphi(xa) - \varphi(x) \leqslant \varphi(\xi a) - \varphi(\xi),$$

or equivalently

$$\varphi(xa) + \varphi(\xi) \leqslant \varphi(\xi a) + \varphi(x).$$

Repeated replacements of x by xa yield

$$\varphi(xa^n) + \varphi(\xi) \leqslant \varphi(\xi a) + \varphi(xa^{n-1})$$

and by summing up and dividing by n,

$$n^{-1}\,\varphi(xa^n) + \varphi(\xi) \leqslant \varphi(\xi a) + n^{-1}\,\varphi(x).$$

Finally, $\varphi(\xi) \leqslant n^{-1}\,\varphi(x) + \varphi(\xi a)$, and since n is arbitrary, for every $a \in G$ there exists ξ in V such that $\varphi(\xi) \leqslant \varphi(\xi a)$, hence such that $\inf_{x \in V} \varphi(x) \leqslant \varphi(\xi a)$. By Proposition 4.1, we know that $\varphi(a) - \varphi(\xi a)$ converges to zero whenever $a \to \varDelta$, and we may therefore conclude that

$$\varliminf_{a \to \varDelta} \varphi(a) \geqslant \inf_{x \in V} \varphi(x). \qquad (4.1)$$

Now let L be a finite cluster point for φ and $\{a_n'\}$ a sequence converging to $\varDelta$ and such that $L = \lim_n \varphi(a_n')$. We may select from $\{a_n'\}$ a sub-sequence $\{a_n\}$ such that

$$\lim_n \varphi(\xi a_j^{-1} a_n) = L \qquad \text{uniformly if } \xi \in V \text{ and } j < n,$$

$$\lim_n \varphi(\xi a_n^{-1} a_j) = +\infty.$$

This may be done recursively in the following way. The points $a_1, \ldots, a_{j+1}$ being already chosen, we choose a_{j+1} in such a way that

$$\varphi(\xi a_k^{-1} a_{j+1}) - \varphi(a_{j+1}) \leqslant 2^{-j}$$

for every $\xi \in V$ and $k \leqslant j$; this is possible on account of Proposition 4.1. But we may also choose a_{j+1} in order that $\varphi(\xi a_{j+1}^{-1} a_k) \geqslant 2^k$ for every $k \leqslant j$ and $\xi \in V$; indeed, by Proposition 4.6, $\varphi(a_n'^{-1} a_k)$ converges to $+\infty$, and by Proposition 4.1, $(I - \tau_\xi)\,\varphi(a_n'^{-1} a_k)$ converges to zero uniformly for ξ in a compact set.

Let us next set

$$\varPhi = n^{-1} \sum_{i=1}^{n} \varphi(\cdot\, a_i).$$

The function is also the negative of a potential, and therefore may be applied the inequality (4.1). On the other hand it is plain from Proposition 4.1 that

$$\varliminf_{x \to \varDelta} \varPhi(x) = \varliminf_{x \to \varDelta} \varphi(x).$$

It follows that

$$\inf_{\substack{\xi \in V \\ 1 \leqslant k \leqslant n}} \left(n^{-1} \sum_{i=1}^{n} \varphi(\xi a_k^{-1} a_i) \right) \leqslant \varliminf_{x \to \varDelta} \varphi(x),$$

and a fortiori

$$n^{-1} \sum_{i=1}^{n} \inf\{\varphi(\xi a_k^{-1} a_i) : \xi \in V, \, 1 \leqslant k \leqslant n\} \leqslant \varliminf_{x \to \varDelta} \varphi(x).$$

As soon as i is sufficiently large, the above infimum is assumed for a number $k \leqslant i$ and thus is near L; as a result, we obtain $L \leqslant \underline{\lim}_{x \to \Delta} \varphi(x)$, and consequently $L = \underline{\lim}_{x \to \Delta} \varphi(x)$. It follows that L is the only finite cluster point.

Definition 4.8. A type I random walk is said to be of *type Ib* if γ has a finite cluster point; it is otherwise said to be of *type Ia*.

There cannot be type Ib random walks on any recurrent abelian group, and our next goal is to give the relevant classification of groups. The process is somewhat parallel to the proof of the renewal theorem for transient random walks. In the following proofs we use the additive notation for the operation in G.

Lemma 4.9. *If G has an open, non-compact, compactly generated sub-group G_1 such that G/G_1 is finite, then every random walk is of type Ia.*

Proof. We use the notation of the proof of Theorem 4.7, and assume that X is *type Ib*. By Theorem 4.7, and the same device as in the proof of ch. 5, Proposition 4.1, we may find a sequence $\{z_n\}$ of points in G such that the sets $z_n G_1$ are pairwise disjoint and such that $\lim_n \varphi(z_n) = L < \infty$.

Since G_1 is compactly generated but not compact, we can choose $x \in G_1$ such that $nx \to \Delta$ as $n \to \infty$, and by Proposition 4.1 and Theorem 4.7, we can suppose that $\lim_n \varphi(nx) = +\infty$.

Arguing as in ch. 5, Proposition 4.1, it is easily seen that for n sufficiently large, there is an integer $k_n > 0$ such that

$$\varphi(z_n + k_n x) < L + 1, \qquad \varphi(z_n + (k_n + 1)\,x) \geqslant L + 1.$$

Now $z_n + kx \to \Delta$ uniformly in k as $n \to \infty$, so that by Proposition 4.1 we get

$$\lim_n \varphi(z_n + k_n x) = L + 1,$$

which contradicts Theorem 4.7.

Corollary 4.10. *If G has a closed sub-group isomorphic to $\mathbf{R}^{d_1} \oplus \mathbf{Z}^{d_2} \oplus K$, where K is a compact group and $d_1 + d_2 \geqslant 2$, then all random walks are type Ia.*

Proof. We choose x and y in G such that $nx + ky \to \infty$ as $n + k \to \infty$, and use the proof of Lemma 4.9. One could also argue as in ch. 5, Corollary 4.2.

Lemma 4.11. *If every element of G is compact, then every Harris random walk on G is of type Ia.*

Proof. We suppose that X is of type Ib, and we denote by H an open compact sub-group containing the support of f (we recall that $\varphi = -Af$). Then G/H is infinite, and arguing as in Lemma 4.9, we may pick a sequence $\{z_n\}$ such that $z_0 = e$ and the co-sets $z_n H$ are disjoint, and $\lim_n \varphi(z_n) = L < +\infty$. By Theorem 4.7, $\lim_n \varphi(-z_n) = +\infty$. By the hypothesis, for every element z in G, the sequence $\{nz\}_{n \geqslant 0}$ intersects H, so that we can set for every n

$$h_n = \inf\{m \geqslant 1 : mz_n \in H\}.$$

For $n \geqslant 1$, $h_n > 1$, and since $(h_n - 1) z_n \in z_n^{-1} H$, we have $\lim_n \varphi((h_n - 1) z_n) = +\infty$. Thus $h_n > 2$ for n sufficiently large, and we can choose k_n to be the largest positive integer less than $h_n - 1$ such that $\varphi(k_n z_n) \leqslant 2L + 2$. Then for n sufficiently large,

$$\varphi(k_n z_n) \leqslant 2L + 2 \leqslant \varphi((k_n + 1) z_n).$$

Now, by using the identities of ch. 8, Theorem 2.1, we can write

$$\varphi(x + y) - \varphi(x) - \varphi(y) = -Af(x + y) + Af(x) + Af(y)$$

$$= -A(\tau_y f)(x) + Af(x) + A(\tau_y f)(e)$$

$$= -G^H(\tau_y f)(x) - P_H A(\tau_y f)(x) - (\Gamma u_H(x) - C_H) m(f)$$

$$+ G^H f(x) + P_H Af(x) + (\Gamma u_H(x) - C_H) m(f)$$

$$+ G^H(\tau_y f)(e) + P_H A(\tau_y f)(e) + (\Gamma u_H(e) - C_H) m(f).$$

Since the support of f is contained in H, we have $G^H f(x) = 0$; on the other hand, $\Gamma u_H = C_H$ in e, since $e \in H$. Finally, owing to the definitions of P_H and G^H, we get, after cancellation,

$$\varphi(x + y) - \varphi(x) - \varphi(y) = -G^H(\tau_y f)(x) - P_H A(\tau_y f)(x) + P_H Af(x) + A(\tau_y f)(e).$$

We may suppose that Af is negative, since this amounts to adding to A a multiple of $1 \otimes m$. On the other hand, as a consequence of Proposition 4.1, we have

$$\lim_{y \to A}[A(\tau_y f)(e) - P_H A(\tau_y f)(x)] = 0$$

uniformly in x. We may thus conclude that, uniformly in $x \in G$,

$$\varphi(x + y) - \varphi(x) - \varphi(y) \leqslant 0(y)$$

where $0(y) \to 0$ as $y \to \varDelta$. Letting $y = z_n$ and $x = k_n z_n$, we get that

$$\varphi((k_n + 1) z_n) - \varphi(k_n z_n) \leqslant \varphi(z_n) + 0_n(1),$$

where $0_n(1) \to 0$ as $n \to \infty$. For n sufficiently large, we thus have

$$L + 1 \leqslant \varphi(k_n z_n) \leqslant 2L + 2 \leqslant \varphi((k_n + 1) z_n) \leqslant 3L + 3.$$

Since either $\{k_n z_n\}$ or $\{(k_n + 1) z_n\}$ has a sub-sequence which converges to infinity, we have a contradiction with Theorem 4.7.

Theorem 4.12. *If the random walk is of type Ib, then* $\mathbf{G}$ *is isomorphic either to* $\mathbf{R} \oplus \mathbf{K}$ *or* $\mathbf{Z} \oplus \mathbf{K}$, *where* $\mathbf{K}$ *is a compact group. Furthermore, there is a finite number* L *such that (with the obvious meaning for* $\pm \infty$)

$$\lim_{x \to +\infty} Af(x) = L\, m(f), \qquad \lim_{x \to -\infty} Af(x) = -\infty$$

or

$$\lim_{x \to +\infty} Af(x) = -\infty, \qquad \lim_{x \to -\infty} Af(x) = L\, m(f)$$

for every special function f.

Proof. The first part is shown in the same way as ch. 5, Theorem 4.4. The second part then follows easily from the above results and the arguments in ch. 5, Theorem 3.1.

Unfortunately we do not know of a characterization of the laws of type Ib walks. Exercise 4.16, however, gives some information on this subject.

Exercise 4.13. (1) Prove that type II random walks are normal in the sense of ch. 8 §3.

[*Hint*: Observe that in Proposition 2.10, $\hat{\gamma}$ may be replaced by a multiple of γ.]

(2) Derive that the resolvent of linear Brownian motion is normal in the sense of ch. 8 §3.

Exercise 4.14. Prove that with the notation of Exercise 2.15, if X is a recurrent random walk on $\mathbf{Z}$, then $\alpha(x) = \lambda x$ for all $x \leqslant 0$ if and only if X is left continuous (see ch. 3, Exercise 4.15) with $\lambda = -\sigma^{-2}$. Compute the potential kernel of the Bernoulli random walk $(\mu(1) = \mu(-1) = 2^{-1})$.

Exercise 4.15. For a type I random walk on $\mathbf{R}$ or $\mathbf{Z}$, prove that $\lim_{x \to \Delta} x^{-1} \gamma(x) = 0$.

Exercise 4.16. (1) All recurrent random walks on $\mathbf{Z}$ have the property that $\alpha(x) < 0$ for $x \neq 0$ with one single exception: left- or right-continuous random walks of type I. In the left-continuous case, $\alpha(x) = 0$ for $x \leqslant 0$ and $\alpha(x) < 0$ for $x > 0$. The reader is invited to return to ch. 8, Exercise 4.18.

(2) Prove that if a random walk on $\mathbf{Z}$ is type I, and $\mu(x) = 0$ for all but a finite number of positive entries x, then there is a finite cluster point for γ.

(3) Use the random walks described in (1) to prove that there exist random walks which are not normal in the sense of ch. 8 §3.

CHAPTER 10

CONSTRUCTION OF MARKOV CHAINS AND RESOLVENTS

We have seen that the potential kernels of Markov chains and resolvents satisfy maximum principles in the recurrent as well as in the transient case. We will deal here with the converse problem: is any kernel satisfying an appropriate maximum principle the potential kernel of a Markov chain or of a resolvent? The answer is negative (cf. Exercise 1.10) in general, but can be made positive by mean of additional conditions. The research for the best of these conditions does not seem to be yet closed.

1. Preliminaries and bounded kernels

In this and the following section, we study positive and proper kernels denoted by G or V. We denote by $\mathscr{B}$ the set of functions h in $b\mathscr{E}$ such that $G|h|$ (or $V|h|$ according to the context) is bounded, and by $\mathscr{B}_+$ the set of positive functions in $\mathscr{B}$. Once for all, we remark that two measures which are equal on $\mathscr{B}_+$ are equal.

These kernels are supposed to satisfy some of the maximum principles defined in ch. 2. From now on we abbreviate "complete maximum principle" into C.M.P. and "reinforced complete maximum principle" into R.C.M.P., and shall write $G \in$ (R.C.M.P.) or $V \in$ (C.M.P.) to mean that $G(V)$ satisfies the corresponding principle.

It may happen that the kernels satisfy the maximum principles only for subclasses of $\mathscr{E}_+$, for instance $\mathscr{B}_+$; when this is the case it will be explicitly stated.

Proposition 1.1. *The kernel V satisfies the C.M.P. if and only if for every f in $\mathscr{E}$ such that Vf is meaningful and assumes positive values,*

$$\sup_{x \in E} Vf(x) = \sup_{x \in \{f > 0\}} Vf(x).$$

Proof. Let a be the right-hand side of the above equation. We have $Vf^+ \leqslant a \vee 0 + Vf^-$ on $\{f^+ > 0\}$, hence everywhere, and $Vf \leqslant a \vee 0$. Since Vf assumes positive values, we have $a \vee 0 = a > 0$, which proves the necessity.

Assume conversely that $Vf \leqslant a + Vg \ (a > 0)$ on $\{f > 0\}$; then $V(f - g) \leqslant a$ on $\{f - g > 0\} \subset \{f > 0\}$, and if V satisfies the above equation we get $V(f - g) \leqslant a$ everywhere, which completes the proof.

Proposition 1.2. *If* $V \in (C.M.P.)$ *and* $f \in \mathscr{E}_+$, *the kernel* $VI_f \in (C.M.P.)$.

Proof. Left to the reader as Exercise 1.9.

Proposition 1.3. *If* $V \in (C.M.P.)$, *then for every* $\alpha > 0$, $I + \alpha V \in (R.C.M.P.)$. *If* $G \in (R.C.M.P.)$, *then* $G \in (C.M.P.)$ *and* G *is a one-to-one operator and may be written* $G = I + V$, *where* V *is a proper kernel.*

Proof. Let $f, g \in \mathscr{E}_+$ and assume that

$$f + \alpha Vf \leqslant a + g + \alpha Vg - g = a + \alpha Vg$$

on $\{f > 0\}$. A fortiori $Vf \leqslant a/\alpha + Vg$ on $\{f > 0\}$, hence everywhere. On $\{f = 0\}$, we consequently have

$$f + \alpha Vf \leqslant a + g + \alpha Vg - g,$$

so that $I + \alpha V \in (\text{R.C.M.P.})$.

Now let $G \in (\text{R.C.M.P.})$ and assume that $f, g \in \mathscr{E}_+$ are such that $Gf \leqslant a + Gg$ on $\{f > 0\}$. It would be easy to show that this inequality holds everywhere if g vanished on $\{f > 0\}$; we reduce the problem to this case by setting $f' = f - f \wedge g$ and $g' = g - f \wedge g$. We then have

$$Gf' \leqslant a + Gg' \quad \text{on } \{f > 0\} \supset \{f' > 0\}.$$

Since $g' = 0$ on $\{f' > 0\}$, we get

$$Gf' \leqslant a + Gg' - g' \quad \text{on } \{f' > 0\},$$

hence everywhere, and a fortiori $Gf' \leqslant a + Gg'$ everywhere, which implies

$$Gf = Gf' + G(f \wedge g) \leqslant a + Gg' + G(f \wedge g) = a + Gg$$

everywhere.

Let now $f \in \mathscr{B}$ be such that $Gf \geqslant 0$. We have

$$Gf^+ - f^+ \geqslant Gf^- \quad \text{on } \{f^- > 0\};$$

hence $Gf \geqslant f^+ \geqslant f$. If $Gf = 0$, it follows that $f^+ = 0$, and symmetrically that $f^- = 0$, which proves that G is one-to-one.

On the other hand if we set $V = G - I$, it is clear that the mapping V from $\mathscr{B}$ to b$\mathscr{E}$ is positive and majorized by G, hence is a positive proper kernel.

Corollary 1.4 (Uniqueness theorem). *If* $V \in (C.M.P.)$, *there is at most one resolvent such that* $V_0 = V$. *More precisely, for every* $\alpha \geqslant 0$, *there is at most one operator* V_α *such that*

$$\alpha V V_\alpha = \alpha V_\alpha V = V - V_\alpha.$$

If $G \in (R.C.M.P.)$, *there is at most one T.P. such that* $G = \sum_0^\infty P_n$.

Proof. Assume that there are two such operators, V_α and $\tilde{V}_\alpha$: then for $f \in \mathscr{B}_+$,

$$(I + \alpha V)\,(V_\alpha f - \tilde{V}_\alpha f) = 0,$$

and since $I + \alpha V$ is one-to-one, $V_\alpha f = \tilde{V}_\alpha f$.

In the same way, if P and $\tilde{P}$ are two T.P.'s with potential operator G, we have

$$GP = G\tilde{P} = G - I,$$

and the result follows once more from the fact that G is one-to-one.

As we have already pointed out, there does not always exist such a resolvent (transition probability). We begin with the special case of *bounded* kernels. A kernel V is said to be bounded if $V1$ is bounded; the space $\mathscr{B}$ is then equal to b$\mathscr{E}$, and V is a bounded endomorphism of b$\mathscr{E}$ with norm $\|V\|$. The following result is basic for the sequel.

Theorem 1.5. *A bounded kernel* V *satisfies the complete maximum principle if and only if there exists a submarkovian resolvent* $\{V_\alpha\}_{\alpha>0}$ *such that* $V_0 = V$.

Proof. The sufficiency was shown in ch. 2 §4. We proceed to the necessity. Suppose that there exists an operator V_α, $\alpha > 0$, on b$\mathscr{E}$ such that

$$\alpha V V_\alpha = \alpha V_\alpha V = V - V_\alpha. \tag{1.1}$$

This operator is positive; indeed, let g be a negative function in b$\mathscr{E}$ such that $V_\alpha g = V(g - \alpha V_\alpha g)$ assumes a positive maximum. By Proposition 1.1, this maximum is assumed on $\{g > \alpha V_\alpha g\}$, that is on the set where $V_\alpha g$ is strictly negative, which is a contradiction.

Furthermore, $\|\alpha V_\alpha\| \leqslant 1$; indeed, V_α being positive, it suffices to check that $\alpha V_\alpha 1 \leqslant 1$. First, we observe that it is not true that $1 \leqslant \alpha V_\alpha 1$ everywhere, since we would then have

$$0 \geqslant V[\alpha(1 - \alpha V_\alpha 1)] = \alpha V_\alpha 1 \geqslant 1.$$

Then $V[\alpha(1 - \alpha V_\alpha 1)] \leqslant 1$ on the non-empty set $\{\alpha(1 - \alpha V_\alpha 1) > 0\}$, and hence everywhere, by the complete maximum principle.

For $\alpha > 0$, we now set

$$V_\alpha = V(I - \alpha V + \alpha^2 V^2 - \cdots);$$

this series converges for $\alpha < \|V\|^{-1}$, and thus defines an operator V_α which satisfies eq. (1.1); it follows that V_α is positive and that $\|V_\alpha\| < \alpha^{-1}$. Now choose $\alpha < \|V\|^{-1}$ and $\beta < \alpha$, and set

$$V_{\alpha+\beta} = V_\alpha(I - \beta V_\alpha + \beta^2 V_\alpha^2 - \cdots); \tag{1.2}$$

the operator thus defined satisfies the relation

$$\beta V_{\alpha+\beta} V_\alpha = \beta V_\alpha V_{\alpha+\beta} = V_\alpha - V_{\alpha+\beta}. \tag{1.3}$$

The operator V commutes with V_α, hence with $V_{\alpha+\beta}$, and multiplying the two members of eq. (1.3) by V yields

$$(\alpha + \beta) V V_{\alpha+\beta} = (\alpha + \beta) V_{\alpha+\beta} V = V - V_{\alpha+\beta},$$

which is eq. (1.1) for $\alpha + \beta$. We have thus defined operators V_α satisfying eq. (1.1) for $\alpha \in [0, 2\|V\|^{-1}[$. The same pattern permits us then to define V_α for $\alpha \in [0, 4\|V\|^{-1}[$, and by iteration for all $\alpha > 0$. We notice that the map $\alpha \to V_\alpha$ is continuous for the uniform topology of operators.

We now show that the operators V_α satisfy the resolvent equation on $b\mathscr{E}$. Since $I + \alpha V$ is one-to-one, it suffices to prove that for $f \in b\mathscr{E}$

$$(I - \alpha V)(V_\alpha - V_\beta) f = (I + \alpha V)(\beta - \alpha) V_\alpha V_\beta f,$$

but this is an obvious consequence of eq. (1.1).

Finally if $\{f_n\}_{n \geqslant 0}$ is a sequence of functions in $b\mathscr{E}_+$ decreasing to zero, for every $\alpha > 0$,

$$\lim_n V_\alpha f_n \leqslant \lim_n V f_n = 0,$$

which proves that the operators V_α are the restrictions to $b\mathscr{E}$ of kernels $V_\alpha(x, \cdot)$. It is now easy to see that these kernels build the desired resolvent.

Corollary 1.6. *Under the same hypotheses, if moreover E is locally compact and V maps C_K into C_0, the kernels V_α have the same property.*

Proof. The above proof may be performed by using the Banach space C_0 instead of $b\mathscr{E}$.

To proceed with the general problem, we shall have to use resolvents of the kind just described. We shall need the notion of reduced functions in the cone of supermedian functions relative to this resolvent.

Proposition 1.7. *Let $\{V_\alpha\}_{\alpha>0}$ be a proper resolvent and $A \in \mathscr{E}$. With each supermedian function f we may associate a supermedian function $R_A f$ called the reduced function of f on A, which satisfies the following properties:*

(i) *$R_A f$ is the smallest supermedian function which dominates f on A; $R_A f = f$ on A and if f, g are two supermedian functions such that $f \leqslant g$ on A, then $R_A f \leqslant R_A g$;*

(ii) *if $\{f_n\}$ is a sequence of supermedian functions increasing to f, then $R_A f = \lim_n R_A f_n$;*

(iii) *if $h \in \mathscr{E}_+$ vanishes outside A, then $R_A V_0 h = V_0 h$;*

(iv) *$R_A(f + g) = R_A f + R_A g$;*

(v) *if $A \subset B$, then $R_A f \leqslant R_B f$.*

Proof. We use the notation of ch. 2 §4. We first prove that if $\alpha < \beta$, then the functions which are superharmonic for X^β are superharmonic for X^α. It suffices to consider the bounded potentials $f = (I + \beta V_0) h$, and then

$$\alpha V_\alpha f = \alpha V_\alpha(I + \beta V_0) h = \alpha V_\alpha h + \beta(V_0 h - V_\alpha h)$$

$$= (\alpha - \beta) V_\alpha h + \beta V_0 h \leqslant \beta V_0 h \leqslant f.$$

Consequently, if f is supermedian $P_A^\alpha f \leqslant P_A^\beta f$, so that the limit

$$R_A f = \lim_{\alpha \to \infty} P_A^\alpha f$$

is well defined. We proceed to show that the operator R_A thus defined has the desired properties (i)–(v).

We first prove that $R_A f$ is a supermedian function. Pick a $\beta > 0$; for every $\alpha > \beta$, $P_A^\alpha f$ is P^β-superharmonic, so $R_A f$ is P^β-superharmonic. Since this is true for all β, the function $R_A f$ is supermedian. Next we note that if $f \leqslant g$ on A, then $P_A^\alpha f \leqslant P_A^\alpha g$, and consequently $R_A f \leqslant R_A g$; since clearly $R_A g \leqslant g$, it follows that $R_A f \leqslant g$, and the proof of (i) is complete.

The property (ii) follows at once from interchanging increasing limits. Now let h be finite and vanish outside A; by the known properties of balayage operators,

$$P_A^\alpha (I + \alpha V_0)\, h = (I + \alpha V_0)\, h,$$

whence, dividing by α and letting α tend to infinity, we get $R_A V_0 h = V_0 h$. The proof of (iii) is then completed by using approximation by potentials.

Properties (iv) and (v) are obvious.

We need one more definition.

Definition 1.8. A supermedian function f is called *excessive* if

$$\lim_{\alpha \to \infty} \alpha V_\alpha f = f.$$

Excessive functions are studied in ch. 2, Exercise 4.15, which the reader is invited to solve, since the results therein will be used freely in the sequel.

Exercise 1.9. Prove Proposition 1.2.

Exercise 1.10. (1) Let V be the potential kernel of a proper Markovian resolvent $\{V_\alpha\}$. Define a new space $\tilde{E}$ by adjoining to E a point Δ, and let $\tilde{\mathscr{E}}$ be the σ-algebra $\sigma(\mathscr{E}, \{\Delta\})$. Define a kernel $\tilde{V}$ on $(\tilde{E}, \tilde{\mathscr{E}})$ be setting

$$\tilde{V}(x, \cdot) = V(x, \cdot) + \varepsilon_\Delta(\cdot), \qquad x \in E,$$

$$\tilde{V}(\Delta, \cdot) = \varepsilon_\Delta(\cdot).$$

Prove that $\tilde{V} \in$ (C.M.P.).

(2) Assume that there is a resolvent $\{\tilde{V}_\alpha\}$ on E such that $\tilde{V} = \tilde{V}_0$. Then $\alpha \tilde{V}_\alpha 1_E = 1_E$ for every $\alpha > 0$, and this is not consistent with the definition of $\tilde{V}$.

Exercise 1.11. In Proposition 1.7, prove that the operator $R_A V_0$ is given by a proper kernel. Is this still true for R_A?

Exercise 1.12. Prove that a positive kernel V satisfying the C.M.P. for the functions in $\mathscr{B}_+$ satisfies the C.M.P. for the functions in $\mathscr{E}_+$.

Exercise 1.13. One could think of generalizing the problem dealt with in this section in the following manner. Let $V \in$ (C.M.P.) and $h \in b\mathscr{E}_+$. Does there exist a kernel V_h such that

(i) $V = V_h + VI_hV_h$,   (ii) $V = V_h + V_hI_hV$,   (iii) $V = \sum_n (V_hI_h)^n V_h$?

Clearly, if V_h satisfies (iii) it satisfies (i) and (ii).

(1) Prove that there exists at most one kernel V_h satisfying (i) and hence (iii). If h, k are in $b\mathscr{E}_+$ and $h \leqslant k$, and if there exist two operators V_h and V_k satisfying (i), then

$$V_h = V_k + V_hI_{k-h}V_h.$$

(2) Prove by an example that a kernel V_h can satisfy (i) without satisfying (ii).

(3) If $h \in \mathscr{B}_+$, then there exists a kernel V_h satisfying (iii) and such that $V_h(h) = 1$. If f is V-supermedian (see next section) then $V_h(hf) \leqslant f$.

2. The reinforced principle. Construction of transient Markov chains

We now study a proper kernel G satisfying the R.C.M.P. for the functions of $\mathscr{B}_+$, and we shall give a necessary and sufficient condition under which it is the potential kernel of a transient Markov chain. Exercise 2.18 provides an example of a kernel which satisfies the R.C.M.P. and is nevertheless not the potential kernel of a transient Markov chain.

Recalling the results of ch. 2, we lay down the following.

Definition 2.1. A function $f \in \mathscr{E}_+$ is called *G-superharmonic* if the inequality $Gg \leqslant f$, $g \in \mathscr{B}$, holds everywhere provided it holds on $\{g > 0\}$.

The following result provides important examples of G-superharmonic functions.

Proposition 2.2. *Let $a \in \mathbf{R}_+$ and $f \in \mathscr{B}_+$; the functions $a + Gf$ and $a + Gf - f$ are G-superharmonic.*

Proof. For the first one it follows at once from the fact that G satisfies the C.M.P. (cf. Proposition 1.1).

Assume next that, for $g \in \mathscr{B}$, we have

$$a + Gf - f \geqslant Gg \quad \text{on } \{g > 0\};$$

this implies

$$a + G(f + g^-) - (f + g^-) \geqslant Gg^+ \quad \text{on } \{g^+ > 0\},$$

hence everywhere, since $G \in$ (R.C.M.P.). It follows that

$$a + Gf - f \geqslant Gg$$

everywhere, which completes the proof.

By ch. 2 §1.15 and Proposition 1.2 there exists a bounded strictly positive function f such that the kernel $V = GI_f$ is a bounded kernel satisfying the C.M.P. for the functions in $b\mathcal{E}_+$ and such that $V(b\mathcal{E}_+) = G(\mathcal{B}_+)$. By the preceding section there exists one and only one resolvent $\{V_\alpha\}$, $\alpha > 0$, such that $V_0 = V$ and we have the following

Proposition 2.3. *The following three families of functions are equal*:
   (i) *the supermedian functions with respect to* $\{V_\alpha\}$;
   (ii) *the excessive functions with respect to* $\{V_\alpha\}$;
   (iii) *the G-superharmonic functions*.

Proof. To prove the equality of (i) and (ii) it suffices by ch. 2, Exercise 4.15 to prove that the empty set is the only set of potential zero. But $V1_A = G(f1_A) = 0$ implies, from Proposition 1.3, that $f1_A = 0$, and since f is strictly positive, A is empty.

As f is strictly positive, the equality of (iii) and (i) follows from ch. 2, Proposition 4.6.

As a result, neither the cone of supermedian functions relative to $\{V_\alpha\}$ nor the operator R_A in this cone depend on the choice of f. Making use of Proposition 1.7, we may therefore speak of the reduced function R_Ah of the G-superharmonic function h on the set A, and the operator R_A enjoys the properties of Proposition 1.7. The following definition is basic.

Definition 2.4. A G-superharmonic function h is said to *vanish at the boundary* if there exists a decreasing sequence $\{A_n\}_{n\geqslant 0}$ of sets in $\mathcal{E}$ such that:
   (i) $\bigcap_n A_n = \emptyset$ and $G(\cdot, A_n^c)$ is bounded for all n;
   (ii) $\inf_n R_{A_n}h = 0$.

Let us further recall that if $h = f + g$, where f and g are G-superharmonic, then h is said to be *specifically greater* than f or g. This is the intrinsic or proper order in the cone of superharmonic functions.

Lemma 2.5. *Let* $\{h_p\}$ *be a specifically increasing sequence of G-superharmonic functions vanishing at the boundary relative to one and the same sequence* $\{A_n\}$. *If* $h = \sup h_p$ *is finite, it vanishes at the boundary relative to* $\{A_n\}$.

Proof. For every p we may write $h = h_p + g_p$, where g_p is G-superharmonic. Then by Proposition 1.7, $R_{A_n}h = R_{A_n}h_p + R_{A_n}g_p \leqslant R_{A_n}h_p + g_p$. Given $x \in E$ and $\varepsilon > 0$, we may find an integer p such that $g_p(x) < \varepsilon$, and then an integer n such that $R_{A_n}h_p(x) < \varepsilon$, which yields the desired result.

Proposition 2.6. *The following three conditions are equivalent:*

(i) *there exists a strictly positive function $g \in \mathcal{B}_+$ such that Gg vanishes at the boundary;*

(ii) *there exists a sequence $\{K_m\}$ of sets in $\mathcal{E}$ with $\bigcup K_m = E$ and such that $G1_{K_m}$ is bounded and vanishes at the boundary for all m, relative to one and the same sequence $\{A_n\}$;*

(iii) *for all $f \in \mathcal{B}_+$, Gf vanishes at the boundary relative to one and the same sequence $\{A_n\}$.*

Proof. (ii) implies (i). Indeed, there exists a sequence of numbers $b_m \in {]0, 1]}$ such that the series $\sum_m b_m 1_{K_m}$ and $\sum_m b_m G1_{K_m}$ converge uniformly. Setting $g = \sum_m b_m 1_{K_m}$, the result follows from Lemma 2.5.

Next, (i) implies (iii). Let $f \in \mathcal{B}_+$, and set $f_n = ng \wedge f$; then Gf_n increases specifically to Gf and each Gf_n vanishes at the boundary relative to any sequence $\{A_n\}$ for which Gg vanishes at the boundary. We conclude the result once more from Lemma 2.5.

Finally, that (iii) implies (ii) is obvious.

As has been proved in ch. 2, if G is the potential kernel of a Markov chain, then all potentials Gg vanish at the boundary. We are going to show that, conversely, this condition is sufficient to assert that G is the potential kernel of a Markov chain. We must first make some preparation.

Lemma 2.7. *Let h be a bounded superharmonic function, and set*

$$D_n h = nf(h - nV_n h);$$

then $GD_n h$ increases to h as n tends to infinity.

Proof. The lemma follows from the fact that h is excessive for $\{V_\alpha\}$, and the equalities

$$GD_n h = V(D_n h/f) = V(n(h - nV_n h)) = nV_n h.$$

Lemma 2.8. *Let h be a bounded superharmonic function, and $\{u_n\}$ a sequence of functions in $\mathcal{B}_+$ such that Gu_n increases to h. The sequence $\{u_n\}$ converges boundedly to a function u and if $h = Gg$ $(g \in \mathcal{B}_+)$, then $u = g$ and $Gu = h$.*

Proof. From the inequalities $h \geqslant Gu_n \geqslant u_n$, we get that the sequence $\{u_n\}$ is uniformly bounded. Furthermore, since for $n \geqslant m$ we have $Gu_n \geqslant Gu_m$, it follows from Proposition 1.3 that $G(u_n - u_m) \geqslant u_n - u_m$, which can be written as

$$u_n \leqslant u_m + G(u_n - u_m).$$

Pick a point x in E, and two sequences $\{n_k\}$ and $\{m_k\}$ such that $n_k \geqslant m_k$,

$$\lim_k u_{n_k}(x) = \overline{\lim} \, u_n(x)$$

and

$$\lim_k u_{m_k}(x) = \underline{\lim} \, u_n(x);$$

letting k tend to infinity in the above inequality yields $\overline{\lim} \, u_n(x) \leqslant \underline{\lim} \, u_n(x)$, which proves the existence of the limit u. The inequality $Gu \leqslant h$ follows from Fatou's lemma.

If $h = Gg$, the inequality $G(g - u_n) \geqslant 0$ implies, as above, that $g \leqslant u_n + G(g - u_n)$ and, passing to the limit, that $g \leqslant u$. As a result, $h = Gg \leqslant Gu$; hence $Gg = Gu$. The operator G being one-to-one, it follows that $u = g$.

Lemma 2.9. *Let $\{u_n\}$ be a sequence in $\mathcal{B}_+$ converging to a function u and such that the potentials Gu_n are smaller than a G-superharmonic bounded function h vanishing at the boundary. Then $Gu = \lim_n Gu_n$.*

Proof. Let $\{A_n\}$ be a sequence relative to which h vanishes at the boundary, and choose a decreasing sequence of numbers a_n such that the series $\sum_n a_n G(\cdot, A_n^c)$ converges uniformly. The function

$$w = \sum_n a_n 1_{A_{n-1} \setminus A_n}$$

is in $\mathcal{B}_+$ and bounded from below on each set A_n^c.

We assume that for every x in E,

$$\lim_{a \to \infty} \int_{\{u_n > aw\}} G(x, dy) \, u_n(y) = 0 \qquad (2.1)$$

uniformly in n. By a classical argument we have

$$|Gu(x) - Gu_n(x)| \leqslant \int_{\{u_n > aw\}} G(x, dy) \, (u_n(y) + u(y))$$

$$+ \int_{\{u_n \leqslant aw\}} G(x, dy) \, |u_n(y) - u(y)|;$$

by first choosing a in order that the first integral be small, then letting n tend to infinity, we get the desired result.

It thus remains to prove the uniform integrability property of eq. (2.1). The integral therein is majorized by

$$G(u_n 1_{C_a})(x) = \int_{C_a} G(x, \mathrm{d}y)\, u_n(y),$$

where $C_a = \{h > aw\}$ contains $\{Gu_n > aw\}$, hence also $\{u_n > aw\}$. But on C_a we have

$$R_{C_a} Gu_p = Gu_p \geqslant G(u_p 1_{C_a}),$$

and since $R_{C_a} Gu_p$ is G-superharmonic, we get $R_{C_a} Gu_p \geqslant G(u_p 1_{C_a})$ everywhere. A fortiori $G(u_p 1_{C_a}) \leqslant R_{C_a} h$, and since h vanishes at the boundary, it suffices to show that $C_a \subset A_n$ for sufficiently large a. Since w is bounded from below by a_n on A_n^c we have $C_a \subset A_n$ as soon as $\|h\| < aa_n$, and the proof is complete.

Theorem 2.10. *Let G be a proper kernel satisfying the R.C.M.P.; then the two following conditions are equivalent:*

(i) *G is the potential kernel of a transition probability P;*

(ii) *every bounded potential vanishes at the boundary.*

Proof. We know from ch. 2 that (i) implies (ii). We proceed to prove the converse.

If (i) is true and if $g \in \mathcal{B}_+$, then $GPg = Gg - g$. We therefore set $Pg = \lim_n D_n(Gg - g)$, which is meaningful by Lemmas 2.7 and 2.8. Let us study the properties of the operator P thus defined on $\mathcal{B}_+$.

The G-superharmonic function $Gg - g$ vanishes at the boundary, since it is majorized by the bounded potential Gg. By Lemma 2.9, we have therefore $GPg = Gg - g$, so that Pg is also in $\mathcal{B}_+$, and we can define the iterates $P_n g$. From the equality $GP_n g = GP_{n-1} g - P_{n-1} g$, we derive

$$Gg = g + Pg + \cdots + P_n g + GP_{n+1} g.$$

This implies that $P_n g \to 0$ as $n \to \infty$, and since Gg vanishes at the boundary it follows from Lemma 2.9 that $GP_{n+1} g \to 0$, and hence that

$$Gg = g + Pg + \cdots + P_n g + \cdots.$$

Now let $\{g_n\}$ be a sequence of functions in $\mathcal{B}_+$ decreasing to zero. By Lebesgue's theorem the sequence $\{Gg_n\}$ also decreases to zero; since $Pg_n \geqslant 0$, it follows from Proposition 1.3 that $Pg_n \leqslant GPg_n = Gg_n - g_n$, and the sequence $\{Pg_n\}$ also decreases to zero.

Finally, let g be a function in $\mathscr{B}_+$ with $g \leqslant 1$; from the inequality $1 \geqslant g = G(g - Pg)$, we get

$$G(g - Pg)^+ \leqslant 1 + G(g - Pg)^- - (g - Pg)^-$$

on $\{(g - Pg)^+ > 0\}$, hence everywhere. This implies that

$$Pg = G(g - Pg) - (g - Pg) \leqslant 1.$$

The space $\mathscr{B}$ being clearly a lattice, the last two properties prove, by means of Daniell's theorem, that P is given by a T.P. still denoted P defined on the σ-algebra generated by $\mathscr{B}$. Since G is proper, the σ-algebra generated by $\mathscr{B}$ is equal to $\mathscr{E}$, and the proof is easily completed.

The above condition (ii) is not easy to check, but it yields some useful corollaries if some additional assumptions are made. One of these is given in Exercise 2.19; another is obtained in a topological setting.

Corollary 2.11. *If E is locally compact and countable at infinity, and if G is a kernel on E mapping C_K into C_0, then G is the potential of a Markov chain. If, moreover, $G(C_K)$ is dense in C_0, then the Markov chain is a Feller chain.*

Proof. The condition of Proposition 2.6(ii) is satisfied by taking for $\{K_m\}$ as well as for $\{A_n\}$ any increasing sequence of compact sets whose interiors cover E; consequently the preceding theorem applies, and G is the potential kernel of a transition probability P.

If $g \in C_K$, from $PGg = g + Gg$ it is easily deduced that PGg is in C_0, and the second part of the corollary follows.

We now apply the same methods to the problem of kernels satisfying the C.M.P.

Definition 2.12. Let V be a kernel satisfying the C.M.P. A function $h \in \mathscr{E}_+$ is called *supermedian* if for every $g \in \mathscr{B}$, the inequality $Vg \leqslant h$ holds everywhere whenever it holds on $\{g > 0\}$.

The potentials $Vf (f \in \mathscr{B}_+)$ are supermedian functions.

Since V is proper, there is a strictly positive function f in $\mathscr{B}_+$. The kernel $\tilde{V} = VI_f$ is bounded and satisfies the C.M.P., so that there is a resolvent $\{\tilde{V}_\alpha\}$ such that $\tilde{V}_0 = \tilde{V}$. The supermedian functions are the same for V and

$\tilde{V}$, and therefore by following the pattern of §1 we can define the reduced functions in the cone of supermedian functions. We define the functions vanishing at the boundary in the same way as above and clearly Proposition 2.6 is still available.

For every $\alpha > 0$, the kernel $G^\alpha = I + \alpha V$ satisfies the R.C.M.P., and the space $\mathscr{B}$ is the same for V and G^α. Furthermore, the supermedian functions are G^α-superharmonic, as is easily checked. As a result, if h is supermedian, its reduced function on A in the cone of G^α-superharmonic functions is smaller than its reduced function on A in the cone of supermedian functions. We may thus state

Lemma 2.13. *Let $\{u_n\}$ be a sequence of functions converging to u and such that $\{G^\alpha u_n\}$ is majorized by a potential Vg vanishing at the boundary; then $G^\alpha u = \lim_n G^\alpha u_n$.*

Proof. The same as the proof of Lemma 2.9.

This enables us to state

Theorem 2.14. *If every bounded potential Vf vanishes at the boundary there exists a sub-markovian resolvent $\{V_\alpha\}$ such that $V_0 = V$.*

Proof. Let $g \in \mathscr{B}_+$. Since Vg is G^α-superharmonic, by Lemma 2.7 there is a sequence $\{l_n\}$ such that $G^\alpha l_n$ increases to Vg. Since the sequence $\{G^\alpha l_n - l_n\}$ increases and is majorized by Vg, it converges, and consequently the sequence

$$\{l_n\} = \{G^\alpha l_n - (G^\alpha l_n - l_n)\}$$

converges to a limit which we call $V_\alpha g$. By Lemma 2.13, we have $G^\alpha V_\alpha g = Vg$, and therefore $V_\alpha g$ does not depend on the particular sequence $\{l_n\}$, since G^α is one-to-one. Finally $V_\alpha g$ lies in $\mathscr{B}_+$.

As in the proof of Theorem 2.10, it is verified that if $g \leqslant 1$, then $\alpha V_\alpha g \leqslant 1$. That the operators V_α satisfy the resolvent equation is seen as in the proof of Theorem 1.5. Finally Daniell's theorem enables us to show that V_α is given by a kernel. It remains to show that $V_0 = V$.

We already know that $V_\alpha g \leqslant Vg$ for every α, hence that $V_0 g \leqslant Vg$. Now the identity $(I + \alpha V) V_\alpha g = Vg$ implies that, for every n,

$$(I + \alpha V)(\alpha V_\alpha)^n g = \alpha V(\alpha V_\alpha)^{n-1} g,$$

and summing up these equations yields

$$\sum_1^n (\alpha V_\alpha)^k g + \alpha V (\alpha V_\alpha)^n g = Vg.$$

This proves that $V(\alpha V_\alpha)^n g \leqslant Vg$ and $\lim_n (\alpha V_\alpha)^n g = 0$, which implies $\lim_n \alpha V(\alpha V_\alpha)^n g = 0$. Finally, it follows that

$$\sum_1^\infty (\alpha V_\alpha)^k g = \alpha Vg,$$

which proves, on account of ch. 2, Proposition 4.4, that $V_0 = V$.

As before we have the corollary

Corollary 2.15. *If E is locally compact and countable at infinity, and if V maps C_K into C_0, there is a sub-markovian resolvent $\{V_\alpha\}$ such that $V_0 = V$. If, in addition, $V(C_K)$ is dense in C_0, then V_α maps C_0 into C_0 for each $\alpha > 0$.*

Proof. The same as for Corollary 2.11.

Remark. This corollary is not the best available, as is pointed out in the exercises and in the notes and comments.

Exercise 2.16. Prove that $h - Gu$ in Lemma 2.8 is superharmonic.

Exercise 2.17. Show that every bounded G-superharmonic function vanishing at the boundary is a potential.

Exercise 2.18. By a slight change of Exercise 1.10, prove that there exist kernels satisfying the R.C.M.P. which are not the potential kernels of Markov chains.

Exercise 2.19. Prove that if $V \in$ (C.M.P.) and $V1$ is finite, then there is a submarkovian resolvent $\{V_\alpha\}$ such that $V_0 = V$. Solve the same problem for a kernel $G \in$ (R.C.M.P.).

Exercise 2.20. Resume the hypotheses of Theorem 2.14. Let $\{K_n\}$ be an increasing sequence of sets such that $\bigcup K_n = E$ and $V1_{K_n}$ is bounded for all n. Let $\{b_n\}$ be a sequence of numbers in $]0, 1[$ such that if we set $a = \sum_n b_n 1_{K_n}$, then a and Va are bounded. Set $a_n = na \wedge 1$ and $V^n = VI_{a_n}$; define $\{V^n_\alpha\}$ to be the resolvent with $V^n_0 = V$. Finally define $\mathscr{E}_K$ to be the set of functions g such that $\{g \neq 0\} \subset K_m$ for some m.

(1) Prove that if $g \in \mathscr{E}^+_K$, then for fixed α, $V^n_\alpha(g/a_n)$ is a decreasing function of n.

(2) Give a proof of Theorem 2.14 by setting $V_\alpha g = \lim_n V^n_\alpha(g/a_n)$.

(3) Prove that Corollary 2.15 holds without the density hypothesis.

3. The semi-complete maximum principles

The goal of this section is essentially to raise the following problem. As we have seen in ch. 8, the recurrent counterpart of the C.M.P. is the so-called semi-complete maximum principle; does there exist a characterization of recurrent potential kernels by means of this principle similar to the characterization found in §§1 and 2 for the transient kernels? This problem has not yet received a general and satisfactory solution, and we shall content ourselves here with some remarks and a very incomplete answer.

Once for all, a measure m is given on $(E, \mathscr{E})$, and any word such as "negligible" will refer to this measure.

Definition 3.1. A kernel $W(\Gamma)$ is said to satisfy the (reinforced) *semi-complete maximum principle* if, for every bounded integrable function f such that $m(|f|) > 0$, $m(f) = 0$, and $Wf(\Gamma f)$ is bounded, the inequality $Wf(\Gamma f) \leqslant a$, $a \in \mathbf{R}$, on $\{f > 0\}$ implies $Wf \leqslant a$ everywhere ($\Gamma f \leqslant a - f^-$ everywhere, or equivalently $\Gamma f - f \leqslant a$ everywhere).

As in the preceding sections, we shall use the simplifying notations R.S.C.M. and S.C.M. We call $\mathscr{N}$ the space of functions f having the properties in the definition; of course $\mathscr{N}$ depends on m and on the kernel studied. It may happen that some kernels satisfy the principles only for subclasses of $\mathscr{N}$. We may now state our problem in a proper way: is the kernel Γ in Definition 3.1 the potential kernel of a Harris Markov chain?

We start with some easy remarks. In what follows we suppose $\Gamma \in$ (R.S.C.M.).

Proposition 3.2. *If* $W \in$ (S.C.M.), *then* $I + \alpha W \in$ (R.S.C.M.) *for every* $\alpha > 0$.

Proof. Easy and left to the reader.

Proposition 3.3. *If* $f \in \mathscr{N}$ *then* Γf *cannot be constant on* $\{f \neq 0\}$. *In particular,* Γ *is one-to-one on* $\mathscr{N}$.

Proof. If $\Gamma f = a$ on $\{f \neq 0\}$, in particular $\Gamma f = a$ on $\{f > 0\}$; hence $\Gamma f \leqslant a - f^-$ everywhere, and in particular on $\{f^- > 0\}$. It follows that $f^- = 0$, and consequently that f^+ is negligible.

A clue to the difficulty of the problem is given by the following theorem, which states that Harris chains are not the only chains which give rise to potential kernels satisfying R.S.C.M. We do not strive for the greatest generality.

Theorem 3.4. *Let E be L.C.C.B. and G be a proper kernel on E satisfying the R.C.M.P. and mapping C_K into C_b. If the set of measures $\{G(x, \cdot), x \in E\}$ has a non-zero cluster point m as $x \to \Delta$, then G satisfies the R.S.C.M. with respect to m for functions in $\mathcal{N} \cap C_K^{\cdot}$.*

Proof. There exists a function $u \in C_0$ which is strictly positive everywhere and such that the kernel $V = GI_u$ is bounded and satisfies the C.M.P. There exists therefore a resolvent $\{V_\alpha\}$ such that $V_0 = V$, and we denote by P_A^α the balayage operator relative to A and the chain X^α of T.P. αV_α. If h vanishes outside A, then

$$P_A^\alpha (I + \alpha V) h = (I + \alpha V) h.$$

Let $f \in C_K$ be non-zero and such that $m(f) = 0$, $m(f^+) > 0$, and $Gf \leqslant a$ on $\{f > 0\}$. If we let $\tilde{f} = fu^{-1}$ then $\langle um, \tilde{f} \rangle = 0$ and $V\tilde{f} \leqslant a$ on $A = \{\tilde{f} > 0\}$. We have

$$(I + \alpha V) \tilde{f}(x) \leqslant (\|\tilde{f}\| + \alpha a) P_A^\alpha 1(x).$$

Let $\{x_n\}$ be a sequence converging to Δ such that $V(x_n, \cdot)$ converges to um. Passing to the limit along $\{x_n\}$ in the above equation yields

$$(\|\tilde{f}\| + \alpha a) \varlimsup_n P_A^\alpha 1(x_n) \geqslant 0.$$

Now, passing to the limit in the same way in the relation

$$(I + \alpha V) f^+ = P_A^\alpha (I + \alpha V) f^+,$$

we get

$$0 < \alpha \langle um, f^+ \rangle \leqslant (\|f^+\| + \alpha \|Vf^+\|) \varlimsup_n P_A^\alpha 1(x_n).$$

It follows that $\varlimsup_n P_A 1(x_n) > 0$; hence $\|\tilde{f}\| + \alpha a \geqslant 0$ for all α, and consequently $a \geqslant 0$. As a result we have

$$Gf^+ \leqslant a + Gf^- - f^- \quad \text{on } \{f^+ > 0\} \quad \text{with } a \in \mathbf{R}_+$$

and we get the desired result by applying the R.C.M.P. to G.

This theorem holds as well with the C.M.P. and S.C.M. in place of the reinforced principles, and if G is the potential of a transient chain or resolvent, then m is an excessive measure. We remark that there are indeed many kernels satisfying the hypotheses of this theorem: for instance, the potential kernels of transient random walks of type II. Furthermore, if G satisfies the R.S.C.M. with respect to m, then the kernel $G + 1 \otimes \nu + \varphi \otimes m$, where φ is a bounded function and ν a measure such that $\nu(|f|) < \infty$ for every $f \in \mathcal{N}$, also satisfies the R.S.C.M. This shows that there are plenty of kernels satisfying the R.S.C.M. that are nevertheless not the potential kernels of Harris chains. This will be made plain by the following result.

Finally, it is worth recording that the kernels dealt with in the above result are precisely those for which Corollaries 2.11 and 2.15 do not apply.

We now turn to a result parallel to Corollary 1.4. The notion of modification refers to m.

Proposition 3.5 (Unicity theorem). *If $(E, \mathscr{E})$ is separable, and if G is a proper kernel satisfying the R.S.C.M., there exists at most one chain up to modification such that G is its potential kernel either in the sense of ch. 2 or in the sense of Harris chains.*

Proof. If P is a T.P. such that $G = \sum_0^\infty P_n$, then for every $f \in b\mathscr{E}_+$ and such that $Gf \in b\mathscr{E}_+$, $G(I - P) f = 0$. If P is a Harris chain such that G is one of its potential kernels in the sense of ch. 6 §5, then there is a measure ν such that $G(I - P) f = \nu(f)$.

Now let P and $\tilde{P}$ be two T.P.'s for which G is a potential kernel in any of the two meanings which we deal with. It follows that if $g \in b\mathscr{E}_+ \cap \mathscr{L}^1(m)$ is such that Gf is bounded, then $G(Pf - \tilde{P}f)$ is constant. Proposition 3.3 implies therefore that $Pf = \tilde{P}f$ m-a.e. The usual arguments prove that P is a modification of $\tilde{P}$.

Remark. It suffices of course that G satisfies the R.S.C.M. for a sufficiently rich subclass of $\mathcal{N}$.

We will now give a partial answer to our problem. We will assume that E is L.C.C.B. and that m is a Radon measure such that the only open set with zero measure is the empty set. (See ch. 8 §4.) For any compact set K, we denote by $\mathscr{B}(K)$ the space of Borel functions vanishing outside K and by $\mathscr{C}(K)$ the space of functions continuous on K and vanishing outside K. We study a kernel G satisfying the R.S.C.M. for the functions with compact support; but we assume further that G may be written $G = I + U$, where U has the following property: for every compact K, the map $f \to (Uf) \, 1_K$ is compact from $\mathscr{B}(K)$ into $\mathscr{C}(K)$, the spaces being endowed with the usual supremum norm. These conditions are satisfied by the potential kernels of Harris chains whose T.P. is strong Feller in the strict sense, hence in particular if E is countable.

The following proposition should be compared with ch. 8, Theorem 2.1.

Proposition 3.6. *For every compact K such that $m(K) > 0$, there exists a unique Radon measure v_K on K such that:*
  (i) $\langle v_K, 1 \rangle = 1$;
  (ii) $\langle v_K, Gf \rangle = 0$ *for every* $f \in \mathscr{N} \cap \mathscr{B}(K)$.

Proof. In view of our hypotheses, the map $f \to (Uf) \, 1_K$ is compact from $\mathscr{C}(K)$ into $\mathscr{C}(K)$, hence from $\mathscr{N} \cap \mathscr{C}(K)$ into $\mathscr{C}(K)$. The subspace $\mathscr{N} \cap \mathscr{C}(K)$ has co-dimension 1 in $\mathscr{C}(K)$. The operator I is thus of index 1 from $\mathscr{N} \cap \mathscr{C}(K)$ into $\mathscr{C}(K)$; hence by the index theorem, the operator

$$f \to f + (Uf) \, 1_K = (Gf) \, 1_K$$

is also of index 1. By Proposition 3.3, this operator is one-to-one on $\mathscr{N}$; its range is thus of co-dimension 1, and therefore is closed by an application of Banach's theorem. On the other hand, Proposition 3.3 asserts also that 1_K is not in this range. There exists, therefore, a unique probability measure v_K on K such that $\langle v_K, Gf \rangle = 0$ for every $f \in \mathscr{N} \cap \mathscr{C}(K)$.

Now let f be any function in $\mathscr{C}(K)$; the function $m(K) f - m(f) \, 1_K$ is in $\mathscr{N} \cap \mathscr{C}(K)$, and therefore

$$0 = v_K G(m(K) f - m(f) \, 1_K) = m(K) \, v_K G f - m(f) \, \langle v_K, G1_K \rangle.$$

The measure $v_K G$ is thus a multiple of m on K, and the proof is complete.

For $g \in b\mathscr{E}$ define $h^K = (g - v_K(g)) \, 1_K$; the function h^K is in $\mathscr{B}(K)$ and $v_K(h^K) = 0$. By the above result there is a function f^K in $\mathscr{N} \cap \mathscr{B}(K)$ such that $h^K = (Gf^K) \, 1_K$. Keeping in mind the formulae of ch. 8, Theorem 2.1 we define

$$P_K g = G f^K + v_K(g),$$

$$\Pi_K g = G f^K + v_K(g) - f^K = P_K g - f^K = U f^K + v_K(g).$$

We notice that if $g \in \mathcal{B}(K)$, then $P_K g = g$, and that $\Pi_K g$ is a continuous function. On the other hand, $P_K g = \Pi_K g$ on K^c.

Finally, we have:

Proposition 3.7. *The operators P_K and Π_K are given by transition probabilities. The measures $P_K(x, \cdot)$ and $\Pi_K(x, \cdot)$ vanish outside K and furthermore*

(i) $m I_K \Pi_K = m I_K$;

(ii) $(I - \Pi_K) Gf = f$ *for every* $f \in \mathcal{N} \cap \mathcal{B}(K)$.

Proof. If g vanishes on K, then $h^K = 0$; hence $f^K = 0$ and consequently $P_K g = \Pi_K g = 0$. If $g \in \mathcal{B}(K)_+$, since $P_K g = g$ on K, we have $G f^K + v_K(g) \geqslant 0$ on K; hence

$$G(- f^K) \leqslant v_K(g) \quad \text{on } \{ f^K \neq 0 \},$$

and by R.S.C.M., $G(- f^K) \leqslant v_K(g) - (- f^K)^-$ everywhere. As a result, $P_K g \geqslant 0$, and

$$\Pi_K g = G f^K + v_K(g) - f^K \geqslant 0.$$

That P_K and Π_K are kernels is clear from the form of Π_K as a function of U. Finally if $g = 1$, then $h^K = f^K = 0$, and therefore $P_K 1 = \Pi_K 1 = v_K(1) = 1$.

Next, for any $g \in b\mathcal{E}_+$, we have

$$\langle m 1_K, \Pi_K g \rangle = \langle m 1_K, P_K g - f^K \rangle = \langle m 1_K, P_K g \rangle = \langle m, 1_K g \rangle,$$

since f^K is in $\mathcal{N} \cap \mathcal{B}(K)$ and $P_K g = g$ on K. This proves (i).

To prove (ii), pick f in $\mathcal{N} \cap \mathcal{B}(K)$; then Gf is in $b\mathcal{E}$ and $v_K(Gf) = 0$. If we put $g = Gf$, we have $h^K = g 1_K$; hence $f^K = f$, and consequently

$$\Pi_K Gf = Gf - f.$$

The T.P.'s Π_K and P_K must be the balayage kernels of the chain we are looking for. The following result goes further in this direction.

Lemma 3.8. *If H and K are two compact sets with $H \subset K$, then*

(i) $P_K P_H = P_H$;

(ii) $\Pi_K P_H = \Pi_H$;

(iii) *for any* $g \in \mathcal{B}(H)_+$, $\Pi_K(g) \leqslant \Pi_H(g)$.

Proof. Set $h = P_H g = G f^H + v_H(g)$, where $f^H \in \mathcal{N} \cap \mathcal{B}(H)$. There is a function $f^K \in \mathcal{N} \cap \mathcal{B}(K)$ such that $P_K h = G f^K + v_K(h)$. Since $P_K h = h$ on K, we have

$$G(f^H - f^K) = v_K(h) - v_H(g) \quad \text{on } K;$$

hence, by Proposition 3.3, $f^H = f^K$ and $v_K(h) = v_H(g)$, so that $P_K P_H g = P_H g$. Next, from $f^H = f^K$ we derive

$$\Pi_K P_H g = P_K P_H g - f^K = P_H g - f^H = \Pi_H g.$$

Finally, if $g \in \mathscr{B}(H)_+$, then $P_H g \geqslant g$, and therefore $\Pi_K g \leqslant \Pi_H g$. We are now ready to state

Theorem 3.9. *There exists a strong Feller transition probability P with excessive measure m and such that, for any $f \in \mathscr{N}$ with compact support,*

$$(I - P)\, Gf = f.$$

Proof. Let $\{K_n\}$ be a sequence of compact sets whose interiors cover E and are increasing to E. If $g \in b\mathscr{E}_+$ has compact support, the preceding lemma implies that the sequence $\Pi_{K_n} g$ decreases everywhere (at least for n sufficiently large) to a limit that we call Pg. We have

$$Pg(x) = \lim_n \Pi_{K_n} g(x) = \lim_n (U f^{K_n}(x) + v_{K_n}(f^{K_n})).$$

As soon as K_n contains the support of g, we have $\Pi_{K_n} g = g - f^{K_n}$; hence $\|f^{K_n}\| \leqslant 2\|g\|$. It follows that the family $\{U f^{K_n}\}$ is equi-continuous on each compact set; one may therefore find a sub-sequence converging uniformly on every compact set, and as a result the function Pg is continuous. Clearly P is a transition probability.

Furthermore $1_{K_n} \Pi_{K_n} g$ converges to Pg, and since

$$\langle m, 1_{K_n} \Pi_{K_n} g \rangle = \langle m, 1_{K_n} g \rangle,$$

by Fatou's lemma, passing to the limit yields $\langle m, Pg \rangle \leqslant m(g)$, and thus m is excessive for P.

Now let $f \in \mathscr{N}$ have compact support, and set

$$g = Gf + \|Gf\| = f + Uf + \|Gf\|.$$

We have, by Proposition 3.7,

$$Pg \leqslant \underline{\lim} \, \Pi_{K_n} g = Gf - f + \|Gf\|;$$

hence $PGf \leqslant Gf - f$. Applying this to $(-f)$ yields

$$PGf = Gf - f,$$

and the proof is complete.

Unfortunately we do not know of a satisfactory criterion to decide whether the T.P. of the preceding theorem is recurrent or transient. (See, however, Exercise 3.12 and the notes and comments.) But we have the following partial answer.

Theorem 3.10. *If m is bounded, the T.P. of Theorem 3.9 is Harris, and m is its invariant measure.*

Proof. If m is bounded we may, in the preceding proof, apply Lebesgue's theorem instead of Fatou's lemma, and we get the equality $m(Pg) = m(g)$; thus m is invariant by P.

Since m is bounded and invariant, it is easily seen that for $f \in C_K^+$ the series $\sum_0^\infty P_n f$ is either $+ \infty$ or 0, or equivalently that P is a conservative contraction of $L^1(m)$. We prove that it is ergodic. If P were not ergodic, we could find two functions f, g in $L^1(m)$ such that $h = f - g$ is in $\mathcal{N}$, and a set A with $m(A) > 0$ such that for $x \in A$, $\sum P_n f(x) = + \infty$ and $\sum P_n g(x) = 0$. From the equality $(I - P) Gh = h$ we derive

$$\sum_0^k P_n(f - g)(x) \leqslant Gh(x) - P_{n+1}Gh(x).$$

Since Gh is bounded, we get a contradiction on letting k tend to infinity.

Thus, for any $A \in \mathcal{E}$ with $m(A) > 0$, we have $U_A(1_A) = 1$ m-a.s.; but since P is strong Feller, it follows by the usual continuity argument that $U_A(1_A) = 1$, and hence that P is Harris. This proof could also be completed by calling upon ch. 4, Exercise 2.17.

If E is compact, then m is bounded and the preceding theorem applies.

Exercise 3.11. Assume that the operator U used in the proof of Proposition 3.6 satisfies the S.C.M., and then prove that it is the potential operator of a strong Feller resolvent. Assume further that m is bounded, and prove that the resolvent is Harris.

Exercise 3.12. Let E be countable and m a measure on E; G a kernel on E satisfying the R.S.C.M. for the functions of $\mathcal{N}$ (relative to m) with compact supports.

(1) Fix an arbitrary state e in E and define

$$G^e(x, y) = G(x, y) - G(e, y) - (G(x, e) - G(e, e))\, m(y)/m(e).$$

Prove that the kernel G^e satisfies the R.C.M.P. on $E\setminus\{e\}$. The reader is invited to look at ch. 8, Exercise 2.11 to see the significance of G^e.

(2) Prove that if every bounded potential $G^e f$ vanishes at the boundary in the sense of § 2, then there is a Harris chain on E for which G is a potential operator. Prove that if m is bounded, then the above condition on G^e-potentials is satisfied, which thus gives another proof of Theorem 3.10 for countable state space.

NOTES AND COMMENTS

Before we proceed to comment on the text we feel that the title of the book deserves an explanation. There is currently some confusion on what is meant by "chain". According to the author, this word refers sometimes to the discreteness of the set of time parameters, and sometimes to the discreteness of the state space. In our opinion the most important feature is the time: a denumerable state space is a special case of a general state space, whereas discrete time is not a particular case of continuous time. In particular, the set of integers has only one accumulation point, namely $+\infty$, whereas the set of positive reals has plenty. As a result, most of the problems in discrete-time processes concern the asymptotic behaviour at $+\infty$. For continuous-time processes, the analogous problems are often solved by straightforward applications of the results known for discrete time. But a host of new problems, with no discrete counterpart, arises in connection with the other accumulation points: for instance, the study of local properties of sample paths. A good terminology must thus stress the nature of the set of time parameters. We therefore stick to using "chain" when the time is discrete and "process" when it is continuous. If one wants to specify the kind of state space or analytical properties, one can add an adjective or a noun. For instance a chain can be Harris, discrete, ..., a process can be a diffusion process, a Feller process, a Hunt process.

Although this book is devoted to chains, (continuous-time) processes will be alluded to by means of resolvents.

Chapter 1

The first three sections are of standard character. Some proofs are taken from Blumenthal and Getoor [1]. The proof of Theorem 2.8 is from Ionescu-Tulcea [1].

Section 5. The important Lemma 5.3 is taken from Doob [2] and Theorem 5.7 is from Mokobodzky [1]. The results on strong Feller kernels are taken from Girsanov [1] and Meyer [4].

An ergodic theory without measure has been developed for Feller kernels. We refer the reader to the expository paper by Foguel [2].

Chapter 2

Most of the results of this chapter are originally due to Deny [1] and Doob [3]. We have also used Meyer [2] and Neveu [1]. The introduction and systematic use of the kernels U_h is due to Neveu [5]. It is interesting to describe their continuous-time counterpart. If X is a standard process with resolvent $\{V_\alpha\}$, and we study the chain with T.P. $P = V_1$, then for $h \in \mathscr{U}_+$ and $f \in \mathscr{E}_+$,

$$U_h f(x) = E_x \int_0^\infty M_t f(X_t) \, dt$$

where $M_t = \exp[-\int_0^t h(X_s) \, ds]$.

The proof of Theorem 2.3 has been borrowed from Meyer [6]. The proof of 2.2 is related to the work of Rost [1, 2]; following Meyer [7, 8] one could think of deducing many results in the sequel from the results by Rost.

Let us mention that the identity between harmonic functions for random walks on symmetric spaces and harmonic functions in the classical sense is shown by Furstenberg [1]. Exercise 3.21, as well as all the subsequent ones dealing with the same example, are taken from Karlin and McGregor [1]. This was generalized by Kemeny [1].

The goal of the section on resolvents is twofold. The first aim is to prepare for the discussion in ch. 10, and the second is to show by numerous exercises how the results obtained for chains may be translated to the continuous-time situation. Exercise 4.14 is taken from Meyer [3] and Exercises 4.15–4.16 from Watanabe [2].

Chapter 3

Section 1 is of standard nature and is intended as an introduction to the sequel as well as to provide examples for the more general situation. Corollary 1.11 has not been extended yet to general state spaces, but using the same argument as in Azema et al. [1] it would certainly be possible to do so. The matrix pattern of 1.12 may be used also for countable state spaces, as is done extensively in the book by Kemeny et al. [1].

Section 2. The main results on irreducible chains, namely Theorems 2.6–2.7, are due to Jain and Jamison [1], but the proofs in the text, as well as most of the subsequent ones, are from Neveu [5]. The whole subject was started by Harris [2] who proved the implication (iii) ⇒ (i) in Proposition 2.9. The proof of Lemma 2.3 uses the same pattern as Harris' original proof. Theorem 2.14 is from Neveu [6] whereas Theorem 2.16 is suggested by Foguel [1]. The useful remark in Exercise 2.19 is from Doob [1].

Some attempts have been made to drop the assumption of separability of the space. See Doob [2] and Meyer [7].

Section 3. The ideas of this section are mostly from Blackwell [2].

Section 4. The first results are from Chung and Fuchs [1] in the case of the real line. The extension to arbitrary groups is straightforward. Theorem 4.11 seems to have been widely known, at least for abelian groups; the present proof is probably new. The proof in Exercise 4.22 was given by Bretagnolle and Dacunha–Castelle [1]. Exercise 4.15 was taken from the basic book by Spitzer [1] and Exercise 4.16 from Chung and Ornstein [1]. Spread-out (in French *étalées*) random walks are generally referred to in the literature as "non-singular".

Section 5. For the few results of harmonic analysis which are used in this section we refer to Rudin [1] and to Hewitt and Ross [1]. The structure theorem used at the end of the section is in Hewitt and Ross, p. 389.

The main result of this section, namely Criterion 5.2, is due to Chung and Fuchs [1] in the case of the real line. It was extended to arbitrary abelian groups by Loynes [1]. Theorem 5.11 was proved by Dudley [1]. The structure theorem used in its proof may be found in Kurosh [1].

The characterization of non-abelian recurrent groups is not yet known. The interested reader may however find fairly complete results for Lie groups in Guivarc'h and Keane [1]. Exercises 5.19–23 give some easy results on this subject.

In this book, we aimed at keeping the use of Fourier transform to a minimum, as is seen from chs. 5 and 9 on random walks. The reader who wishes to study random walks by means of Fourier transforms is referred to the book by Spitzer [1] and to the papers by Port and Stone, especially their final paper [1].

Chapter 4

Section 1. This owes much to the fifth chapter of the book by Neveu [2]. Exercise 1.10 is from Chacon and Krengel [1].

Section 2. The results of this section are due to Hopf [1]. The simple proof of the basic Maximal ergodic lemma is from Garsia [1].

Exercise 2.12 is from Krengel [1], Exercise 2.13 from Ackoglu and Brunel [1] and Exercise 2.18 from Brunel [unpublished].

Section 3. This proof of the Chacon–Ornstein theorem is due to Neveu [3], Lemma 3.1 being an original lemma of Chacon and Ornstein. Exercise 3.9 was proved by Doeblin (at least the existence of the limit), and was the first result of this kind upon which the following ones were patterned.

Section 4. The form of Brunel's lemma given here is due to Ackoglu [1] and the proof is from Garsia [2]. The other proofs of this section are taken from Meyer [1].

This chapter might have included a section on invariant measures. We refer to the books by Foguel [1] and Friedman [1] and also to the paper by Brunel [2].

Chapter 5

Section 1. The Choquet–Deny theorem was announced in Choquet and Deny [2] and its proof given in Deny [2]. The proof presented here is from Guivarc'h, Lemma 1.1 being from Brunel [2]. The proof in Exercise 1.7 is from Doob et al. [1]. Example 1.10 is taken from the fundamental paper by Furstenberg [1]. Further work in this direction was accomplished by Azencott [1] and Guivarc'h [1]. They establish Choquet–Deny theorems for large classes of solvable groups; but some questions remain open.

Section 2. For the history of the renewal theorem, we refer the reader to the book by Feller [3]. To write this section, we used the book by Feller already quoted and the paper by Herz [1], from which the proof of Theorem 2.6 is taken. Exercise 2.10 is taken from Spitzer [1].

Section 3. The most general form of the renewal theorem for the real line was given by Feller and Orey [1]. We follow here the presentation of Feller [3].

Section 4. The renewal theorem (4.4) was shown by Port and Stone [1] after Kesten and Spitzer [2] had opened the way.

Renewal theorems for non-abelian groups have been given by Guivarc'h and Keane [2] and Derriennic and Guivarc'h [1], but the most general result is not yet known.

Section 5. Theorem 5.1 was first shown by Stone [1] for the real line and with the assumption of a finite second moment, then by Bretagnolle and Dacunha–Castelle [1] with the assumption of a finite first moment. The general result for abelian groups is given in Port and Stone [1]. The present proof is from Bellaïche–Fremont and Sueur–Pontier [1].

Proposition 5.6 is taken from Spitzer [1] in the case of integers and from Bretagnolle and Dacunha–Castelle [1] for the real line. Further results on recurrent sets of transient random walks may be found in Spitzer [1] and in Jain and Orey [1]. Exercise 5.13 is borrowed from Spitzer [1].

Chapter 6

Section 1. For discrete chains, the results of this section as well as some of the next one have been known for a long time (see Chung [2]). They were extended to Harris chains by Orey [1]. We follow closely Orey [5] in our presentation.

Section 2. Orey's theorem was first shown for discrete chains in Orey [3]. It was a sharpening of earlier results due to Kolmogoroff. The present pattern of proof is from Blackwell and Freedman [1] and was carried out for Harris chains in Jamison and Orey [1]. Theorem 2.11 and its proof are from Jain [1]. We refer to Foguel [1] for another presentation in the more "abstract" setting described in ch. 4, §1.

Exercise 2.16 was taken from Orey [5], 2.18 from Ehrenfeucht [1] and 2.23 from Duflo [1].

The question of what can be said in place of Exercise 2.12 when X is null has been investigated by Krickeberg [1, 2]. This is related to the study of the asymptotic behaviour of the ratios $P_{n+m}(x, A)/P_n(y, B)$, which has been tackled by several authors. We refer the reader interested in this topic to Orey [5]. For the study of point transformations and the notions of mixing, see the book by Friedman [1].

Section 3. The bulk of this section is due to Yosida and Kakutani [1]. We borrowed our method of presentation from Neveu [2]. The important Theorem 3.10 is due to Horowitz [1]. For the general case of Proposition 3.11 see Doob [2].

Section 4. Special functions which generalize the former "bounded sets" (Orey [5], Metivier [1], Brunel [3]) appear in Neveu [5]. Together with the potential kernels of the next section, they constitute a major progress in the theory of Harris chains, permitting one to simplify and sharpen all the previous results. Neveu proved all the results of this section up to Proposition 4.8. Proposition 4.9 and 4.10 are from Brunel and Revuz [1]. The idea of relating "boundedness" of sets to quasi-compactness appears in Brunel [3]. Horowitz [1] has shown that if a chain is conservative and ergodic in the sense of ch. 4 and possesses a "bounded" set, then it is Harris, a result which was extended to special functions by Lin [2]. (See Exercise 4.15.) The results on Harris resolvents of this and the following section are mostly from Brancovan [1].

Section 5. Almost all this section is taken from Neveu [5] where, however, Theorem 5.2 is proved only for strictly positive functions; Proposition 5.4 was first stated by Orey [4] in the case of discrete chains, and enables one to simplify the proof of Corollary 5.5. Proposition 5.7 and its sharpening in Exercise 5.16 had been obtained before for "bounded" sets by Ornstein [1], Metivier [1] and Duflo [1].

Section 6. The first ratio limit theorem for recurrent discrete chains was given by Doeblin. The proofs of this section are due to Neveu [7]; they are patterned after Levitan [1]. The reader will find another interesting proof in Metivier [2]. For earlier work, see Jain [1], Isaac [1] and Metivier [1]. A counterexample which shows that the most general ratio limit theorem fails to be true was designed by Krengel [1]. The important Exercise 6.8 is from Brunel et al. [1]; the result is still true for general recurrent random walks.

Chapter 7

Section 1. The results of Martingale theory needed in this section may be found in Neveu [2].

The ideas involved in the proof of Theorem 1.11 are originally due to Hunt [2] in the case of discrete chains and were used by Abrahamsee [1] for general state space. The observation contained in Theorem 1.13 is from Roudier [1]. For the important Exercise 1.18 see Furstenberg [1] and Azencott [1].

Section 2. The Martin boundary for Markov chains was introduced independently by Doob [3] and Watanabe [1]. The metric we use here to complete the space is the metric of Hunt [2]. To extend the theory to a case more general than discrete chains we have used the paper by Derriennic [1]. Unfortunately, the integral representation of harmonic functions has not yet been carried over to this situation.

Section 3. The boundary M of §2 is not easily computed. The third section gives a way of computing its interesting part and at the same time gives the desired integral representation of harmonic functions. What lies beneath the present discussion is the theory of convex cones of Choquet. We refer the reader to Neveu [1] for an exposition of the Martin boundary relying on the theory of Choquet. In this line, the results of Mokobodzky (see Meyer [5]) would perhaps lead to some generalizations in more general state spaces.

The Martin boundary has now be worked out for several important classes of discrete chains. The reader should look in Doob et al. [1], Dynkin and Malyutov [1], Lamperti and Snell [1], Blackwell and Kendall [1] and Ney and

Spitzer [1]. For random walks on groups and symmetric spaces see also Furstenberg [2] and Azencott and Cartier [1]. Their results use the theory of Poisson spaces, sketched in Exercise 1.18. The most general non-bounded harmonic functions are not known for all groups. See, however, Furstenberg [3] and Deny [2].

Chapter 8

Section 1. This is taken from Brunel and Revuz [1].

Section 2. This is taken mostly from Neveu [5], but these kinds of results were already known for discrete chains (see, for instance, Neveu [1] or Kemeny et al. [1]). The observation in Exercise 2.11 is due to Orey [4]. Exercise 2.13 is due to Chung in the case of discrete chains; the proof hinted at is from Lin [2].

Section 3. The theory of normal chains is due to Kemeny and Snell [1] in the case of discrete chains. Their results are also contained in the book by Kemeny et al. [1]. It was shown by Orey [2] that there exist non-normal chains (see Exercise 3.11). Exercise 3.9 for the case in which X is discrete was taken from Kemeny et al. [1].

Section 4. The theory of boundaries is only sketched in this section. We refer the reader to the last chapter in the book of Kemeny et al. [1] and to the paper of Orey [4] (see also Neveu [1]). Theorem 4.13 may be seen as a sharpening of a result by Orey.

We feel that the use of special functions should allow one to sharpen and illuminate the already known results. It would be desirable to give a theory subsuming those of discrete chains and random walks. In the latter case, it is shown in ch. 9 that the conditions of Theorem 4.9 hold, but furthermore that the convergence of the powers P_n hold for all special and co-special functions, whether continuous or not. This is due in particular to the fact that for Harris random walks, P_n is "asymptotically" strong Feller. Are similar results true for all chains? More precisely, if a chain satisfies the equivalent conditions of Theorem 4.9 what can be said of the class of functions on which P_n converges?

Chapter 9

The study of potential theory for recurrent random walks was initiated by Spitzer, who treated the case of $\mathbf{Z}^p$ and discovered the main features such as the classification into types I and II. His results are collected in his basic book [1].

The theory was enlarged to abelian discrete groups by Kesten and Spitzer [2], to discrete groups by Kesten [4], to the real line by Ornstein [1], and to general abelian locally compact groups by Port and Stone [1]. They deal also with non-Harris recurrent random walks. Finally, in Brunel and Revuz [2] the case of general non-abelian groups is dealt with in the more general setting of special functions.

Chapter 9 follows mostly the paper by Brunel and Revuz [2] with the exception of the end of §4, which comes from Port and Stone [1], but the original ideas are due to Kesten and Spitzer [2]. Many exercises are borrowed from Spitzer's book. The Fourier criterion (2.20) is taken from Kesten and Spitzer [2]. It is also true for general groups and non-Harris recurrent random walks, as was shown by Ornstein [1] and Stone [3] for the real line and by Port and Stone [1] in full generality.

Many results which lie beyond the scope of this book, especially asymptotic theorems of probabilistic nature, have been shown for random walks. We refer the reader to the papers by Kesten, Spitzer, Ornstein and by Port and Stone.

Chapter 10

The subject was started by Hunt in his fundamental paper [1]. He proves the basic Theorem 1.5 and Corollary 2.15 by means of probabilistic methods. In fact he proves not only the existence of a resolvent but also of a semi-group.

Section 1. Aside from 1.5, the results in this section are taken mostly from Meyer [3]. Exercise 1.13 is from Bronner [1] to which we refer for further results in this line.

Section 2. The main result, namely Theorem 2.10, as well as its proof, are from Meyer [3]. The proof of 2.14 follows Kondo [1]. Another proof, outlined in Exercise 2.20, is due to Taylor [1]. It follows in part the proof given by Lion [1], who showed that the density hypothesis in 2.15 may be dropped, and gave a purely analytical proof. Actually it is known from the work of Hirsch [1] that the countability assumption on E may also be dropped. The reader is also referred to Hansen [1] and Mokobodzky and Sibony [1].

The notion of "vanishing at the boundary" was emphasized in Meyer [3]. Proposition 2.6, which clarifies the matter, is due to Taylor [1]. In view of Proposition 1.3, one could think of deriving Theorem 2.10 from Theorem 2.14 or Theorem 2.14 from Theorem 2.10 without having to repeat the proof. Unfortunately this does not seem to work.

Section 3. The proof of Theorems 3.9 and 3.10 were given by Kondo [2] for countable E. The proof in the text is merely an extension of Kondo's proof to strong Feller kernels. Theorem **3.4** and the related remarks seem to be new.

It is clear that more work has to be done to bring the subject of this section to a satisfactory state. First, a proof must be given avoiding the use of topological hypothesis, and we believe that if the relevant measure is sufficiently "spread out", as for instance in the hypothesis of Theorem **3.9**, a kernel satisfying R.S.C.M. is either a transient (up to addition of $1 \otimes \nu + \varphi \otimes m$) or a recurrent potential kernel. Then it would be interesting to find handy criteria to separate the two possibilities. Such a criterion (see Exercise **3.12**) has been given by Oshima [1], and was extended to strong Feller kernels by Kondo and Oshima.

Added in proof. It has since been shown by Hirsch and by Taylor that the condition in Theorem **2.14** is also necessary.

REFERENCES

I.J.M. = *Illinois J. Math.*; *T.A.M.S.* = *Trans. Am. Math. Soc.*; *T.P.* = *Theory Probab. Appl.* (translation of *Teor. Verojatnostei i eë Primeneniya*); *A.I.F.* = *Ann. Inst. Fourier*; *A.I.H.P.* = *Ann. Inst. Henri Poincaré*; *Z.W.* = *Z. Wahrscheinlichkeitstheorie Verw. Geb*; *A.M.S.* = *Ann. Math. Statist.*; *C.R.A.S.* = *Comptes Rendus Acad. Sci. Paris.*

A. F. ABRAHAMSEE
[1] The Martin Potential kernel for improperly essential chains, *Z.W.* **18** (1971) 2.18–2.26.

M. A. ACKOGLU
[1] An ergodic lemma, *Proc. Am. Math. Soc.* **16** (1965) 388–392.
[2] Pointwise ergodic theorems, *T.A.M.S.* **125** (1966) 296–309.

M. A. ACKOGLU and A. BRUNEL
[1] Contractions on L^1-spaces, *T.A.M.S.* **155** (1971) 315–325.

M. A. ACKOGLU and R. W. SHARPE
[1] Ergodic theories and boundaries, *T.A.M.S.* **132** (1968) 447–460.

J. AZEMA, M. DUFLO and D. REVUZ
[1] Propriétés relatives des processus de Markov recurrents, *Z.W.* **13** (1969) 286–314.

R. AZENCOTT
[1] *Espaces de Poisson des Groupes Localement Compacts*, Lecture Notes in Math. **148** (Springer, Berlin, 1970).

R. AZENCOTT and P. CARTIER
[1] Martin boundaries of random walks on locally compact groups, in: *Proc. 6th Berkeley Symp. on Mathematical Statistics and Probability*, Vol. III (Univ. of California Press, Berkeley, Calif., 1970) 87–129.

C. BELLAÏCHE-FREMONT and M. SUEUR-PONTIER
[1] Théorème de renouvellement pour groupes abéliens localement compacts, in: *Astérisque* **4** (Soc. Math. de France, Paris, 1973).

D. BLACKWELL
[1] A renewal theorem, *Duke Math. J.* **15** (1948) 145–150.
[2] On transient Markov processes with a countable number of states and stationary transition probabilities, *A.M.S.* **26** (1955) 654–658.

D. BLACKWELL and D. FREEDMAN
[1] The tail σ-field of a Markov chain and a theorem of Orey, *A.M.S.* **35** (1964) 1291–1295.

D. BLACKWELL and D. KENDALL
[1] The Martin boundary for Polya's urn scheme and an application to stochastic population growth, *J. Appl. Probab.* **1** (1964) 284–296.

A. BLANC-LAPIERRE and R. FORTET
[1] *Théories des Fonctions Aléatoires* (Masson, Paris, 1953).

R. M. BLUMENTHAL and R. K. GETOOR
[1] *Markov Processes and Potential Theory* (Academic Press, New York, 1968).

M. BRANCOVAN
[1] Quelques propriétés des resolvantes récurrentes au sens de Harris, *A.I.H.P.* **9** (1973) 1–18.

J. BRETAGNOLLE and D. DACUNHA-CASTELLE
[1] Sur une classe de marches aléatoires, *A.I.H.P.* **3** (1967) 403–431.

F. BRONNER
[1] Principe du maximum et résolvantes sous-markoviennes, *C.R.A.S.* **277** (1973) 221–223.

A. BRUNEL (see Ackoglu)
[1] Sur un lemme voisin du lemme de E. Hopf et sur une de ses applications, *C.R.A.S.* **256** (1963) 5481–5484.
[2] New conditions for existence of invariant measures, in: *Contributions to Ergodic and Probability*, Lecture Notes in Math. **160** (Springer, Berlin, 1970).
[3] Chaines abstraites de Markov vérifiant une condition de Orey. Extention à ce cas d'un théorème ergodique de M. Métivier, *Z.W.* **19** (1971) 323–329.

A. BRUNEL, P. CRÉPEL, Y. GUIVARC'H and M. KEANE
[1] Marches aléatoires récurrentes sur les groupes localement compacts, *C.R.A.S.* **275** (1972).

A. BRUNEL and D. REVUZ
[1] Quelques applications probabilistes de la quasi-compacité, *A.I.H.P.* **10** (1974) 301–337.
[2] Marches de Harris sur les groupes localement compacts I, *Ann. Sci. École Norm. Sup.* (4) **7** (1974) 273–310.

R. V. CHACON
[1] Identification of the limit of operator averages, *J. Math. Mech.* **11** (1962) 961–968.

R. V. CHACON and V. KRENGEL
[1] Linear modulus of a linear operator, *Proc. Am. Math. Soc.* **15** (1964) 553–559.

R. V. CHACON and D. S. ORNSTEIN
[1] A general ergodic theorem, *I.J.M.* **4** (1960) 153–160.

G. CHOQUET
[1] *Lectures in Analysis* (Benjamin, New York, 1969).

G. Choquet and J. Deny
[1] Modèles finis en théorie du potentiel, *J. Anal. Math.* **5** (1956/1957) 77–135.
[2] Sur l'équation de convolution $\mu = \mu * \sigma$, *C.R.A.S.* **250** (1960) 799–801.

K. L. Chung
[1] The general theory of Markov processes according to Doeblin, *Z.W.* **2** (1964) 230–250.
[2] *Markov Chains with Stationary Transition Probabilities*, 2nd ed. (Springer, Berlin, 1967).

K. L. Chung and W. H. Fuchs
[1] On the distribution of values of sums of random variables, *Mem. Am. Math. Soc.* **6** (1951).

K. L. Chung and D. S. Ornstein
[1] On the recurrence of sums of random variables, *Bull. Am. Math. Soc.* **68** (1962) 30–32.

J. Deny (see Choquet)
[1] Familles fondamentales, noyaux associés, *A.I.F.* **3** (1951) 73–101.
[2] Sur l'équation de convolution $\mu = \mu * \sigma$, in: *Sem. de Théorie du Potentiel* (Inst. Henri Poincaré, Paris, 1959/60) 4me année.

Y. Derriennic
[1] Sur la frontière de Martin des processus de Markov à temps discret, *A.I.H.P.* **9** (3) (1973) 233–258.

Y. Derriennic and Y. Guivarc'h
[1] Théorème de renouvellement pour les groupes non moyennables, *C.R.A.S.* (A) **277** (1973) 613–615.

J. L. Doob
[1] Asymptotic properties of Markoff transition probabilities, *T.A.M.S.* **63** (1948) 393–421.
[2] *Stochastic Processes* (Wiley, New York, 1953).
[3] Discrete potential theory and boundaries, *J. Math. Mech.* **8** (1959) 433–458.

J. L. Doob, J. L. Snell and R. E. Williamson
[1] Application of boundary theory to sums of independent random variables, in: *Contributions to Probability and Statistics* (Stanford Univ. Press, Stanford, Calif., 1960).

R. M. Dudley
[1] Random walk on abelian groups, *Proc. Am. Math. Soc.* **13** (1962) 447–450.

M. Duflo (see Azema)
[1] Opérateurs potentiels des chaines et des processus de Markov irréductibles, *Bull. Soc. Math. France* **98** (1970) 127–163.

N. Dunford and J. T. Schwarz
[1] *Linear Operators, Part I: General Theory* (Interscience, New York, 1953).

E. B. Dynkin and M. B. Maljutov
[1] Random walks on groups with a finite number of generators, *Soviet Math. Dokl.* **2** (1961) 399–402 (English Transl.).

328   REFERENCES

D. A. EDWARDS
[1] On potentials and general ergodic theorems for resolvents, *Z.W.* **20** (1971) 1–8.

A. EHRENFEUCHT
[1] A criterion for a finitely generated group to be finite, *Nederl. Akad. Wetensch.* **74** (= *Indag. Math.* **33**) (1971) 47–48.

J. FELDMAN
[1] Subinvariant measures for Markov operators, *Duke Math. J.* **29** (1962) 71–98.
[2] Integral kernels and invariant measures for Markov transition functions, *Ann. Math. Statist.* **36** (1965) 517–523.

W. FELLER
[1] Boundaries induced by non-negative matrices, *T.A.M.S.* **83** (1956) 19–54.
[2] A simple proof for renewal theorems, *Commun. Pure Appl. Math.* **14** (1961) 285–293.
[3] *An Introduction to Probability Theory and its Applications*, Vol. 2 (Wiley, New York, 1966).

W. FELLER and S. OREY
[1] A renewal theorem, *J. Math. Mech.* **10** (1961) 619–624.

S. R. FOGUEL
[1] *The Ergodic Theory of Markov Processes* (Van Nostrand, New York, 1969).
[2] The ergodic theory of positive operators on continuous functions, *Ann. Scuola Norm. Sup. Pisa* **27** (1973) 19–51.

S. R. FOGUEL and M. LIN
[1] Some ratio limit theorems for Markov operators, *Z.W.* **23** (1972) 55–66.

N. A. FRIEDMAN
[1] *Introduction to Ergodic Theory* (Van Nostrand, New York, 1970).

H. FURSTENBERG
[1] A Poisson formula for semi-simple Lie groups, *Ann. Math* (2) **77** (1963) 335–386.
[2] Non-commuting random products, *T.A.M.S.* **108** (1963) 377–428.
[3] Translation-invariant cones of functions on semi-simple Lie groups, *Bull. Am. Math. Soc.* **71** (2) 271–326 (1965).

A. GARSIA
[1] A simple proof of E. Hopf's maximal ergodic theorem, *J. Math. Mech.* **14** (1965) 381–382.
[2] More about the maximal ergodic lemma of Brunel, *Proc. Nat. Acad. Sci.* **67** (1967) 21–24.
[3] *Topics in Almost Everywhere Convergence*, Lectures in Adv. Math. (Markham, Chicago, Ill., 1970).

I. V. GIRSANOV
[1] Strong Feller processes I. General properties, *T.P.* **5** (1960) 7–28.

Y. GUIVARC'H (see Brunel and Derriennic)
[1] Croissance polynomiale et périodes des fonctions harmoniques, *Bull. Soc. Math. France*, to appear.

Y. GUIVARC'H and M. KEANE
[1] Transience des marches aléatoires sur les groupes nilpotents, in: *Astérisque* **4** (Soc. Math. de France, Paris, 1973).
[2] Un théorème de renouvellement pour les groupes nilpotents, in: *Astérisque* **4** (Soc. Math. de France, Paris, 1973).

W. HANSEN
[1] Konstruktion von Halbgruppen und Markoffschen Prozessen, *Invent. Math.* **3** (1967) 179–214.

T. E. HARRIS
[1] Recurrent Markov processes II, *A.M.S.* **26** (1955) 152–153 (abstract).
[2] The existence of stationary measures for certain Markov processes, in: *Proc. 3rd Berkeley Symp. on Mathematical Statistics and Probability* Vol. **2** (Univ. of California Press, Berkeley, Calif., 1956) 113–124.

P. L. HENNEQUIN
[1] Les processus de Markov en cascades, *A.I.H.P.* (12) **18** (1963) 109–196.

C. S. HERZ
[1] Les théorèmes de renouvellement, *A.I.F* **15** (1) (1965) 169–188.

K. HEWITT and K. A. ROSS
[1] *Abstract Harmonic Analysis I* (Springer, Berlin, 1963).

F. HIRSCH
[1] Familles résolvantes, générateurs, cogénérateurs, potentiels, *A.I.F.* **22** (1972) 89–210.

E. HOPF
[1] The general temporally discrete Markov process, *J. Rational. Math. Mech. Anal.* **3** (1954) 13–45.
[2] On the ergodic theorem for positive linear operators, *J. Reine Angew. Math.* **205** (1960/61) 101–106.

S. HOROWITZ
[1] Transition probabilities and contractions of L^∞, *Z.W.* **24** (1972) 263–274.

G. A. HUNT
[1] Markov processes and potentials I, II, III, *I.J.M.* **1** (1957) 44–93, 316–389, **2** (1958) 151–213.
[2] Markov chains and Martin boundaries, *I.J.M.* **4** (1960) 119–132.
[3] La théorie du potentiel et les processus récurrents, *A.I.F.* **15** (1) (1965) 3–12.

C. IONESCU-TULCEA
[1] Méasures dans les espaces produits, *Atti Accad. Naz. Lincei. Rend.* **7** (1949) 208–211.

R. ISAAC
[1] On the ratio-limit theorem for Markov processes recurrent in the sense of Harris, *I.J.M.* **11** (1967) 608–615.

N. C. JAIN
[1] Some limit theorems for a general Markov process, *Z.W.* **6** (1966) 206–223.

N. C. JAIN and B. JAMISON
[1] Contributions to Doeblin's Theory of Markov processes, *Z.W.* **8** (1967) 19–40.

N. C. JAIN and S. OREY
[1] Some properties of random walk paths, *J. Math. Anal. Appl.* **43** (1973) 795–815.

B. JAMISON and S. OREY
[1] Tail σ-field of Markov processes recurrent in the sense of Harris, *Z.W.* **8** (1967) 41–48.

S. KARLIN and J. McGREGOR
[1] Random walks, *I.J.M.* **3** (1959) 66–81.

J. G. KEMENY
[1] Representation theory for denumerable Markov chains, *T.A.M.S.* **125** (1966) 47–62.

J. G. KEMENY and J. L. SNELL
[1] Potentials for denumerable Markov chains, *J. Math. Anal. Appl.* **3** (1961) 196–260.
[2] Notes on discrete potential theory, *J. Math. Anal. Appl.* **3** (1961) 117–121.
[3] Boundary theory for recurrent Markov chains, *T.A.M.S.* **106** (1963) 495–520.
[4] A new potential operator for recurrent Markov chains, *J. London Math. Soc.* **38** (1963) 359–371.

J. G. KEMENY, J. L. SNELL and A. W. KNAPP
[1] *Denumerable Markov Chains* (Van Nostrand, New York, 1966).

J. H. B. KEMPERMAN
[1] *The Passage Problem for a Stationary Markov Chain* (Chicago Univ. Press, Chicago, Ill., 1961).

H. KESTEN
[1] Symmetric random walks on groups, *T.A.M.S.* **92** (1959) 336–354.
[2] Full Banach mean values on countable groups, *Math. Scand.* **7** (1959) 146–156.
[3] Ratio theorems for random walks II, *J. Anal. Math.* **11** (1963) 323–379.
[4] The Martin boundary of recurrent random walks on countable groups, in: *Proc. 5th Berkeley Symp. on Mathematical Statistics and Probability*, Vol. II (Univ. of California Press, Berkeley, Calif., 1967) 51–75.

H. KESTEN and F. SPITZER
[1] Ratio theorems for random walks I, *J. Anal. Math.* **11** (1963) 285–322.
[2] Random walk on countably infinite Abelian groups, *Acta. Math.* **114** (1965) 237–265.

R. KONDO
[1] On potential kernels satisfying the complete maximum principle, *Proc. Japan. Acad.* **44** (1968) 193–197.
[2] A construction of recurrent Markov chains, *Osaka. J. Math.* **6** (1969) 13–28.
[3] A construction of recurrent Markov chains II, *T.P.* **15** (1970) 499–507.

R. KONDO and Y. OSHIMA
[1] A characterization of weak potential kernels for strong Feller recurrent Markov chains, to appear.

U. KRENGEL (see Chacon)
[1] On the global limit behaviour of Markov chains and of general nonsingular Markov processes, *Z.W.* **6** (4) (1966) 302–316.

K. KRICKEBERG
[1] Strong mixing properties of Markov chains with infinite invariant measures, in: *Proc. 5th Berkeley Symp. on Mathematical Statistics and Probability* (California Univ. Press, Berkeley, Calif., 1966).
[2] Mischende Transformationen auf Mannigfaltigkeiten unendlichen Maßes, *Z.W.* **7** (1967) 235–247.

A. G. KUROSH
[1] *The Theory of Groups* (Chelsea, New York, 1955).

J. LAMPERTI and J. L. SNELL
[1] Martin boundaries for certain Markov chains, *J. Math. Soc. Japan* **15** (1963) 113–128.

M. L. LEVITAN
[1] Some ratio limit behaviour of Markov processes, *Z.W.* **15** (1970) 29–50.
[2] A generalized Doeblin ratio limit theorem, *Ann. Math. Stat.* **42** (1971) 904–911.

M. LIN (see Foguel)
[1] Mixed ratio limit theorems for Markov processes, *Israel J. Math.* **8** (1970) 357–366.
[2] On quasi-compact Markov operators, (1973).

G. LION
[1] Familles d'opérateurs et frontière en théorie du potentiel, *A.I.F.* **16** (1966) 389–453.

M. LOÈVE
[1] Probability Theory, 2nd edition (Van Nostrand, New York, 1960).

R. M. LOYNES
[1] Products of independent random elements in a topological group, *Z.W.* **1** (1963) 446–455.

M. METIVIER
[1] Existence of an invariant measure and an Ornstein's ergodic theorem, *A.M.S.* **40** (1969) 74–96.
[2] Théorème limite quotient pour les chaines de Markov récurrentes au sens de Harris, *A.I.H.P.* **8** (2) (1972) 93–105.

P. A. MEYER
[1] Théorie ergodique et potentiels, *A.I.F.* **15** (1) (1965) 89–102.
[2] *Probability and Potentials* (Blaisdell, Waltham, Mass., 1966).
[3] Caractérisation des noyaux potentiels des semi-groupes discrets, *A.I.F.* **16** (2) (1966) 225–240.
[4] Les resolvantes fortement Felleriennes d'après Mokobodzky, in: *Sém. de Probabilités II*, Lecture Notes in Math. **51** (Springer, Berlin, 1968).

[5] Representation intégrale des fonctions excessives, résultats de Mokobodzky, in: *Sém. de Probabilités V*, Lecture Notes in Math. **191** (Springer, Berlin, 1971).

[6] Deux petits résultats du théorie du potentiel, in: *Sém. de Probabilités V*, Lecture Notes in Math. **191** (Springer, Berlin, 1971).

[7] Travaux de H. Rost et théorie du balayage, in: *Sém. de Probabilités V*, Lecture Notes in Math. **191** (Springer, Berlin, 1971).

[8] Solutions de l'équation de Poisson dans le cas récurrent, in: *Sém. de Probabilités V*, Lecture Notes in Math. **191** (Springer, Berlin, 1971).

G. MOKOBODZKY

[1] Noyaux absolument measurables et opérateurs nucléaires, *C.R.A.S.* **270** (1970) 1673–1675.

G. MOKOBODZKY and D. SIBONY

[1] Cones de fonctions et théorie du potentiel II: Résolvantes et semi-groupes subordonnés à un cone de fonctions, in: *Sém. de Théorie du Potentiel* (Inst. Henri Poincaré, 1967) 11me année.

S. T. C. MOY

[1] Period of an irreducible positive operator, *I.J.M.* **11** (1967) 24–39.

[2] λ-continous Markov chains, *T.A.M.S.* **117** (1965) 68–99.

J. NEVEU

[1] Potentiels markoviens discrets, *Ann. Univ. Clermont* **24** (1964) 37–89.

[2] *Mathematical Foundations of the Calculus of Probability* (Holden Day, San Francisco, Calif., 1965).

[3] Relations entre la théorie des martingales et la théorie ergodique, *A.I.F.* **15** (1965) 31–42.

[4] Existence of bounded invariant measures in ergodic theory, in: *Symp. 5th Berkeley Symp. on Mathematical Statistics and Probability* (Univ. of California Press, Berkeley, Calif., 1966).

[5] Potentiel markovien recurrent des chaines de Harris, *A.I.F.* **22** (2) (1972) 85–130.

[6] Sur l'irréductibilité des chaines de Markov, *A.I.H.P.* **8** (3) (1972) 249–254.

[7] Généralisation d'un théorème limite-quotient, in: *Trans. 6th Prague Conf. on Information Theory, Statistical Decision Functions, Random Processes* (Czech. Acad. Sci., Prague, 1973).

P. NEY and F. SPITZER

[1] The Martin boundary for random walk, *T.A.M.S.* **121** (1966) 116–132.

S. OREY (see Feller, Jain and Jamison)

[1] Recurrent Markov chains, *Pacific J. Math.* **9** (1959) 805–827.

[2] Sums arising in the theory of Markov chains, *Proc. Am. Math. Soc.* **12** (1961) 847–856.

[3] An ergodic theorem for recurrent Markov chains, *Z.W.* **1** (1962) 174–176.

[4] Potential kernels for recurrent Markov chains, *J. Math. Anal. Appl.* **8** (1964) 104–132.

[5] *Limit Theorems for Markov Chain Transition Probabilities* (Van Nostrand, New York, 1971).

D. S. Ornstein (see Chacon and Chung)
[1] Random walks I, II, *T.A.M.S.* **138** (1969) 1–43, 45–60.

D. S. Ornstein and L. Sucheston
[1] An operator theorem on L^1-convergence to zero with applications to Markov kernels, *A.M.S.* **41** (1970) 1631–1639.

Y. Oshima (see Kondo)
[1] A necessary and sufficient condition for a kernel to be a weak potential kernel of a recurrent Markov chain, *Osaka J. Math.* **6** (1969) 29–37.

S. C. Port and C. J. Stone
[1] Potential theory of random walks on abelian groups, *Acta Math.* **122** (1969) 19–114.

D. Revuz (see Azema and Brunel)
[1] Théorèmes limites pour les résolvantes récurrentes, *Rend. Circ. Mat. Palermo* **19** (1970) 294–300.
[2] Sur la théorie du potentiel pour les processus de Markov récurrents, *A.I.F.* **21** (1971) 245–262.
[3] Le principe semi-complet du maximum, in: *Sém. de Probabilités VI*, Lecture Notes in Math. **258** (Springer, Berlin, 1972).

Roudier
[1] Chaine de Markov μ-continue à l'infini, *A.I.H.* **8** (3) (1972) 241–248.

H. Rost
[1] Darstellung einer Ordnung von Massen durch Stoppzeiten, *Z.W.* **15** (1970) 19–28.
[2] Markoff-Ketten bei sich füllenden Löchern im Zustandsraum, *A.I.F.* **21** (1) (1971) 253–270.

W. Rudin
[1] *Fourier Analysis on Groups* (Interscience, New York, 1967).

F. Spitzer
[1] *Principle of Random Walks* (Van Nostrand, New York, 1964).

C. J. Stone (see Port)
[1] On absolutely continuous components and renewal theory, *A.M.S.* **37** (1966) 271–275.
[2] Ratio limit theorem for random walks on groups, *T.A.M.S.* **125** (1966) 86–100.
[3] On the potential operator for one-dimensional recurrent random walks, *T.A.M.S.* **136** (1969) 413–426.

J. C. Taylor
[1] On the existence of sub-Markovian resolvents, *Invent. Math.* **17** (1972) 85–93.

T. Ueno
[1] Some limit theorems for temporally discrete Markov processes, *J. Fac. Sci. Univ. Tokyo* (I) **7** (1957).

T. Watanabe
[1] On the theory of Martin boundaries induced by countable Markov processes, *Mem. Coll. Sci. Univ. Kyoto* (A) **33** (1960) 39–108.

[2] On balayees of excessive measures and functions with respect to resolvents, in: *Sém. de Probabilités V*, Lecture Notes in Math. **191** (Springer, Berlin, 1971).

K. YOSIDA and S. KAKUTANI
[1] Operator-theoretical treatment of Markov's process and mean ergodic theorem, *Ann. Math.* **42** (1941) 188–228.

INDEX